Geology of the country ~~ Great Yarn

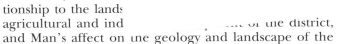

This memoir descri[ ] Broadland, the histo [ ] tionship to the land[ ] agricultural and ind [ ] [ ] [ ] [ ] [ ] [ ] [ ] of the district, and Man's affect on the geology and landscape of the Broads in historical times, are also described.

The landscape of the district, with its gently undulating uplands and wide, flat marshland, was shaped by the geological and climatic events of the last 500 000 years; the so-called 'Ice Age' in Britain. About half a million years ago ice sheets originating from Scandinavia and northern Britain advanced across East Anglia. They moulded the landscape by smearing it with thick deposits of stony clay and sandy clay, whilst meltwaters issuing from them spread sheets of sand and gravel, and carved out valleys and channels. The ice retreated and alternations of temperate and cold climates followed until, about 13 000 years ago, the melting of the last great northern ice sheet caused the sea-level to rise. The valleys were flooded and silted up, ultimately giving rise to the familiar marshlands of the present day. Peat, formed by the decay of plants growing around the marshes, was extensively dug by Man in historical times. The flooded workings are now the famous 'Broads'.

Deep below the glacial deposits, the oldest known rocks in the district, slates of Silurian age (about 400 million years old), form a basement massif. In the north-east of the district, rocks of Carboniferous, Permian and Triassic age, some of which accumulated as sediments in the subsiding North Sea Basin, rest on the flank of this massif. None of these rocks crop out at the surface and are known only from boreholes and seismic records. Younger rocks, the Chalk, Tertiary clays and the shelly sands and clays of the Crag, are well known from outcrops or shallow boreholes and wells. Volcanic eruptions in the North Atlantic some 60 million years ago are recorded as ash layers in the Tertiary clays, while oscillations in the Earth's climate during the last 2 million years are known from pollen preserved in the Crag and younger sediments.

Cover photograph

Great Yarmouth spit and Haven viewed from the south. The present haven mouth was cut by the Dutch engineer Joas Johnson in the 16th and 17th centuries, when the spit extended several kilometres to the south. Caister Ness and the eastern extremity of the Broadland marshes may be seen in the middle distance. A history of the formation of the spit is given in Chapter eight. *(Photograph by ADAS, Cambridge)*

BRITISH GEOLOGICAL SURVEY

R S ARTHURTON
S J BOOTH
A N MORIGI
M A W ABBOTT and
C J WOOD

CONTRIBUTORS
General stratigraphy
D McC Bridge
R W Gallois
P M Hopson

Biostratigraphy
H W Bailey
K C Ball
D K Graham
R Harland
A A Morter
I P Wilkinson

Offshore geology
P S Balson
D J Harrison

Water supply and hydrogeology
K M Hiscock

Engineering geology
M G Culshaw

Tertiary clay mineralogy
R J Merriman

Geology of the country around Great Yarmouth

Memoir for 1:50 000 geological sheet 162
(England and Wales)

with an appendix on the Upper Cretaceous
biostratigraphy of the Trunch Borehole (Sheet 132)
by C J Wood and A A Morter

LONDON: HMSO   1994

iv

ISBN 011 884491 1

Bibliographical reference

ARTHURTON, R S, BOOTH, S J, MORIGI, A N, ABBOTT, M A W, and WOOD, C J. 1994.   Geology of the country around Great Yarmouth.   *Memoir of the British Geological Survey*, Sheet 162 (England and Wales).

Authors

R S Arthurton, BSc, S J Booth, BSc, A N Morigi, BSc, and M A W Abbott, BSc
British Geological Survey, Keyworth
C J Wood, BSc, FGS
formerly British Geological Survey

Contributors

P S Balson, BSc, PhD, D McC Bridge, BSc, M G Culshaw, MSc, R W Gallois, BSc, DIC, PhD, CEng, CGeol, FIMM, R Harland, DSc, D J Harrison, MSc, P M Hopson, BSc, R J Merriman, BSc, and I P Wilkinson, MSc, PhD
British Geological Survey, Keyworth

D K Graham, BSc
British Geological Survey, Edinburgh

H W Bailey, BSc, PhD
Paleoservices Ltd

K C Ball, BSc, PhD, A A Morter, BSc
formerly British Geological Survey

K M Hiscock, BSc, PhD
School of Environmental Sciences
University of East Anglia

Other publications of the Survey dealing with this and adjoining districts

BOOKS
British Regional Geology
East Anglia and adjoining areas (4th edition)
Memoirs
Geology of the country around Norwich (Sheet 161)
Geology of the country around Diss (Sheet 175)
Assessment of British Sand and Gravel Resources
Sand and gravel resource sheet TG 20 (south-east of Norwich)
Well catalogue
Records of wells in the area of the New Series one-inch Geological Sheet 162 (Great Yarmouth)

MAPS
1:250 000
52N 00 East Anglia: Solid geology, Quaternary geology, Sea bed sediments, Aeromagnetic anomaly, Bouguer gravity anomaly (separate maps)
Hydrogeological map of northern East Anglia

1:50 000 (Solid and Drift)
Sheet 145 and part sheet 129 (King's Lynn and The Wash)
Sheet 161 (Norwich)
Sheet 173 (Ely)
Sheet 175 (Diss)
Sheet 189 (Bury St Edmunds)

Printed in the UK for HMSO
Dd 292034   C8   03/94

CONTENTS

NOTES

Throughout the memoir the word 'district' refers to the area (including the offshore area) covered by the 1:50 000 Great Yarmouth (162) Sheet.

References in the memoir to 'the published map' are specifically to the 1:50 000 Great Yarmouth (162) Sheet, including the geological sections and other marginal information shown thereon.

National Grid references are given in square brackets; they lie within the 100 km squares TG and TM unless otherwise stated. Numbers prefixed by 'E' refer to the National Sliced Rock Collection of the British Geological Survey, housed at Keyworth, Nottingham.

PREFACE

The coastal region is of particular importance to Britain. It is where many of us live and work and where we undertake many of our recreational activities. However, it is also the region where the environmental impacts of development are most apparent. East Anglia is one such area, where a comprehensive knowledge of the geology of the coastal region is essential if we are to assess the direct environmental impact not only of human activity but also the longer-term impact of changing sea levels.

This memoir and its accompanying 1:50 000-scale geological map identify the geological events that have led to the formation of the present-day landscape of central Broadland and its adjoining coastline, and highlight the particular relevance of the geology of the district to a wide range of environmental and economic issues.

The study has produced a detailed new interpretation of the structural history of the district, in particular the dominant influence of the Lower Palaeozoic London–Brabant Massif, on the northern margin of which the district is situated. Younger Palaeozoic and Triassic rocks of the North Sea Basin show recurrent restricted onlap against this massif. Late Mesozoic and Tertiary formations including the Chalk and the London Clay extend across the massif within the district and their stratigraphy is known largely from boreholes. Two boreholes, at Hales and Ormesby, drilled for this survey have provided much new information on the Tertiary clays, including the identification of many layers of volcanic ash.

The Chalk and Tertiary clays as well as the overlying shelly sands and clays of the Crag are of importance to the distribution of groundwater in the district, and the interfaces of these formations have been plotted from a borehole database constructed for this survey. The plots highlight previously unrecognised structural and sedimentary features, such as a sub-basin of Crag sands lying in the lee of a north-west-facing buried scarp formed by the London Clay Formation in the west-central part of the district.

Because of their widespread and superficial distribution, the Quaternary deposits are of particular environmental and economic significance. Besides having an importance influence on groundwater recharge, they include aggregate resources both on land and offshore, and their included estuarine deposits present hazards in engineering construction whether for urban infrastructure or flood defence. The estuarine silts and clays are described from an engineering geological as well as from a stratigraphical standpoint, and special attention is given to the form of the buried valley system that accommodates these deposits.

Environmentally, the youngest Quaternary deposits, those of Flandrian age including those forming in the present day, are of major importance in that they control much of the essential character of Broadland and its adjoining coastal zone. From the mapping of the Flandrian deposits onshore and offshore, this survey has produced an interpretation of the history of marine and estuarine erosional and depositional events resulting from the global sea-level rise that has occurred during this period. This understanding of the past will help us to develop strategies for managing coastal change in the future.

Peter J Cook, DSc
Director

British Geological Survey
Kingsley Dunham Centre
Keyworth
Nottingham
NG12 5GG

December 1993

ACKNOWLEDGEMENTS

This memoir has been written by Messrs M A W Abbott (concealed formations and their structure), C J Wood (Upper Cretaceous rocks), R S Arthurton, S J Booth and A N Morigi, and incorporates a compilation of the published work and unpublished 1:10 000 sheet reports of Messrs D McC Bridge and P M Hopson. Dr P S Balson and Mr D J Harrison contributed the sections dealing with the offshore geology, and Mr M G Culshaw compiled the section on engineering geology from an earlier report produced jointly by the British Geological Survey and the Geotechnical Consulting Group. Mr C J Wood and Mr A A Morter prepared the biostratigraphical account of the Chalk in the Trunch Borehole (Sheet 132) given in Appendix 1. Mr R J Merriman provided petrographical notes on the Tertiary formations. The section on water supply and hydrogeology was written with the generous assistance of Dr K M Hiscock (University of East Anglia) and the guidance of Mr M Price, Ms J M Parker and Mrs M A Lewis. We are also pleased to acknowledge the additional details on the Holocene succession and palaeogeography provided by the University of East Anglia under the NERC contract F60/G2/32; this work, supervised by Professor B M Funnell and Dr N K Tovey, was carried out by Messrs D S Brew, M L Goodwin and D C Tisdale.

Micropalaeontological identifications were made by Drs K C Ball, R Harland and I P Wilkinson (BGS) and Dr H W Bailey (Paleoservices); macropalaeontological determinations by Mr D K Graham. The detailed logging and interpretation of the Survey's Ormesby and Hales boreholes were carried out by Dr R W O'B Knox and Mr A N Morigi, and the geophysical logging by Mr D K Buckley and Dr J D Cornwell. The computer database of surface and subsurface geological information was assembled under the supervision of Mr S J Booth, and the marine geophysical surveys were executed by Messrs C P Brett, T Fitton, A C Skinner and D J Smith under Mr Brett's direction. Land geophysical investigations in support of the survey were carried out by Dr J D Cornwell with assistance of Mr P G Greenwood, Mr M G Raines, Mr C P Royles and Mrs S J Self.

This work has benefitted from the generous assistance afforded by the Hydrographic Department of the Ministry of Defence and by staff of various university departments, in particular Professors B M Funnell, J Rose and R G West and Mr W M Corbett in respect of the Quaternary and Tertiary stratigraphy. There has been fruitful collaboration with the Soil Survey of England and Wales (now the Soil Survey and Land Research Centre), in particular Messrs R G O Burton and J Hazelden; also with civil engineeering consultants of the Geotechnical Consulting Group, in respect of the geotechnical data. Contributions to the account of the Chalk were provided by Messrs N B Peake and P S Whittlesea, and Dr A J Pitchford.

We gratefully acknowledge the willing co-operation of many public and private bodies for supplying borehole and survey information, and for arranging access to construction sites and nature reserves during the course of the survey. These bodies include the former Anglian Water Authority, Anglian Water Services Ltd (Dr P Matthews, Mr J Ferry), the National Rivers Authority (Anglian Region) (Dr D Burgess), Atlas RMC plc, Ambrit Resources Ltd, British Coal, M Folkes and Son (Welcome Pit), the East Anglian Water Company, Norfolk County Council Highways Department (Mr J D Pitchford) and Planning Department (Mr J Brigham), the Broads Authority, Great Yarmouth Borough Council, Great Yarmouth Port and Haven Commissioners, the Ministry of Agriculture, Fisheries and Food, the Nature Conservancy Council, the Norfolk Naturalists Trust and the Castle Museum, Norwich. Finally, we acknowledge the co-operation of the many landowners, wardens and tenants of the district during the execution of the fieldwork.

The photographs were taken by Mr H J Evans, with some exceptions, which are indicated in the captions. The memoir was edited by Dr R G Thurrell, Regional Geologist and Mr R J Wyatt.

HISTORY OF SURVEY OF THE GREAT YARMOUTH SHEET

The district covered by the Great Yarmouth (162) sheet of the 1:50 000 Geological Map of England and Wales was originally surveyed on a scale of one inch to one mile by J H Blake, C Reid and H B Woodward between 1875 and 1882 and published on the one-inch scale as Old Series sheets 66 NE and SE and 67 (Solid and Drift) in 1881–82.

The district was resurveyed on the scale of 1:10 000 over three periods: initially during 1967–69 by Dr F C Cox as overlap from the resurvey of the adjoining Norwich (161) sheet, secondly during 1983–85 by Messrs D McCBridge and P M Hopson as part the Survey's East Anglian Regional Research Project of the early 1980s, then finally during 1985–89 by Messrs A N Morigi, S J Booth and R S Arthurton. The published 1:50 000-scale map of the district covers both the onshore and the offshore areas; it depicts both the Solid geology and that part of the geological succession of Quaternary age that has traditionally been referred to as Drift.

The following is a list of 1:10 000- and 1:10 560-scale geological maps included wholly, or in part, in the area of the 1:50 000 Great Yarmouth (162) Geological Sheet, with the initials of the surveys and the date of survey for each map.

Manuscript copies of these maps have been deposited for public reference in the library of the British Geological Survey, Keyworth, Nottingham and in the British Geological Survey Information Point at the Geological Museum, Exhibition Road, South Kensington, London. They contain more detail than appears on the 1:50 000 map. National Grid dyeline copies are available except for those marked with an asterisk.

TG 20 NE	Postwick	FCC	1967
TG 20 SE	Yelverton	FCC	1967
TG 21 SE	Rackheath	FCC	1969
TG 30 NW	Blofield	ANM, FCC	1985–86
TG 30 NE	Lingwood	ANM, FCC	1986–88
TG 30 SW	Rockland St Mary	ANM	1988
TG 30 SE	Langley	ANM	1986–87
TG 31 SW	Salhouse	ANM	1989
TG 31 SE	South Walsham	RSA	1989
TG 40 NW	Halvergate	SJB	1989
TG 40 NE	Breydon Water (west)	SJB	1988–89
TG 40 SW	Reedham	SJB, PMH	1985–89
TG 40 SE	Belton	SJB	1988
TG 41 SW	Acle	RSA	1988
TG 41 SE	Filby	RSA	1988
TG 50 NW	Great Yarmouth	SJB	1987
TG 50 SW	Gorleston-on-Sea	SJB	1987–88
TG 51 SW	Caister-on-Sea	RSA	1987
TM 29 NE	Brooke	FCC	1969
TM 39 NW	Seething	ANM	1987–88
TM 39 NE	Loddon	ANM	1985–86
TM 39 SE *	Ellingham	AH	1980
TM 49 NW	Thurlton	PMH	1985
TM 49 NE	Somerleyton	PMH, DMCCB	1984
TM 49 SW*	Beccles (north)	PMH	1983
TM 49 SE*	Burgh St Peter	PMH	1983
TM 59 NW/NE	Blundeston	DMCCB	1983
TM 59 SW/SE*	Lowestoft (northern margin only)	SJB	1989

ONE

Introduction

This memoir describes the geology of the district covered by the Great Yarmouth Sheet (New Series 162) of the 1:50 000 Geological Map of England and Wales. The district extends to include the adjoining part of the nearshore zone of the North Sea (Figure 1).

The district lies within the county of Norfolk, with the exception of the Blundeston area (Lothingland) in the south-east which lies in Suffolk. Topographically, it mostly comprises two contrasting types of terrain: upland areas of a dissected plateau, rising in the south-west to some 40 m above Ordnance Datum (OD), which are largely given over to agricultural use, and tracts of marshland that form part of the extensive system of wetlands, broads and drained marshes known as Broadland. The marshlands are crossed by the tidal rivers Bure, Yare and Waveney, and include an area of intertidal mud flats known as Breydon Water.

The town of Great Yarmouth is a sea port and industrial base, as well as being a leisure resort; it is built largely on a spit that forms a barrier between the Broadland marshes and the North Sea. The nearshore zone includes the Yarmouth Roads and the Lowestoft North Roads, and is generally an area of shifting sandbanks that constrain the navigation channels.

Extractive industries currently operating within the district comprise sand and gravel workings at Burgh Castle. Historically, however, parts of the marshland have yielded peat, and the uplands have served variously as a source of sand, gravel, marling clay, brick clay and even iron ore. Sand has also been worked from time to time for local use from the spit at Great Yarmouth. Groundwater is pumped to meet agricultural demand as well as to augment the public supply, the needs of which are met largely by surface abstraction from lakes, themselves fed largely by groundwater. Abandoned excavations have been used for landfill operations, either for the piecemeal private dumping of agricultural and domestic waste or for large-scale disposal under local authority control. Reclamation for industrial development by the use of various fill materials is a feature of the marshland on the fringes of Great Yarmouth.

The district is a focus of many conservation interests. The Broads Authority plays a central role in conservation issues that concern Broadland as a whole, while there are many other bodies, both local and national, with specific

Figure 1 Principal topographical features of the district.

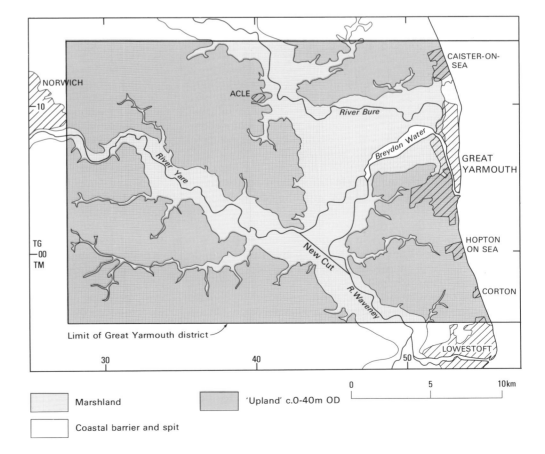

Marshland

Coastal barrier and spit

'Upland' c.0–40m OD

0   5   10km

interests, mostly concerning the marshland and Breydon Water.

OUTLINE OF GEOLOGICAL HISTORY

The oldest rocks at outcrop within the district belong to the Chalk Group. This group forms the main part of a layer of Cretaceous sedimentary rocks some 400 m thick that completely overlaps the much older rocks of the London–Brabant Massif, which extends from southern Britain eastwards under the southern North Sea to Belgium. The northern margin of this massif extends under the north-eastern part of the district.

Rocks of the massif proved in the vicinity of the district are metasediments of probable Silurian age, including cleaved mudstones, siltstones and sandstones. These are believed to belong to a folded and metamorphosed, turbiditic shelf succession, which forms part of the concealed Caledonide (end-Silurian) fold belt known elsewhere in eastern England.

The massif formed a structural high and was flanked by sedimentary basins throughout the Upper Palaeozoic and Mesozoic; sedimentary formations that accumulated in the adjoining North Sea Basin thinned out southwards against its northern margin. Within the district, dolomitic limestones and mudstones of Dinantian (Lower Carboniferous) age lap onto Lower Palaeozoic rocks with marked unconformity, representing a marine transgression characteristic of this period worldwide. Westphalian sedimentary rocks (Coal Measures), preserved just to the north, may also have been deposited within the district but, if so, they were eroded before the accumulation of Permian sediments, which overlapped onto the massif; both the Lower and the Upper Permian are represented. The Lower Permian Leman Sandstone Formation (Rotliegendes) accumulated in desert fluvial (wadi) or aeolian conditions, after which a eustatic rise in sea level in the Upper Permian led to the marine flooding of the desert basin and the consequent deposition of a cyclic (Zechstein) succession comprising limestones, dolomites and mudstones, with some anhydrite.

The hot, arid climate that characterised the Permian continued through the Triassic. Short-lived rejuvenation of the London–Brabant Massif introduced clastic sediment, forming the Hewett Sandstone Member, and this was followed by the development of a playa-lake environment which produced the evaporitic mudstones, siltstones and subordinate sandstones of the Bunter Shale Formation. These mainly argillaceous deposits were succeeded diachronously by the coarser clastic sediments of the Bunter Sandstone Formation, prograding northwards from the basin margin. The Haisborough Group marks a return to an evaporitic environment, with gypsum- and anhydrite-bearing mudstones and interbedded siltstones and sandstones.

Although Jurassic strata overlap the massif margin in adjoining areas to the north and west, none is known to be preserved in the district. If such deposits were formerly present, then they were removed by the late-Cimmerian (late Jurassic–early Cretaceous) erosion that was widespread in this region. The succeeding, overlapping strata are marine rocks of Lower Cretaceous age; they rest with marked unconformity on the Haisborough Group or, by southward overstep, directly on the Lower Palaeozoic basement. The Carstone is the oldest of the Lower Cretaceous formations to be preserved throughout the district. Its deposition marks the commencement of a period of sea-level rise that extended through most of the Upper Cretaceous, such that the surface of the massif became progressively buried, notably by the micritic limestones of the Chalk Group. The Chalk was formed in a warm sea protected from the influx of terrigenous detritus, the contemporary landmasses being distant and of subdued relief.

A phase of regional uplift and erosion during the late Cretaceous was followed by sustained subsidence of the southern North Sea Basin, on the western margin of which the district lies. This subsidence continued through the Tertiary and Quaternary, with the exception of possible uplift in mid to late Miocene times. The complex graben system that developed during the Mesozoic as part of the North Atlantic rift system, and which had been the primary control on sedimentation in the North Sea Basin, ceased to subside differentially by early Tertiary times. Subsequently, the subsidence formed a saucer-shaped basin along the axis of the graben system.

In the Great Yarmouth district, the Thanet Formation, represented by the Ormesby Clay, marks the transgression of the Palaeocene sea over the eroded Chalk surface, but it is not clear whether this transgression extended to the entire district. A phase of uplift and erosion of the Norfolk area preceded a further southward marine advance during which the mudstones of the London Clay Formation were deposited. Abundant volcanic ash layers in the Tertiary sediments were the result of volcanism in the North Atlantic igneous province.

A period of uplift followed the deposition of the Eocene strata and no further marine sediments accumulated until a late Pliocene (late Tertiary)–early Pleistocene marine transgression affected at least part of the district. The resulting deposits, and those of subsequent early Pleistocene transgressions, make up the Crag Group. Together, they comprise sands, silts and clays formed mainly in shallow-shelf and intertidal environments. These marine conditions were followed, after an hiatus during which slight eastward tilting occurred, by a fluvial to intertidal regime, leading to the accumulation of the Kesgrave Formation. Its deposits, mainly sand and gravel, were formed during the Pre-Pastonian to Cromerian stages on the beds of braided rivers that migrated laterally across much of eastern and southern East Anglia. A further hiatus in sedimention, perhaps accompanied by minor erosion, heralded the onset of the cold climatic conditions of the Anglian stage, represented in this district, as over much of East Anglia, by glacial deposits.

The Anglian deposits record a sequence of two glacial depositional events, separated by an erosional interval. The older of these, represented by the Corton Formation, was associated with ice of Scandinavian origin which advanced from the north-east and from which till and subaqueous sands and gravels where deposited The later event is represented mainly by the widespread sheet of chalk-rich Lowestoft Till, deposited as a lodgement till on an undulating land surface by ice that advanced from the west or north-west. During this later glaciation, irregular channel-like depressions were formed on the surface of the underlying deposits, commonly to depths of several tens of metres; the depressions were subsequently backfilled, largely by Lowestoft Till. During the wasting of the Lowestoft ice, deep valleys were eroded then partially backfilled with glaciofluvial deposits.

The sedimentary record of the Late Pleistocene following the Lowestoft glacial event is fragmentary in this district, as it is over most of East Anglia. No deposits that can definitely be ascribed to the succeeding Hoxnian warm stage have been identified, although the sands and organic silts filling a channel cut in Lowestoft Till at Caister-on-Sea seem likely to be of this age. By Devensian times the principal landforms of the district, produced by dissection of the Lowestoft Till sheet, were probably much as they are at present, though with the drainage graded to a lower sea level, and the uplands extending perhaps several kilometres to the east of the present coastline. During the Devensian, and specifically the late Devensian, when much of Britain (but, with the exception of the Hunstanton coast, not East Anglia) was subject to glaciation, a veneer of silt and fine sand settled from airborne suspension over the land surface, the remnants of which extensively mask the underlying geology. Also during the Devensian, deposits of river sand and gravel, part of the Yare Valley Formation, accumulated on the flood plains of the principal valleys and continued to do so into the succeeding Flandrian Stage, until these floodplains were transformed into an estuarine complex through a global rise in sea level.

This eustatic sea-level rise during the Flandrian led to the substantial accumulation of estuarine sediments, including peats, (the Breydon Formation) over the erstwhile floodplains. At the same time, the coastline suffered major erosion and consequent retreat. During the latter part of the marine transgression, sandbanks formed offshore and, between these, deep channels including Yarmouth Roads were scoured by strong tidal currents. From about the 13th century, a substantial barrier sand spit built southwards across the estuary mouth from Caister-on-Sea and extended almost as far as Lowestoft. This spit became shortened to its present length following the construction of an engineered haven mouth in the 16th and 17th centuries.

PREVIOUS RESEARCH

Early researches relating to the geology of Norfolk in general include those of and H B Woodward, published in 'Geology of the country around Norwich' (1881). Works of particular significance in the understanding of the stratigraphy of the Great Yarmouth district include those by S V Wood and F W Harmer who, both individually and jointly, published papers that established a succession for the glacial and postglacial deposits of Norfolk and Suffolk (e.g. Wood and Harmer, 1868); they also made considerable advances in knowledge of the Crag deposits and the deposits referred to in this account as the Kesgrave Formation. In 1890, J H Blake contributed 'Geology of the country near Yarmouth and Lowestoft', an explanation of Old Series sheet 67.

These comprehensive works incorporate a wealth of field data, including much from sections long since obliterated, as well as providing detailed reviews of previous research. Subsequent investigations of the Quaternary deposits by academic workers led them to refine the stratigraphy employed by the primary surveyors and to revise the nomenclature of the various deposits, but the succession adopted in this account corresponds in essence with that described by Woodward (1881) and Blake (1890).

TWO

Palaeozoic

Evidence for the presence of Lower Palaeozoic, Carboniferous and Permian rocks within the district is inferred from published regional geological evaluations (e.g. Wills, 1978; N J P Smith, 1985) based on scattered borehole data and geophysical studies (e.g. Chroston and Sola, 1982; Allsop, 1985), combined with recent interpretations of seismic records calibrated against the data provided by deep boreholes in the adjoining North Walsham, Norwich and Lowestoft districts (Figure 2).

The district lies on the northern margin of a concealed platform of Palaeozoic rocks, the London–Brabant Massif, which acted as a positive structural feature through Late Palaeozoic and Mesozoic times and was the dominant feature in the geological evolution of the region.

The platform represents the eroded surface of a massif of folded and low-grade regionally metamorphosed, Precambrian volcanic and volcaniclastic rocks, Lower Palaeozoic sedimentary and volcanic rocks, and late Caledonian intrusive rocks (Allsop 1987; Pharaoh et al., 1987), known as the London–Brabant Massif (Wills, 1978). This massif comprises the concealed Caledonide fold belt of eastern England and the eastern margin of the Midlands

Microcraton, a mainly subcrop terrain in which the Precambrian basement is overlain by a thin (less than 3 km) cover of Cambrian to Tremadocian strata (Pharaoh et al., 1987; Smith, 1987; Lee et al., 1990). A concealed north-west-trending belt of calcalkaline volcanic rocks lies largely within the Caledonide fold belt, close to the margin of the microcraton, and represents arc magmatism of probable Ordovician age (Pharaoh et al., 1991).

The interaction of the relatively stable London–Brabant Massif with the peripherally subsiding Southern North Sea Basin resulted in attenuation, nondeposition and erosion of Permian, Triassic and Jurassic sequences within the region. It was not until Albian (Early Cretaceous) times that regional subsidence resulted in the complete overstep of the Palaeozoic platform (Owen, 1971).

The relationships of the Palaeozoic and Mesozoic rocks of the district are illustrated in Figure 56 and on the horizontal section accompanying the published map. The Palaeozoic sequence of the region is affected by two major unconformities related to post-Caledonian and post-Variscan erosion.

LOWER PALAEOZOIC

Information afforded by the limited number of boreholes penetrating to basement throughout East Anglia is reviewed

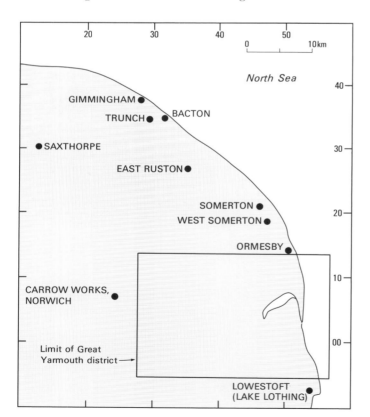

Figure 2 Locations of principal boreholes around the district which penetrate Palaeozoic and Mesozoic rocks.

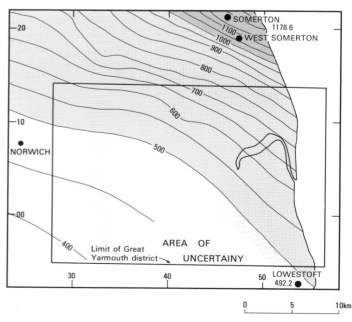

Figure 3 Generalised structure contours (metres below OD) on the top of the pre-Caledonian basement.

in Chroston and Sola (1982); however, much of the research into the nature of the concealed Lower Palaeozoic and Precambrian basement rocks beneath East Anglia has been based on geophysical studies. Early seismic refraction studies by Bullard et al. (1940) have been supplemented by further refraction studies, summarised in Evans and Allsop (1987), and interpretations of the British Geological Survey's gravity and magnetic databases (Chroston and Sola, 1982; Allsop, 1984, 1985; Chroston et al., 1987). Palaeogeological maps of the Lower Palaeozoic (Wills, 1978) and

pre-Permian (Allsop and Jones, 1981; N J P Smith, 1985) surfaces of the region have been compiled utilising borehole and geophysical data. These studies show the district to be underlain by Lower Palaeozoic metasediments of probable Silurian age (Smith, 1985) dipping gently to the north-east from around 400 m below OD in the south-west to about 900 m in the north-east, onshore (Figure 3).

Deep boreholes at Somerton [4607 2120] and Lowestoft [5380 9260], respectively in the adjoining North Walsham and Lowestoft districts (Figure 2, Appendix 2), pro-

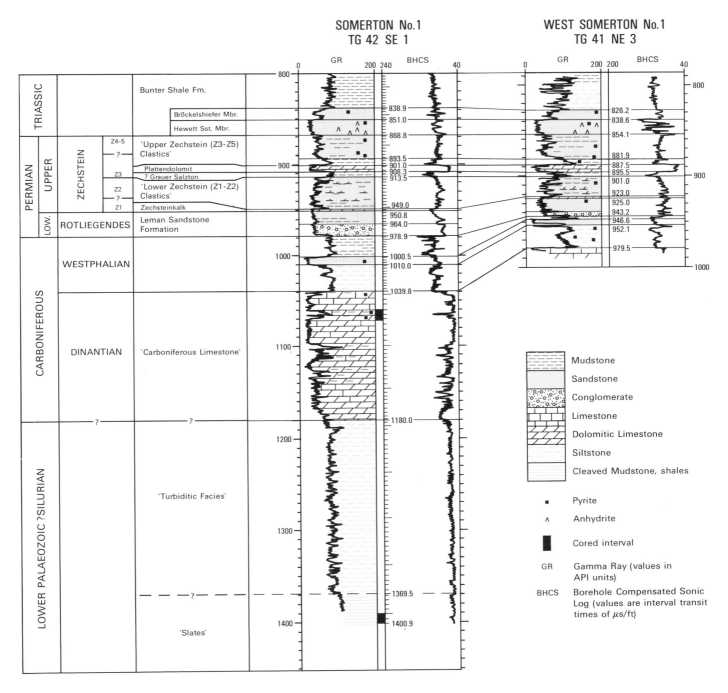

Figure 4 Interpreted stratigraphy and geophysical log characteristics of the Palaeozoic sequences proved in the Somerton No.1 and West Somerton No.1 boreholes.

vide evidence of the subcropping basement lithologies. The Lowestoft (Lake Lothing) borehole (Strahan, 1913), drilled in 1902, penetrated 62.48 m of Lower Palaeozoic rocks at 492.21 m below OD beneath Lower Cretaceous rocks. Poor sample recovery from the basement precluded detailed description; however, in general, the sequence comprises poorly cleaved, indurated, commonly micaceous, pale mudstones and shales, interbedded with lesser amounts of siltstone and sandstone. Cutting samples yielded brachiopod fragments of the genera *Lingula* and *Orbiculoidea,* which were assigned a general Lower Palaeozoic age (Strahan, 1913); more recently, these rocks have been assigned a ?Silurian age (Stubblefield, 1967; Smith, 1985).

The Somerton Borehole penetrated some 220 m of rocks beneath Dinantian (Lower Carboniferous) limestones (1180.8 to 1400.9 m, Figure 4). The sequence can be divided into two distinct units, the upper 188.7 m (1180.8 to 1369.5 m) comprising interbedded mudrocks, siltstones and sandstones assigned a Viséan (late Dinantian) age by oil company geologists, and the lower consisting of 31 m (1369.5 to 1400.9 m) of cleaved shales and siltstones of ?Silurian age.

Coring of the lower unit between 1390.5 and 1400.9 m proved a sequence of cleaved, bluish grey to dark grey, highly compacted, slightly calcareous shales and siltstones which exhibit steep dips (30° to 70°) indicated by sedimentary banding. A complex pattern of hairline and thicker calcite veins and small fractures, some showing slickensided surfaces, were observed. Microcrystallinity studies of white micas have indicated that the sequence has undergone metamorphism to greenschist facies (Pharaoh et al., 1987). Although no palaeontological data are available, the lithological evidence suggests a Lower Palaeozoic, possible Silurian age for this part of the sequence.

The upper unit comprises a sequence of interbedded dark grey to blue-grey, hard, fissile, micaceous and slightly dolomitic shales, and white, pale grey and grey, micaceous, dolomitic, calcite-rich, fine-grained sandstones and siltstones, containing interstitial kaolin and scattered pyrite. The sequence is affected by numerous hairline and thin crystalline calcite veins. The age of this unit is more problematical, but the limited palaeontological results (Owens, 1982) suggest a Viséan age, contrary to the evidence afforded by the physical properties (density and sonic velocity) and the structural and palaeogeological data. However, Owens (1982) noted that the palynological determinations were inconclusive, because of sample contamination by cavings from higher levels in the borehole. The high density and sonic velocities measured through this section are similar to those of Lower Palaeozoic sequences seen elsewhere in the region, for example at East Ruston [3530 2680] and Saxthorpe [1226 3013] (Figure 2). Structural evaluation of seismic reflection data also indicates that this sequence is part of the Lower Palaeozoic (Caledonian) basement. Thus, the interpretation favoured here is that this part of the sequence represents a turbiditic shelf sequence of probable Silurian age.

CARBONIFEROUS

Dinantian limestones proved in the adjoining North Walsham district at Somerton and West Somerton [4736 1935] (Figure 2, Appendix 2) are inferred from seismic evidence to extend into the north-eastern part of the district (Figures 5 and 6). Devonian rocks preserved elsewhere in East Anglia (Allsop, 1985) are absent from the district. Interpretation of gravity data by Allsop (1984) predicted an extensive Coal Measures (Westphalian) basin in the north of the district, extending inland from the coast to near Norwich; however, recent seismic reflection evidence suggests that, although penetrated in the Somerton and West Somerton boreholes, Coal Measures are absent from the district (Figure 6).

Major unconformities mark both the upper (post-Variscan) and lower (post-Caledonian) boundaries of the Carboniferous sequence in the district (Figure 56). A maximum of about 100 m of Carboniferous rocks is inferred in the extreme north-east; the sequence thins to the south-west where it is eventually overstepped by rocks of Permian age. The top of the subcropping Carboniferous rocks falls gently north-eastwards from around 700 to over 800 m below OD in the extreme north-east, onshore (Figure 6).

The West Somerton Borehole terminated at a depth of 987.5 m after penetrating just 8 m of Dinantian limestones; however, at Somerton, 141 m of Dinantian limestones were proved below a depth of 1039.8 m, resting on presumed Lower Palaeozoic rocks (see above) and overlain by a sequence of Coal Measures sandstones. Coring between 1054.3 and 1083.4 m proved grey, brown and reddish brown dolomitic limestones and interbed-

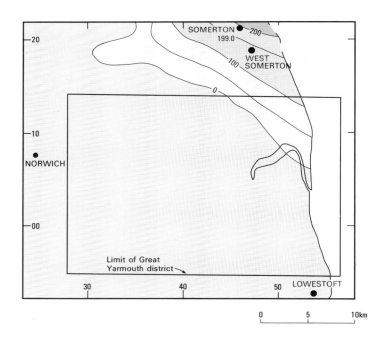

Figure 5 Generalised isopachytes (metres) of Carboniferous rocks.

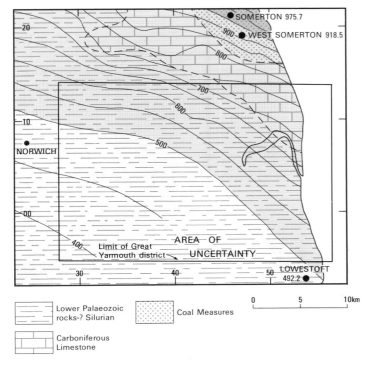

Figure 6 Generalised structure contours (metres below OD) and subcrop at the basal Permian unconformity (in part adapted from Smith, N J P, 1985).

ded pale grey to black mudrocks. Pyrite, galena and calcite mineralisation in the form of subvertical veins, vugs, infilled fossil casts and geodes up to 12 cm across were present throughout. Geophysical log data suggest that below 1100 m the limestone has a higher content of interbedded mudstones; above this depth the limestone appears to be cleaner, but includes some well-defined mudstone interbeds. Samples of *Gigantoproductus* sp. and *?Syringothyris* suggest an Asbian age for the cored interval at Somerton (Mitchell, 1982). Determinations of the foraminifera assemblages suggest that the limestones range in age from Holkerian or early Asbian to late Asbian or Brigantian (Strank, 1982). Conodont determinations (Owens, 1982) also suggest a Holkerian to Brigantian age for the limestones. In addition, fragments of nondiagnostic crinoids, solitary and compound corals, brachiopods and bryozoans have been described from the cuttings.

PERMIAN

Permian rocks proved in boreholes in the adjoining North Walsham district are inferred from seismic evidence to extend into the north-eastern part of the district, where they overstep the Carboniferous and come to rest, with marked unconformity, on Lower Palaeozoic rocks (Figure 6). Totals of 110 m and 89.1 m of Permian rocks were interpreted in the Somerton and West Somerton borehole sequences respectively (Figure 4).

Onshore, a maximum thickness of some 70 m of Permian rocks is predicted beneath the extreme north-east of the district, but they thin to the south-west where they are overstepped by rocks of Triassic age. Structure contours on the base of the Permian are shown in Figure 6.

Following the north–south compression of the Variscan orogeny, the initiation in early Permian times of an east–west tensional stress regime, related to the development of the proto-Atlantic Ocean, resulted in the initial development of the Southern North Sea Basin (Russell, 1976; Ziegler, 1975). The Permian sequence deposited within the basin is divided into a dominantly clastic Lower Permian Rotliegendes sequence and an Upper Permian Zechstein one, dominated by carbonate and evaporitic deposits. The general stratigraphical correlation of the Permian is outlined in detail by Smith et al. (1974), following the nomenclature adopted for the offshore succession (Rhys, 1974). Revisions of the Upper Permian Zechstein nomenclature onshore have been proposed by Smith et al. (1986); the revised nomenclature is compared to that adopted offshore in Table 1. Both the Permian and Triassic sequences of the district have affinities with those of the Southern North Sea Basin (see Chapter three); hence the nomenclature adopted is an adaptation of that outlined by Rhys (1974). No core is available for the Permian successions proved at Somerton and West Somerton, and thus details of lithology are based upon the description of cuttings compared, with the aid of geophysical log correlation, to the sequence cored in the British Coal borehole at Gimmingham (Figure 2).

Lower Permian — Rotliegendes Group

The stratigraphy and sedimentology of the southern North Sea Rotliegendes sequences have been described by Glennie (1972, 1986) and Marie (1975). A summary of the distribution, thickness and properties of the onshore Rotliegendes of the Eastern England Shelf is given in I F Smith, (1985). The economic importance of the Rotliegendes sandstone as a major reservoir formation for the gas fields of the southern North Sea basin has resulted in many detailed studies related to specific gas fields (e.g. van Veen, 1975; France, 1975; Butler, 1975; Gray, 1975; Goodchild and Bryant, 1986). The application in the district of lithostratigraphical divisions is based largely on regional geophysical log correlations. The difficulty in identifying chronostratigraphical divisions in the absence of significant fossil evidence is discussed by Smith et al. (1974).

At Somerton (978.9 m) and West Somerton (943.2m), the Rotliegendes Leman Sandstone Formation rests unconformably on Coal Measures (Westphalian) sandstones (Figure 4). In the north of the district, the Rotliegendes sequence rests directly on Dinantian limestones; in the south, it oversteps these to rest on rocks of Lower Palaeozoic age. The top of the Leman Sandstone is marked by the incoming of a thin muddy carbonate which represents the first carbonate cycle of the Upper Permian Zechstein sequence (Table 1). Some 28.1 m and 18.2 m of Rotliegendes were proved in the Somerton and West Somerton boreholes respectively.

Table 1 Summary of lithostratigraphical nomenclature and correlation of Permian sequences onshore with those in the southern North Sea and the district.

	Cycle		YORKSHIRE PROVINCE (subsurface)	SOUTHERN NORTH SEA BASIN	GREAT YARMOUTH DISTRICT
Z E C H S T E I N	EZ5	GROUP / ESKDALE	ROXBY FORMATION (Upper or Saliferous Marls)	ZECHSTEINLETTEN	'UPPER ZECHSTEIN (Z3-Z5) CLASTICS'
			LITTLEBECK FORMATION (Top Anhydrite)	GRENZANHYDRIT	
			SLEIGHTS (SILTSTONE) FORMATION		
	EZ4	STAINTON-DALE	SNEATON (HALITE) FORMATION; including SNEATON POTASH MEMBER (Upper Halite and Potash)	ALLER HALIT and EQUIVALENTS	
			SHERBURN (ANHYDRITE) FORMATION (Upper Anhydrite)	PEGMATITANHYDRIT and EQUIVALENTS	
			UPGANG FORMATION		
			CARNALLITIC MARL FORMATION	ROTER SALZTON	
	EZ3	TEESSIDE	BOULBY (HALITE) FORMATION; including BOULBY POTASH MEMBER (Middle Halite and Potash)	LEINE HALIT and EQUIVALENTS	
			BILLINGHAM (ANHYDRITE) FORMATION (Billingham Main Anhydrite)	HAUPTANHYDRIT	
			BROTHERTON (MAGNESIAN LIMESTONE) FORMATION (Upper Magnesian Limestone)	PLATTENDOLOMIT	PLATTENDOLOMIT
				GRAUER SALZTON	GRAUER SALZTON
	EZ2	AISLABY	FORDON (EVAPORITE) FORMATION	STASSFURT SALZE	'LOWER ZECHSTEIN (Z1-Z2) CLASTICS'
			KIRKHAM ABBEY FORMATION	HAUPTDOLOMIT	
	EZ1	DON	HAYTON (ANHYDRITE) FORMATION	WERRANHYDRIT	
			CADEBY (MAGNESIAN LIMESTONE) FORMATION	WERRADOLOMIT and ZECHSTEINKALK	ZECHSTEINKALK
			MARL SLATE FORMATION	KUPFERSCHIEFER	? ?
ROTLIEGENDES			YELLOW SANDS (BASAL PERMIAN SANDS)	LEMAN SANDSTONE FORMATION	LEMAN SANDSTONE FORMATION

The Leman Sandstone Formation comprises a red-brown to grey-green sandstone, with subrounded to subangular grains, generally medium grained but ranging from fine to coarse grained; it contains traces of pyrite, calcareous patches and a calcitic and dolomitic cement. At Somerton the lower part of the sequence (964 to 978.9 m) comprises a red and yellow, quartz-rich conglomerate, with clasts of red clay, and a matrix rich in dolomite and silica, with traces of kaolin and pyrite. The sandstones are thought to have been deposited either in ephemeral fluvial/wadi conditions, or in an aeolian environment, adjacent to the emer-gent and eroding London–Brabant Massif, which formed the south-western boundary of the Southern North Sea Basin (Glennie, 1972, 1986; Marie, 1975). The contemporary erosion of the Variscan mountains to the south of Britain provided the main clastic input into the basin, via northerly draining fluvial systems (Marie, 1975).

Upper Permian — Zechstein Group

The Upper Permian Zechstein sequence of the Southern North Sea has been described in outline by Kent (1967) and, with reference to the evaporites, by Brunstrom and Walmsley (1969). The classic work of Taylor and Colter (1975), describing the morphology, distribution and stratigraphy of the five recognised Zechstein cycles (Z1–Z5), based on detailed basinwide borehole correlations, has been updated by the later review of Taylor (1986). The extensive literature for the onshore sequences in eastern England is summarised in Smith et al. (1974, 1986).

By the end of the early Permian, the topography of the sediment source area had been much reduced; hence, the rate of subsidence outstripped sedimentation resulting in a lowering of the level of the Southern North Sea Basin floor. A eustatic rise in sea level, probably related to the deglaciation of Gondwanaland (Smith et al., 1974), resulted in the rapid flooding of the desert basin and the formation of the Zechstein Sea, in which the alternating processes of progressive evaporation and recharge produced complex cycles of carbonate/evaporite sedimentation (Taylor and Colter, 1975; Taylor, 1986). The Zechstein sequence of the district was deposited at the margin of the main Zechstein basin, largely away from marine influence (Taylor and Colter, 1975; Taylor, 1986), and as such shows limited development both of carbonate and of evaporite deposits; it is dominated by the clastic red-bed sequences, which are lateral equivalents of the thick basinal deposits (Taylor, 1986, fig. 4.4). Totals of 82 m and 70.9 m of Zechstein sediments were proved in the Somerton and West Somerton boreholes respectively (Figure 4).

The thin (c. 2 m) basal bed of the Zechstein sequence is the first cycle (Z1) carbonate phase, the Zechsteinkalk (Cadeby [Magnesian Limestone] Formation of Smith et al., 1986), it consists of muddy limestone and calcareous mudstone and rests directly on the Rotliegendes Leman Sandstone Formation (Table 1). Overlying this is a fining-upwards sequence of interbedded, red-brown, white or grey siltstones, very fine- to fine-grained, dolomitic, non- or poorly micaceous, sandstones with angular to subangular grains, and red-brown mudstones. The sequence thins southwards from 35.5 m at Somerton to 22 m at West Somerton, with a predicted maximum development of about 10 m in the north-east of the district. In the absence of chronologically significant fossils, it is not feasible to correlate these beds with those of other similar marginal Permian sequences, such as the Edlington and Roxby formations (Smith et al., 1986), and so the sequence is here broadly classified as the 'Lower Zechstein (Z1–Z2) Clastics'.

At the top of the 'Lower Zechstein Clastics' is a distinctive thin red mudstone (5.2 m at Somerton), probably equivalant to the Grauer Salzton seen offshore (Taylor and Colter, 1975), which is the basal bed of the third Zechstein cycle (Z3) (Table 1). The third cycle carbonate, resting above the mudstone, is the Plattendolomit (Brotherton [Magnesian Limestone] Formation of Smith et al., 1986). The correlative of this at Gimmingham showed a distinctive development of the tabular calcareous alga *Calcinema permiana*, confirming its stratigraphical position. The Plattendolomit is around 8 m thick at Somerton and West Somerton, and comprises a white to pale grey, dominantly fine-grained, crystalline dolomite, with laminations of green, grey and red mudstone and anhydrite. In addition, layers of coarser saccharoidal and coarse vuggy dolomite, and sparse pyrite and sphalerite, have also been described from the sequence. The deposition of the carbonates indicates a period of transgression, the district at this time forming the shelf edge of the Zechstein Sea (Taylor and Colter, 1975). The Z3 carbonate is locally an important seismic reflector; structure contours on the top of the Plattendolomit are shown in Figure 7.

Regression and a return to terrigenous clastic sedimentation at the margins of the London–Brabant Massif resulted in the deposition of the 'Upper Zechstein (Z3–Z5) Clastics'. These sediments comprise a coarsening-upwards sequence of interbedded, white, grey and red siltstones and very fine- to fine-grained sandstones, and red and green mudstones, which attain thicknesses of 32.2m and 33.4 m at Somerton and West Somerton respectively (Figure 4). Little information is available on the detailed sedimentology of the marginal Zechstein clastic sequences, and their conditions of deposition remain somewhat speculative; however, it seems likely that they were formed by a combination of fluvial, aeolian and, with the increased proximity of the Zechstein Sea, possibly even sabkha conditions. Van Adrichem Boogaert and Burgers (1983), working in the Dutch sector of the southern North Sea, have related clastic input during the Z1 cycle to sediments sourced from river systems draining the London–Brabant Massif, supporting the suggestion that similar conditions existed at times within the district. As the Permian sequence thins to the south and

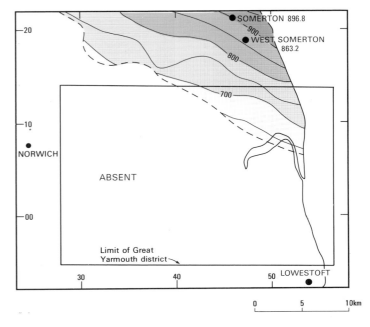

Figure 7 Generalised structure contours (metres below OD) on the top of the Plattendolomit (Brotherton [Magnesian Limestone] Formation).

west beneath the district towards the original basin margin (see section on the published map), it is likely that the carbonates pass laterally into rocks of continental facies, until, at the limits of Zechstein preservation, the sequence is wholly clastic.

The top of the Upper Permian Zechstein sequence in the district is marked by the incoming of the distinctive Hewett Sandstone Member of the Bunter Shale Formation (Bacton Group) of Triassic age (Rhys, 1974).

THREE

Mesozoic

The occurrence of Triassic and Lower Cretaceous sedimentary rocks within the district is inferred from the interpretation of seismic records calibrated against the logs of deep boreholes in the adjoining North Walsham district. The distribution of the Triassic is indicated in Figure 13, and the thickness variations of the Triassic and Lower Cretaceous across the northern flank of the London–Brabant Platform are illustrated in a horizontal section on the published map. The Chalk (Upper Cretaceous) crops out in the Yare valley in the extreme western part of the district and has been penetrated in a number of boreholes sunk for water supply.

Cox et al. (1989, fig. 4) indicated the presence of Jurassic rocks in the north of the district; however, borehole and seismic data suggest that erosion following the late-Cimmerian uplift has removed these from the district (Figure 13).

Figure 56 demonstrates the broad relationship of Mesozoic rocks within the district, which lies at the northern margin of the London–Brabant Platform. The platform continued to act as a positive structural unit throughout the Triassic and Jurassic, it was not until the late Lower Cretaceous that the platform was completely overstepped by the Gault (Owen, 1971). The disposition of the Mesozoic sequence is affected by two major unconformities, related to late-Cimmerian (late Jurassic–early Cretaceous) (Fyfe et al., 1981; Ziegler, 1981) and post-Cretaceous erosion.

TRIASSIC

Early work on the Triassic stratigraphy of the Southern North Sea Basin and its landward continuation by Geiger and Hopping (1968) has been updated by the later reviews of Brennand (1975) and Fisher (1986). Summaries of the relevant work on similar sequences in eastern England are contained in Warrington et al. (1980).

Rocks of Triassic age proved in the adjoining North Walsham district are interpreted from seismic evidence to overstep the Permian sequence and to rest on Lower Palaeozoic (?Silurian) basement beneath much of the northern half of the district. Southerly thinning and progressively deeper erosion has resulted in their eventual overstep by rocks of early Cretaceous age (Figure 56). The stratigraphy of the Triassic sequence proved in the Somerton and West Somerton boreholes to the north of the district (Figure 8, Appendix 2) has been interpreted in terms of the southern North Sea nomenclature outlined by Rhys (1974). These offshore lithostratigraphical units and their eastern England equivalents are shown in Table 2. The Bacton Group corresponds approximately to the Sherwood Sandstone Group and the Haisborough Group to the Mercia Mudstone Group.

The base of the Triassic is taken at the incoming of the distinctive Hewett Sandstone Member, marked by a basal conglomerate and a distinctive geophysical log signature (Figure 8). Youngest Triassic rocks of Rhaetian age are absent from the district, having been removed by early Jurassic erosion.

The hot and arid conditions of the Permian persisted during the Triassic, with rejuvenation of Hercynian massifs in early Triassic times, and gradual peneplanation by late Triassic times resulting in the establishment of low-lying continental-interior basins which underwent stronger subsidence. The London–Brabant Massif was only moderately elevated and provided little coarse detritus.

Bacton Group (Sherwood Sandstone Group equivalent)

The Bacton Group, approximately equivalent to the Sherwood Sandstone Group (Warrington et al., 1980), is divided into a lower, dominantly argillaceous Bunter Shale Formation and an upper, mainly arenaceous, Bunter Sandstone Formation (Table 2). In the north of the district their combined thickness is around 90 m, thinning to the south (Figure 9) where, beneath Gorleston-on-Sea, they are overstepped by the Haisborough Group. Generalised structure contours on the top of the Bacton Group are shown in Figure 11.

BUNTER SHALE FORMATION

At the base of the Bunter Shale Formation is the Hewett Sandstone Member, a distinctive sandstone of limited lateral extent, found to the north of the London–Brabant Platform (Brennand 1975). It comprises a white to grey, quartz-rich, subrounded to rounded, poorly to moderately sorted, fine- to medium-grained sandstone containing traces of pyrite and anhydrite cement. The sediments are thought to have been derived from the moderately rejuvenated London–Brabant Platform (Cumming and Wyndham, 1975). At Somerton and West Somerton (Figure 2; Appendix 2) the Hewett Sandstone Member is 17.8 m and 15.5 m in thickness respectively (Figure 8). It thickens offshore where, in the Hewett Gas Field, up to 61.5 m were proved (Cumming and Wyndham, 1975). Generalised structure contours on the top of the Hewett Sandstone Member are shown in Figure 10.

Between the Hewett Sandstone Member and the main body of the Bunter Shale Formation, there is a gradational fining-upwards sequence of laminated, red-brown, locally anhydritic, silty mudstones, with interbedded argillaceous, slightly dolomitic, fine-grained sandstones and siltstones. These may represent the lateral equivalents of the Bröckelschiefer as described in the Hewett Gas Field by Cumming and Wyndham (1975). A maximum thickness of around 10 m beneath the north of the district is predicted; with 12.1 m and 12.4 m were proved in the Somerton and West Somerton boreholes respectively.

At Somerton and West Somerton, 85.9 m and 81.4 m of Bunter Shale Formation respectively were penetrated.

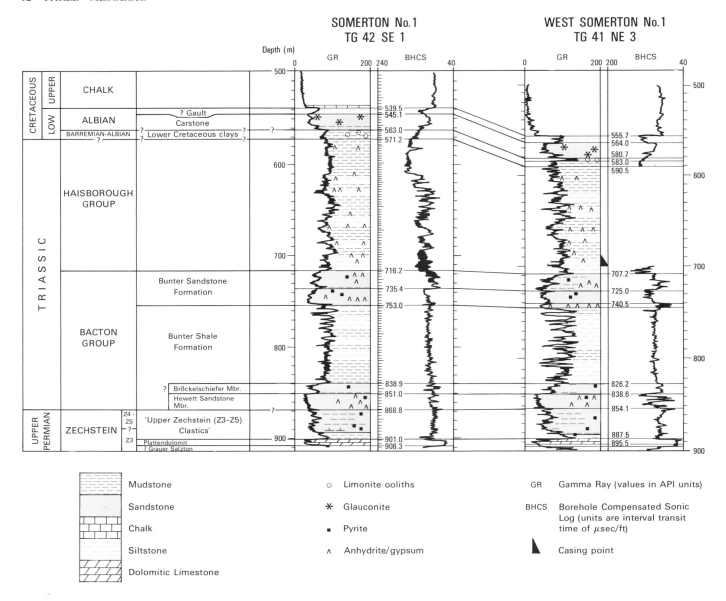

Figure 8 Triassic stratigraphy of the Somerton No.1 and West Somerton No.1 boreholes; borehole locations shown in Figure 2.

The formation comprises a sequence of red to brown, anhydritic mudstones and minor green shales, interbedded with white to greenish white siltstones and fine-grained sandstones, giving the formation a characteristic 'spikey' log signature (Figure 8). The Bunter Shale Formation is thought to have accumulated in lacustrine or floodplain conditions within an early Triassic playa lake or inland sea (Fisher, 1986).

BUNTER SANDSTONE FORMATION

The boundary between the Bunter Shale Formation and the Bunter Sandstone Formation is markedly diachronous in the southern North Sea (Fisher, 1986). At Somerton and West Somerton, 36.8 m and 37.6 m respectively of the latter were penetrated. The lithology of the

formation, described from drill cuttings and analysis of geophysical log data (Figure 8), is dominantly a grey, white or light yellow, subrounded to rounded, poorly sorted, medium- to fine-grained sandstone. Traces of pyrite, calcite and dolomite were recorded; also gypsum, which becomes more abundant towards the base of the formation. Interbedded mudstones are interpreted from the geophysical logs, and coarser-grained beds are represented in the cuttings. A break in the sonic velocity (Somerton 735.4 m, West Somerton 725.0 m) is probably due to an increase in the degree of anhydrite cementation in the upper part of the sandstone.

The Bunter Sandstone Formation is thought to have been deposited under arid conditions in a combination of fluvial, sheet-flood and lacustrine environments (Fisher, 1986).

Table 2   Summary of lithostratigraphical nomenclature and correlation of Triassic sequences onshore with those in the southern North Sea (after Warrington et al., 1980).

		OFFSHORE NOMENCLATURE adapted from RHYS (1974)		EASTERN ENGLAND NOMENCLATURE after WARRINGTON et al. (1980)		GREAT YARMOUTH DISTRICT	
T R I A S S I C	Rhaetian	HAISBOROUGH GROUP	WINTERTON FORMATION	PENARTH GROUP	MERCIA MUDSTONE GROUP	HAISBOROUGH GROUP	
			? ———— ?	?			
	Norian		TRITON ANHYDRITE FORMATION				?
	Carnian		DUDGEON SALIFEROUS FORMATION				
	Ladinian		DOWSING DOLOMITIC FORMATION				
	Anisian						
	Scythian	BACTON GROUP	BUNTER SANDSTONE FORMATION	SHERWOOD SANDSTONE GROUP	NOTTINGHAM CASTLE FORMATION	BACTON GROUP	BUNTER SANDSTONE FORMATION
							BUNTER SHALE FM.
			BUNTER SHALE FM.		LENTON SANDSTONE FORMATION		BRÖCKELSCHIEFER MBR.
			HEWETT SANDSTONE MBR.				HEWETT SANDSTONE MBR.
PERMIAN			? ——— ? ZECHSTEIN	ESKDALE GROUP	Saliferous Marls	ZECHSTEIN	'UPPER ZECHSTEIN CLASTICS'

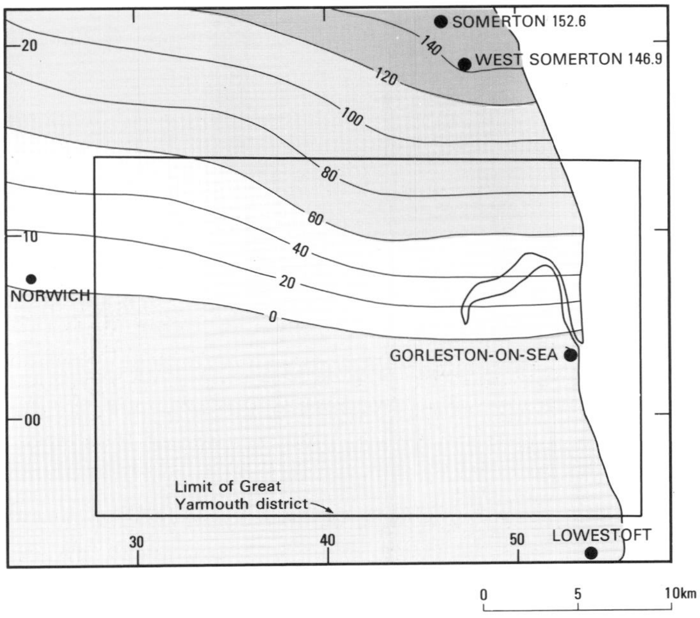

Figure 9   Generalised isopachytes (metres) of the Bacton Group.

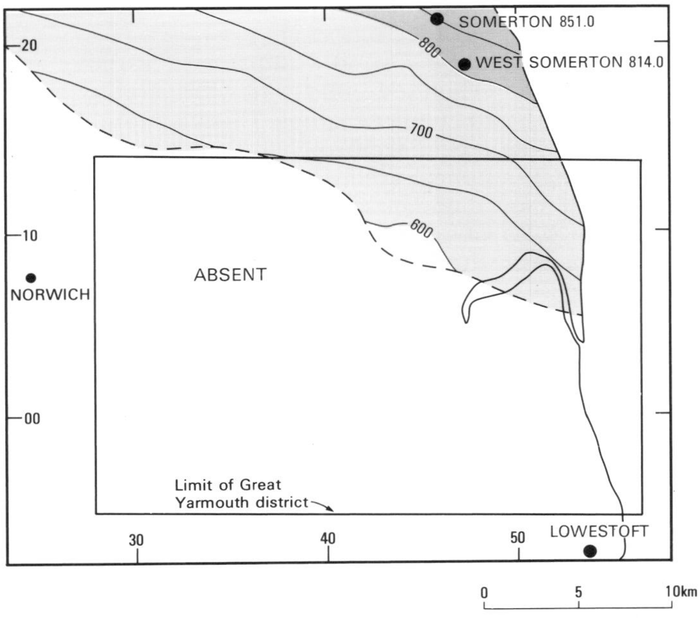

Figure 10   Structure contours (metres below OD) on the top of the Hewett Sandstone Member.

Haisborough Group (Mercia Mudstone Group equivalent)

The Haisborough Group (Rhys, 1974) is a dominantly fine-grained sequence of sedimentary rocks, equivalent to the Mercia Mudstone Group of eastern England (Warrington et al., 1980), with which the sequence in the district has more affinities than the more evaporitic sequence proved in the southern North Sea (Brennand, 1975; Fisher, 1986). However, because the offshore nomenclature is used for the Permian and early Triassic sequences of the district, it is also adopted here for the younger Triassic rocks, for the sake of consistency. (Table 2). None of the subdivisions recognised in the offshore sequences (Rhys, 1974; Brennand, 1975), nor the sequence proved in the East Midlands (Elliott, 1961; Balchin and Ridd, 1970), can yet be reliably identified in the district.

At Somerton and West Somerton the base of the group is indicated by the incoming of fine-grained sediments above the Bunter Sandstone Formation (Figure 8). Elsewhere, this boundary has been shown to represent a period of erosion related to the 'Hardegsen Disconformity' (Geiger and Hopping, 1968), although this cannot be clearly demonstrated within the district. A major unconformity at the top of the group, related to late-Cimmerian (late Jurassic–early Cretaceous) erosion, has resulted in the removal of Jurassic and late Triassic (Rhaetian) rocks from the district. The suceeding Lower Cretaceous beds overstep the Haisborough Group and come to rest on the Lower Palaeozoic to the south of Great Yarmouth (Figure 56 and section on the published map). Structure contours on the top of the Bacton Group (Figure 11) and the base of the Cretaceous rocks (Figure 13), define the thickness of the Haisborough Group within the district (Figure 12). Some 145 m and 116.7 m of Haisborough Group were proved at Somerton (571.2 to 716.2 m) and West Somerton (590.5 to 707.2 m) respectively, with about 80 m inferred in the extreme north-east of the district, onshore.

The Haisborough Group comprises a variable sequence of interbedded mudstones, siltstones, fine-grained sandstones and evaporites. The mudstones range in colour from red or red-brown to light green or grey; they are either noncalcareous or slightly calcareous and locally contain abundant gypsum or anhydrite cement and thin beds of microcrystalline anhydrite. Sporadic thicker beds of white or clear, microcrystalline or fibrous anhydrite or gypsum are present through the sequence (e.g. at about 670 m and about 630 m in the Somerton Borehole, Figure 8). The siltstones and very fine- to fine-grained sandstones are generally white or green, and less commonly red or brown, and are mainly composed of angular and well-sorted, loose quartz grains, with calcite, anhydrite and, towards the base, dolomitic cements.

The Haisborough Group was deposited, during a period of greater tectonic stability than the Bacton Group, within a low-lying basin subject to rapid transgressions related to minor rises in sea level. Sedimentation was mainly in distal floodplain environments alternating with coastal sabkha or shallow-marine environments (Fisher, 1986).

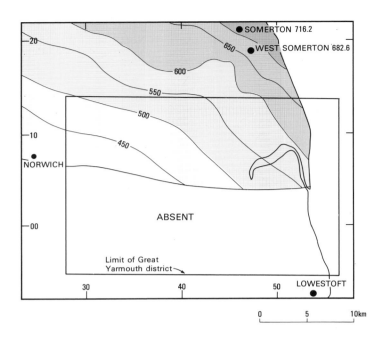

Figure 11 Structure contours (metres below OD) on the top of the Bacton Group.

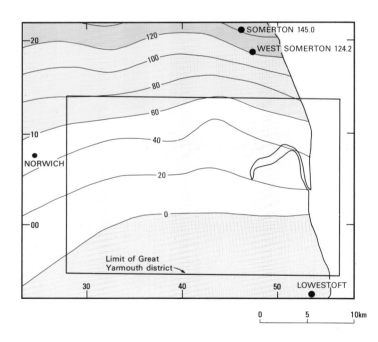

Figure 12 Generalised isopachytes (metres) of the Haisborough Group.

LOWER CRETACEOUS

Rocks of Lower Cretaceous age, proved in the adjoining North Walsham, Lowestoft and Norwich districts, are inferred to be present throughout the Great Yarmouth district. They rest with marked unconformity on Triassic and, in the south, Lower Palaeozoic rocks (Figure 13),

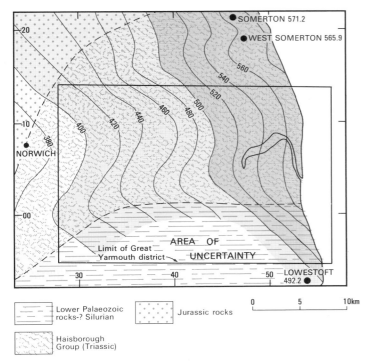

Figure 13 Structure contours (metres below OD) and subcrop at the base Cretaceous unconformity.

Key:
- Lower Palaeozoic rocks-? Silurian
- Jurassic rocks
- Haisborough Group (Triassic)

0   5   10km

which were eroded following the late-Cimmerian uplift; this uplift has been related to a combination of post-extensional isostatic recovery and global sea-level fall (Chadwick, 1985a).

The stratigraphy of the Cretaceous period in Britain is summarised in Rawson et al. (1978). Reviews of the Lower Cretaceous sequence in Norfolk (Larwood, 1961; Chatwin, 1961; Gallois, 1984) and studies of specific Lower Cretaceous formations, for example the Lower Greensand (Casey, 1961), the Gault (Gallois and Morter, 1982) and the various Sandringham Sands, (Casey and Gallois, 1973), give little specific information on the sequence within the district. Hancock (1986) has summarised the offshore Lower Cretaceous succession, termed the Cromer Knoll Group (Rhys, 1974).

Figure 8 shows the Lower Cretaceous sequence to the north of the district at Somerton and West Somerton based, in the absence of any core material or biostratigraphical evidence, on the interpretation of drill cuttings and geophysical log characteristics. In these boreholes, the boundaries between the Lower Cretaceous and Triassic sequences are problematical. Regional geophysical log correlations in north Norfolk demonstrate the removal by erosion of the Rhaetian and upper parts of the Haisborough Group rocks. This work also indicates that much of what have been described as ?Barremian clays are in fact part of the Haisborough Group. However, the presence of abundant goethite ooliths within pink and olive-green soft clays is probably indicative of a Lower Cretaceous age for part of the sequence. The base of the Cretaceous at Somerton and West Somerton is thus tentatively placed at

571.2 m and 590.5 m respectively, with 8.2 m and 9.8 m of clays preserved in these boreholes. Elsewhere in north-eastern Norfolk, strata of Albian age are inferred to rest directly on pre-Cretaceous rocks (see below).

Rocks of Barremian age have not been recognised in this part of East Anglia before. Their thinness in the Somerton boreholes and absence from the Lowestoft Borehole and boreholes to the north of Somerton (e.g. Trunch, Appendix 1) indicate a limited development. However, the presence in west Norfolk of derived Barremian fossils in the Carstone (Casey and Gallois, 1973) provides evidence for a more extensive original deposition of Barremian rocks. It may be that the clays at Somerton and West Somerton can be interpreted as a preserved outlier of such deposits, which would be at a stratigraphical position similar to the Dersingham Beds (?Snettisham Clay equivalent) of west Norfolk (Casey and Gallois, 1973; Rawson et al., 1978). Alternatively, and much more likely, these clays may represent an easterly extension of the succession known in the southern North Sea. However, in the absence of core material and bio-stratigraphical control, their classification remains speculative; hence, they are here described as 'Lower Cretaceous (Barremian) Clays' and identified on the generalised vertical section of the published map as unnamed clays of Barremian age.

The Carstone (Lower Greensand) proved to the north (Somerton, 545.1 to 563.0 m; West Somerton, 564.0 to 580.7 m) (Figure 8), south (Lowestoft, 483.4 to 495.9 m) and west of the district (Cox et al., 1989) is inferred to be present throughout the district. It is of Albian age (Rawson et al., 1978; Gallois and Morter, 1982) and thins southwards from 17.9 m at Somerton to 12.5 m at Lowestoft. It comprises a poorly cemented, green or white, goethitic medium- to coarse-grained sandstone, with minor mudstone interbeds, and coarsens upwards. It is inferred to have been deposited in a relatively high energy, shallow-marine shoreline environment to the north of the London–Brabant Platform.

The succeeding Gault is the oldest preserved formation to have entirely covered the London–Brabant Platform (Owen, 1971); it oversteps earlier Lower Cretaceous formations to rest directly on Lower Palaeozoic rocks to the south of the district (Gallois and Morter, 1982; Millward et al., 1987).

The detailed stratigraphy of the Gault in northern East Anglia has been described by Gallois and Morter (1982). It is proved to the north (Somerton, 539.5 to 545.1 m; West Somerton, 555.7 to 564.0 m) (Figure 8), south (Lowestoft, 469.69 to 483.4 m) and west of the district (Norwich, 351.67 to 362.65 m, the total depth), and is inferred to be present throughout the district. It thins northwards from 13.72 m at Lowestoft to 5.6 m at Somerton and passes laterally into the condensed Red Chalk sequence of north Norfolk (e.g. Trunch Borehole, Appendix 1); it thickens to the west towards its outcrop in west Norfolk (Gallois and Morter, 1982). The Gault comprises fining-upwards cycles of pale to dark grey, silty and sandy mudstones, which contain numerous phosphate- and glauconite-rich erosion surfaces (Gallois and Morter, 1982), and is thought to have been deposited in a shallow marine embayment between the London–Brabant Platform and a shoal of Red Chalk to the north.

To the south of the district, at Lowestoft (Strahan, 1913), and to the west, at Norwich (Whitaker, 1921), a thin development of ?Upper Greensand succeeds the Gault, and is probably present in the southern part of the Great Yarmouth district. The Upper Greensand is described in Lowestoft Borehole as a green clay and chalk, with black sand, 3.35 m in thickness (466.34 to 469.69 m) (Strahan, 1913); at Norwich, only 1.83 m of sands are described in Carrow Works Borehole (349.84 to 351.67 m) (Whitaker, 1921).

UPPER CRETACEOUS — CHALK GROUP

The three lithostratigraphical subdivisions of the Chalk Group, the Lower, Middle and Upper Chalk, underlie the district completely. Exposures are very restricted, occurring on both sides of the Yare valley in the extreme west where the Chalk surface dips generally to the east. The Chalk disappears from view altogether beneath the river bed east of Bramerton Common [297 061]. The exposed Chalk belongs entirely to the Upper Chalk, and specifically to the highest part of the Upper Campanian Zone of *Belemnitella mucronata* sensu lato and the lowest part of the Lower Maastrichtian Zone of *Belemnella lanceolata* sensu lato (Table 3). The boundary between the Campanian and Maastrichtian stages is inferred to lie in the vicinity of Bramerton.

The biostratigraphy, lithology and structure of the Chalk in Norfolk were the subjects of a comprehensive review by Peake and Hancock (1961), and its revision by the same authors (1970). The lithostratigraphy, biostratigraphy and history of research, of the Norwich district, were further updated by Wood (1988) from studies carried out as part of the geological survey of the Norwich (161) Sheet. Wood's account was summarised in the Norwich memoir (Cox et al., 1989).

All three of the Chalk subdivisions have been penetrated in deep boreholes sited just beyond the limits of the district, including those at Norwich, Somerton and West Somerton, and Lowestoft (Figure 2). Abstracts of the logs of these boreholes are given in Appendix 2, and part of the stratigraphy of Somerton Borehole is illustrated in Figure 17. Correlation of the downhole geophysical logs of these boreholes, and of others farther afield, with those of the fully cored sequence of the Trunch Borehole (Figure 17; Appendix 1) has enabled the recognition of the Lower, Middle and Upper Chalk subdivisions, and the estimation of the positions of some zonal boundaries. These results are applicable to the interpretation of the Chalk stratigraphy of the district.

The preserved Chalk Group has a thickness of some 434 m and 423.7 m at Somerton and West Somerton respectively. Its maximum thickness under the Crag at the western boundary of the district was estimated to be in the range 375 to 385 m (Cox et al., 1989), while in the Lowestoft Borehole only 321.6 m were recorded. Generalised isopachs of the Chalk Group (Figure 16) show an extrapolated southerly thinning within the district from about 420 m in the north, near Caister-on-Sea, to less than 340 m south of Corton. Structure contours on the

Table 3 Chalk Group, Trunch Borehole: biostratigraphical zones recognised and the depths of occurrence of zonal boundaries.

UPPER CHALK	*Belemnella lanceolata* s.l.		
		c.61m	
	Belemnitella mucronata s.l.		
		209.07m	
	Gonioteuthis quadrata		
		272.50m	
	Offaster pilula		
		306.72m	
	Marsupites testudinarius		
		?	
	Uintacrinus socialis		
		335.26m	
	Micraster coranguinum		
		411.50m	
	Micraster cortestudinarium		
		432.03m	
	Sternotaxis plana		
		469.32m	
MIDDLE CHALK	*Terebratulina lata*		
		493.97m	
	'*Mytiloides labiatus* s.l.'*		
		500.51m	
LOWER CHALK	*Metoicoceras geslinianum*		
		501.10m	
	Calycoceras guerangeri		
		c.502m	
	Acanthoceras jukesbrownei		
		502.32m?	
	Acanthoceras rhotomagense		
		506.30m?	
	Mantelliceras dixoni		
		509.80m	
	Mantelliceras mantelli		
		512.22m	

*includes an unnamed zone, the *Mytiloides* spp. Zone and the *Neocardioceras juddii* Zone

MIDDLE CHALK	M.Tur.	unnamed Zone	493.97m
			496.00m
	L.Tur.	*Mytilodes* spp.	
			500.07m
LOWER CHALK	Cenomanian	*Neocardioceras juddii*	
			500.51m
		Metoicoceras geslinianum	
			501.10m

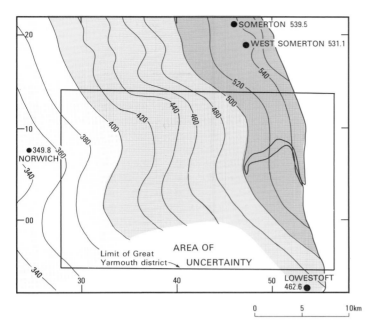

Figure 14 Structure contours (metres below OD) on the base of the Chalk Group.

The principal lithology of the Chalk Group is white, micritic, coccolith limestone that is generally rather poorly cemented and porous. The Lower Chalk, Middle Chalk and basal part of the Upper Chalk of the district can be inferred from the Trunch Borehole to be comparable with the Ferriby Chalk, Welton Chalk and basal Burnham Chalk formations respectively of the Northern Province, in North Yorkshire, Humberside and Lincolnshire (Wood and Smith, 1978; Mortimore and Wood, 1986; Wood, 1992), but considerably condensed. However, the greater part of the Upper Chalk proved in the Trunch Borehole has greater affinity with the Chalk of southern Britain.

On the evidence of borehole provings elsewhere in north-east Norfolk, the Lower Chalk in the district is estimated to be some 12 to 15 m thick and is less pure than the Middle and Upper Chalk. It is grey in colour and flintless, with some hardgrounds and several horizons of dark grey, shell detrital, silty chalk. The Middle Chalk, some 31 m thick in the Trunch Borehole, is almost flintless (flints at only two horizons) and includes seams of marl; beds of shell-detrital chalk are common in the lower part of the sequence. The only reliable data for the thickness of the Upper Chalk come from the Trunch Borehole, where a value of 423.62 m has been determined (see Appendix 1). In the district, a maximum of some 375 m has been inferred in the north-east by extrapolation. The Upper Chalk is mainly white, though has locally been described as yellow at outcrop. It is conspicuously rich in flint, which occurs either as nodules or tabular forms, or, in the higher part of the section, as paramoudras, cylindrical bodies up to 1 to 2 m high and 0.5 m in diameter, formed around the ichnofossil *Bathichnus paramoudrae* (Bromley et al., 1975; Clayton, 1986).

Differential subsidence of the London–Brabant Massif has resulted in northerly thinning of the Lower and Mid-

base of the Chalk (Figure 14) show a gentle (0.25° to 0.5°) easterly to north-easterly dipping surface over most of the district. The top of the Chalk (Figure 15) is formed of two principal erosion surfaces. To the west of the feather-edge of the Thanet Formation subcrop, the erosion surface is that of the Crag marine transgression (see Chapter five; Figure 27); its general dip is similar to that seen in the adjoining Norwich district, where progressively higher Chalk strata are preserved eastwards. The feather-edge of the Thanet Formation marks the preserved western limit of a slightly more steeply (easterly) inclined Thanetian (early Tertiary) erosion surface.

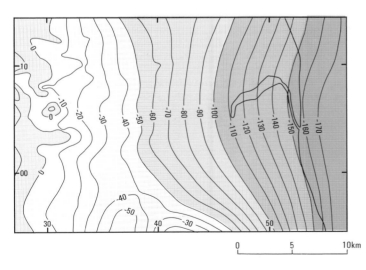

Figure 15 Structure contours (metres below OD) on the top of the Chalk Group (*computer-generated plot derived from the borehole database*).

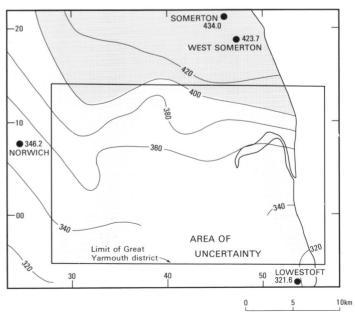

Figure 16 Generalised isopachytes (metres) of the Chalk Group.

dle Chalk within the district (Figure 17) and may be related to the effects of the postulated Wash–Saxthorpe Granite which approaches the northern part of the district (see chapters two and nine). In contrast, the Upper Chalk thickens to the north and east, towards the Southern North Sea Basin, as does the Chalk Group as a whole (see Figure 16).

The Chalk has suffered a number of weathering and erosional episodes. Where the London Clay Formation or the underlying Thanet Formation is preserved, the erosion surface at the top of the Chalk is of Palaeocene age. Where the Crag rests directly on the Chalk, the erosion surface is of late Pliocene or early Pleistocene age; here, the uppermost few centimetres of the Chalk are commonly indurated and stained brown. Over wide areas, the uppermost part of the Chalk is represented by a soft, weak material known as putty chalk, recorded in borehole logs as extending to depths of several metres in places. It is unclear to what extent this condition is an original feature of the rock or has resulted from weathering.

Locally in the Yare valley, at the western margin of the district, Anglian glacial deposits immediately overlie the Chalk; the possibility that some of the Chalk outcrops in this area are not in situ but rather those of glacially emplaced rafts has been suggested (Wood, 1988; Cox et al., 1989). Sites at which there is evidence of glaciotectonic disturbance of superficial Chalk have been documented from adjoining parts of the Norwich district (Woodward, 1881; Wood, 1988). A complex system of valleys cut into the Chalk of East Anglia, and now largely buried by sediments, was documented by Woodland (1970), who proposed that they were eroded by Anglian subglacial streams flowing under hydrostatic pressure. One such valley, known to be cut into Chalk to 14.6 m below OD, in a borehole [253 084] at Thorpe St Andrew, just within the Norwich district, is inferred to extend eastwards into this district under the Yare valley, forming a trench in the Chalk surface.

The Upper Chalk in the now abandoned pit at Thorpe Tollgate [2830 0894] probably provided material to be burnt for use as agricultural lime, and flints to be used mainly for building purposes, but also for gunflints. Farther west, in and around the city of Norwich, the Chalk was worked over many hundreds of years by means of tunnels or galleries driven into the hillsides, thus avoiding the need to remove any overburden. No such underground workings of Chalk are known within the district, though the possibility of their existence should not be ruled out, particularly in view of the potential hazards implicit in subsidence caused by roof collapse (see Cox et al., 1989, p.27).

Biostratigraphy

No comprehensive biostratigraphical record is available for the Chalk of the district. In the adjoining Norwich district, biostratigraphical details are restricted to the upper part of the Upper Chalk (Wood, 1988). For this memoir, the biostratigraphy has been extrapolated from the fully cored Trunch Borehole [2933 3455] (Figure 18; Appendix 1) sunk in the Mundesley (132) district by the Institute of Geological Sciences in 1975. This borehole proved a total

Chalk thickness of 466.52 m and represents the most complete cored sequence of the Chalk Group in Britain.

A preliminary biostratigraphical interpretation was given by Gallois and Morter (1976). The account given in Appendix 1 is based partly on the unpublished, original detailed written and graphic logs of the borehole by A A Morter, and partly on a recent reassessment of the total stratigraphy by C J Wood. Some of the reassessment departs to a greater or lesser extent from the published interpretation, particularly that of the base of the Maastrichtian Stage (*Belemnella lanceolata* s.l. Zone). Some boundaries have been recognised for the first time, in particular the base of the *quadrata* Zone and the two subzones of the underlying *Offaster pilula* Zone. The position of the base of the *Sternotaxis plana* Zone (and consequently the base of Upper Chalk) has been revised downwards by some 15 m from that published by Gallois and Morter (1976) and used subsequently by Whittaker et al. (1985, fig. 40) for the stratigraphical calibration of the sonic log of this borehole. The revised calibration has been applied to the interpretation of the wireline logs of other deep boreholes in north-east Norfolk (Figure 17). Despite this revision, much work remains to be carried out on the biostratigraphy of the Trunch Borehole. A summary of the known biostratigraphy of the borehole is given in Table 3 with the principal lithostratigraphical subdivisions indicated. Depth ranges are quoted, with thicknesses shown in parentheses. Fuller details may be found in Appendix 1.

Details

Postwick–Bramerton

A pit at Thorpe Tollgate [2830 0894] is now backfilled, but must have been very large and deep. It is the third and most easterly of the pits east of Thorpe village recorded by Woodward (1881) and may be the source of some of the fossils in old collections labelled 'Thorpe'. The Chalk is overlain by Crag from which Fitch (1836) recorded a Mastodon tooth. A 1 m section seen in the late 1970s by Wood (1988) comprised richly fossiliferous, hard, yellow chalk with poorly preserved sponges and baculitid ammonites above and below a thalassinoid flint. The fauna included brachiopods and calcitic bivalves, as well as moulds of originally aragonite-shelled bivalves, gastropods and scaphopods; the only belemnite present was the relatively long-ranging late Campanian species *Belemnitella* cf. *najdini*. Despite the fact that no echinoids were collected, a Campanian Paramoudra$_2$ horizon, slightly above that of the nearby Thorpe St Andrews pit [2755 0900] in the adjoining Norwich district, was inferred. It should be noted, however, that the general aspect of the lithology and fauna is similar to that in the presumed Lower Maastrichtian Chalk of the Bramerton sewer trench and river bank sections, discussed below.

The only extant permanent Chalk exposure in the district is the 2 m section in the former river cliff at Postwick Grove [2866 0801]. It lies at or about the stratigraphical level of the Thorpe Tollgate pit and was considered by Wood (1988) probably to represent the highest in-situ Upper Campanian in Norfolk. However, Mr P S Whittlesea (written communication, 1990) considers that this locality is topographically too high in relation to the river bed exposures to be in situ, and it is possible that the section is cut in a glacial erratic. This interpretation is supported by obvious slickensiding on vertical joints. The lower part of the section resembles that at the Thorpe Toll-

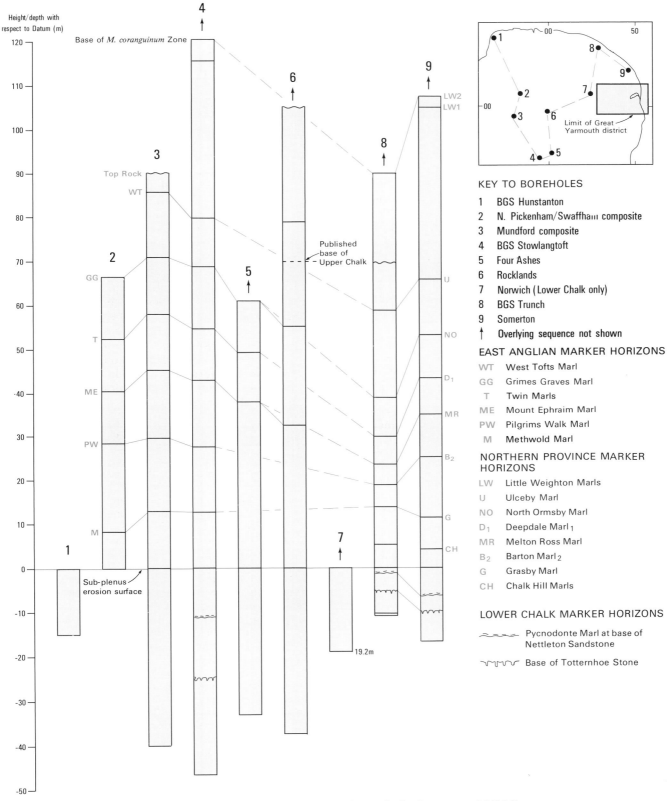

Figure 17 Chalk Group: comparative borehole sections through the Lower and Middle Chalk in northern East Anglia. The datum is taken at the sub-Plenus erosion surface; it approximates to the Lower–Middle Chalk boundary. The horizon GG/NO has been used as the geophysical marker for the base of the Upper Chalk although the actual position lies between GG/NO and T/D$_1$.

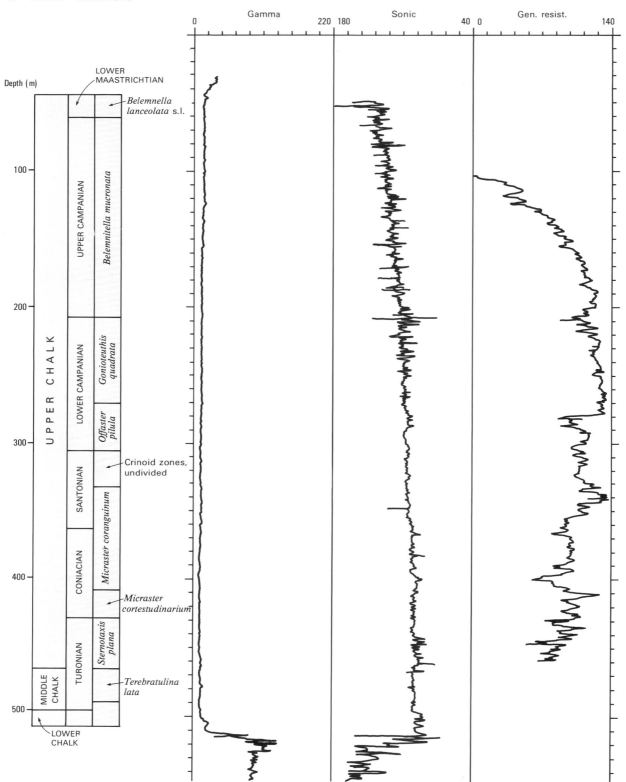

Figure 18   Chalk Group, Trunch Borehole: section showing chronostratigraphical stages, zonal classification and downhole geophysical logs. Details of the Lower and Middle Chalk are shown in Figure 17.

gate pit, in that a thalassinoid burrow-form flint occurs within a bed of hardened orange-yellow chalk containing sponges and moulds of originally aragonite-shelled molluscs including baculitids. Mr P S Whittlesea (written communication, 1990) has collected a well-preserved scaphitid from this bed, which has not yet been investigated. The overlying beds (Wood, 1988) terminate in a single or complex chalkstone with a line of flints, the contact with the Crag being seen at the top of the section. The relative abundance of *Micraster ciplyensis* places this locality in the higher part of the Campanian rather than in the Lower Maastrichtian.

Small beach exposures of Chalk are seen intermittently at low water [2869 0768] on the north side of the River Yare near Postwick, downstream from Postwick Grove; the top of the Chalk was reported to be disturbed (Wood, 1988). The fact that the chalk here is white rather than yellow, as at Postwick Grove and the Thorpe pits immediately to the west, may indicate a correlation with the successions in the two Whitlingham Sewage Works excavations on the opposite (south) side of the river (see below). The limited fauna (Wood, 1988) includes *Micraster* of the *ciplyensis–grimmensis* group, so a high Campanian position can be inferred. This is supported by the foraminiferal assemblage (Swiecicki, 1980), which contains common *Bolivinoides miliaris*; the abundant planktonic foraminifera are dominated by forms transitional between *Archaeoglobigerina cretacea* and *Rugoglobigerina rugosa*. The microfauna indicates an horizon high in the topmost Upper Campanian Zone B4 (Swiecicki, 1980) [= UKB19 of the current benthonic foraminifer zonation].

In an extensive temporary section in the late 1970s at Whitlingham Sewage Works [278 086], the Chalk was situated at about 10 m above OD and overlain by Crag. It appeared to be part of a gigantic glacial raft, since till was observed dipping beneath the Chalk at one end of the excavation. The section exposed very poorly fossiliferous white chalk with one or more bands of small thalassinoid burrow-form flints; no detailed measurements are available. The sparse fauna (housed mainly in Norwich Castle Museum) includes *Cretirhynchia* cf. *arcuata*, *Belemnitella* cf. *najdini*, *Echinocorys* ex gr. *belgica* and *Micraster* ex gr. *ciplyensis–grimmensis*. The *Micraster* indicates a Paramoudra₂ horizon, and the *Echinocorys* are of the distinctive type (*Echinocorys pyramidata* sensu Wright *non* Lambert) that characterises topmost Campanian successions elsewhere; this form is common in the derived blocks of hard yellow chalk on the foreshore reef west of Overstrand, which are inferred to represent a terminal Campanian hardground (Peake and Hancock, 1961, p.339G). *Echinocorys* material collected by Mr P G Cambridge from the raft (housed in the Sedgwick Museum, Cambridge) includes forms of probable Lower Maastrichtian Porosphaera Beds provenance (Whittlesea, 1991), introducing the possibility that the succession may have included glaciotectonic slices comparable with those in the Overstrand Hotel masses (Wood, 1967; Peake and Hancock, 1970), or that it spanned the Campanian–Maastrichtian boundary.

A recent temporary section [281 077], east of the Whitlingham Sewage Works locality and on low ground close to the river, currently exposes up to 4 m of extremely soft, white chalk; an additional 7 m of the same lithology were proved in trenches below the water table. The section is obscured behind shuttering and it has not proved possible to obtain detailed measurements. Material collected from the dumps includes abundant paramoudras and a few circular flints up to 0.6 m in diameter and 0.45 m thick, of a type hitherto unrecorded in Norfolk (Mr N B Peake, personal communication, 1990). Apart from a single *Cardiaster* and uncommon *Belemnitella* sp. (presumably *Belemnitella* cf. *najdini*), the chalk appears to be almost totally devoid of complete macrofossils, possibly due to their low preservation potential in the soft sediment. However, washed residue from bulk samples contains much fragmentary echinoid test material including *Cardiaster, Echinocorys, Galerites*, abundant rostra of *Hagenowia elongata* and *Micraster*, in addition to a rich mesofauna, over 100 taxa having been recorded by Mr P S Whittlesea (personal communication, 1990 and in preparation). The occurrence of *Micraster* places this succession in the Campanian. It may well correlate with the unexposed succession between the foreshore reef opposite Cromer Lighthouse, which contains abundant *Echinocorys* and *Micraster ciplyensis* (Peake and Hancock, 1970, pp. 339F–G), and the hardground with abundant *Echinocorys pyramidata* at Overstrand. In terms of the Norwich succession, it must overlie the richly fossiliferous chalks of Thorpe St Andrews and Thorpe Tollgate (Paramoudra₂) and may constitute a third unit, which may be provisionally termed Paramoudra₃. In view of the low topographical position of this exposure compared with that of the presumed raft to the west, it is likely that the Chalk here is in situ, rather than part of a raft.

Chalk excavated from a gas pipeline west of the Wood's End Inn [291 062] yielded *Echinocorys* of high Upper Campanian aspect (Wood, 1988). Chalk was found in the river bank, but is absent in the river bed, which is formed here by Alluvium. No Chalk is seen in the river bed downstream from this point for some 400 m until it reappears opposite the Bramerton Common pit.

A trench for sewer pipes at Bramerton Common, north of Bramerton, dug in 1983 close to the river and just above river level from 100 m west of the Wood's End Inn [290 062] to the eastern end of the Common [297 061], exposed waterlogged Chalk throughout its length (Whittlesea, 1985). Material from the eastern end of the trench comprised markedly yellow chalk with *Zoophycos* and a rich fauna including brachiopods and 10 species of bivalves. Some of the chalk was hardened, and contained hexactinellid sponges and moulds of originally aragonite-shelled molluscs including baculitid ammonites. An extensive faunal list was given by Whittlesea (1985), who inferred a Campanian rather than Maastrichtian position, based on the occurrence of six specimens of *Belemnitella*. As noted by Wood (1988), these *Belemnitella* could equally well have had a Lower Maastrichtian provenance. However, Mr P S Whittlesea (written communication, 1990) has found several species of bryozoa which he considers to be characteristic of the (Campanian) Paramoudra Chalk but absent from undoubted Maastrichtian Chalk. On balance, the evidence appears to favour a late Campanian age for the beds in the Bramerton trench, depite the presence of unequivocal Maastrichtian Chalk in the nearby river bed (see discussion below).

At the Bramerton Common pit [2950 0601], the contact between the Chalk and the overlying type Bramertonian Crag occurs at about 3 m above the river level (Mr N B Peake, personal communication, 1990). The top of the Chalk is indurated, as is usual at the contact with the Crag throughout Norfolk. The only fossils noted by him were large *Echinocorys* comparable with those found in the Lower Maastrichtian succession at Sidestrand, but these were filled with soft chalk and none could be collected intact.

The contact between the Crag and the Chalk can also be observed in the nearby river bank, just above the level of the river, and approximately 3 m beneath the contact in the Bramerton Common pit. This significant difference in level cannot be explained at present, nor is it clear whether the Chalk in the river bank is in lateral continuity with that in the pit. Mr N B Peake (personal communication, 1990) reports that the river is shallow at this point, with the Chalk visible in the river bed. This latter Chalk is relatively soft and extends downstream for some 30 m as what appears to be a gently tilted raft. Dredging operations into this raft in the 1970s, parallel to the bank and on the Bramerton Common side of the river, brought up several specimens of *Belemnella* (identified in the field by Prof Dr F Schmid, then of Niedersächsisches Landesamt für Bodenforschung, Hanover, Germany). This belemnite genus is restricted to the Maastrichtian and proves without doubt the existence of Maastrichtian Chalk in the river bed here. The relationship between this Maastrichtian Chalk and the topographically higher and apparently Campanian Chalk in the Bramerton trench section cannot be resolved from the present information, but it is possible that it may involve complex glaciotectonic slices comparable with those found on the north Norfolk coast.

In the river bank west of Hill House [2956 0609], a richly fossiliferous section was exposed at about water level, consisting of hard, yellow chalk with large (up to 25 cm) thalassinoid, burrow-form, nodular flints (see Wood, 1988, for details). The fauna included large *Echinocorys* ex gr. *belgica* comparable with those from the Lower Maastrichtian Pre-Porosphaera and Porosphaera Beds of Sidestrand, in addition to *Carneithyris* sp., attributed by Asgaard (1975) to the Upper Campanian species *C. carnea* rather than to the Maastrichtian *C. subcardinalis*. The only belemnites collected were zonally undiagnostic *Belemnitella*. The macrofossil evidence for dating this section is clearly contradictory, but the Chalk is presumably in lateral continuity with that in the Bramerton sewer trench section, discussed above.

A wall next to the riverside path [2965 0610] contained large flints, almost certainly dredged from the adjacent river bed, with large *Echinocorys* ex gr. *belgica* comparable with those from the Lower Maastrichtian at Sidestrand. No belemnites were noted.

The contact between the Chalk and the Bramertonian Crag with its basal Stone Bed was exposed by trenching in the former Blake's Pit at the eastern end of Bramerton Common [301 063] in 1974 (Cambridge, 1975). The top of the Chalk was reported to be stained brownish by iron oxide, and to be penetrated to a depth of about 70 mm by irregular branching fissures. These fissures were attributed to solution at the site of plant roots during a period of exposure under terrestrial conditions. No fossils were recorded. A subsequent excavation made in about 1978 by the Geological Society of Norfolk established that the top of the Chalk lay 1.5 to 2.0 m above river level at normal high tide (Mr P S Whittlesea, written communication 1990). The chalk was intensely hardened and no macrofossils were collected. A large flint was found with its base in situ in the Chalk and its subaerially weathered exposed surface encrusted with Crag barnacles. This specimen is now in the Norwich Castle Museum.

A small cutting made for a boat in the river bank next to Blake's Pit exposed Chalk from which several belemnites were reported to have been collected (Mr N B Peake, personal communication, 1990). The present whereabouts and identity of these fossils is not known.

A bulk sample of chalk from an unspecified locality, labelled 'Bramerton', yielded a micromorphic brachiopod assemblage belonging to the Lower (but not basal) Maastrichtian *Rugia acutirostris–Rugia spinosa* Zone (Johansen and Surlyk, 1990, figs. 2, 3 and p. 832). The topmost Campanian *Terebratulina longicollis—Gisilina jasmundi* Zone was recognised in a sample from the Whitlingham pit [presumably Colman's] in the adjacent Norwich district.

In a borehole at Rockland St Mary (TG30SW/13) [3089 0424], a hardened top to the Chalk was encountered beneath Crag at 35.4 m below surface. No further stratigraphical details are available.

Surlingham–Brundall

Dredging of the bed of the River Yare between Surlingham and Brundall [312 079] brought up Chalk with *Echinocorys* (housed in Norwich Castle Museum) believed by Mr N B Peake to indicate the Lower Maastrichtian Sponge Beds, although the characteristic lithology was not represented (Whittlesea, 1991). Piling operations on the north side of Surlingham Ferry [326 071] proved soft white chalk with abundant *Porosphaera globularis*, suggestive of the Lower Maastrichtian Porosphaera Beds but not unequivocally diagnostic of this unit (Whittlesea, 1991). It is not clear whether this Chalk is in situ or part of a glacial raft.

Loddon

In the Hales Borehole (TM39NE/7; Appendix 2), Chalk was drilled under Thanet Formation from 57.77 to 60.0 m. Recovery was fragmentary and totalled approximately 0.7 m. The upper 0.55 m comprised chalkstone with pyritic ghosts of hexacticellid sponges but no other fossils; the chalkstone graded down into white chalk. The spongiferous chalkstone is reminiscent of the Lower Maastrichtian Sponge Beds. However, on the basis of his analysis of the foraminiferal fauna of the underlying chalk, Dr I P Wilkinson reports that it demonstrates an unequivocal Late Campanian rather than Maastrichtian age. This is based on the concurrent range of *Gavelinella clementiana, G. monterelensis* and *Reussella szajnochae*, all of which became extinct in the Late Campanian according to Hart et al. (1989), and on the occurrence of *Bolivinoides laevigatus laevigatus, Eponides beisseli* and *Rugoglobigerina rugosa*, which first evolve at that level (Hart et al., 1989).

Ormesby St Margaret (North Walsham district)

In the Ormesby Borehole (TG51SW/7; Appendix 2), Chalk was drilled under Thanet Formation from 139.85 down to 148.0 m. Dr K C Ball reports that the foraminiferal faunas recovered between the top of the Chalk and 149.5 m are of Late Campanian–Early Maastrichtian age. However, two of the highest samples, at 140.10 and 142.02 m, gave an unequivocal Late Campanian age on the basis of the occurrence of *Gavelinella clementiana laevigata*. In addition, the assemblage at 143 m included *G. monterelensis*, which does not range above the Campanian. With the exception of the top 0.3 m, the core is no longer available. The top 0.3 m comprises off-white chalk with contrasting grey trace fossils including possible *Zoophycos*. It includes common large bryozoans, seen in section on the slabbed surface, and the serpulids *Ditrupa* sp. and small *Glomerula gordialis*. Although a correlation is not implied, it may be significant that comparable bryozoan-rich chalk was encountered in the Trunch Borehole at 49.40 m.

Wroxham (North Walsham district)

While there are no provings of unequivocal Maastrichtian Chalk in situ in the Great Yarmouth district, only some 3.5 km to the north, in the North Walsham district, a series of site investigation boreholes drilled in 1986–87 [308 174 to 309 176] at Wroxham has proved Lower Maastrichtian Sponge Beds overlying Porosphaera Beds with *Belemnitella* (Whittlesea, 1991). No details of the stratigraphy are available, but it is known that Upper Campanian chalks rich in inoceramid fragments and containing *Belemnitella* were found beneath the Maastrichtian in the lower parts of the boreholes, comparable with the succession between 83 and 102 m in the Trunch Borehole (Appendix 1).

FOUR

Tertiary

The Tertiary strata of the district rest unconformably on the Chalk east of a line between South Walsham and Seething, and are concealed by a widespread cover of Quaternary deposits, including the Crag (Figure 19). Their base slopes gently towards the east-south-east, but at a slightly steeper angle than the dip of the underlying Chalk. The strata have a maximum estimated thickness of 115 m immediately offshore from Great Yarmouth (Figure 20).

The beds were laid down in environments ranging from open marine shelf to shallow brackish, near the margin of the then slowly subsiding Southern North Sea Basin. The deposits have been assigned to the Palaeocene and Eocene epochs of the Palaeogene and, in particular, to the Thanetian and Ypresian stages (Knox et al., 1990). According to Knox (1990), the lack of agreement on the definition of the Thanetian and

Ypresian stages has a bearing on the definition of the Palaeocene/Eocene boundary, because Berggren et al. (1985) and Cavelier and Pomerol (1986) placed it at their Thanetian/Ypresian boundary. Representatives of the Sparnacian stage which occur widely in southern East Anglia and the London Basin are not present in this district (Knox et al., 1990). The possible occurrence of Pliocene strata is discussed in the treatment of the Crag Group in Chapter five. The Palaeogene stratigraphical nomenclature, as applied in this district, is given in Table 4. Until 1860, the northern limit of Eocene and older Tertiary strata was thought to lie in mid-Suffolk, but in that year Prestwich examined the records of, and the carefully collected specimens from a well sunk twenty years before at Lacon's Brewery in Great Yarmouth (Figure 21, Appendix 2). This resulted in the first descrip-

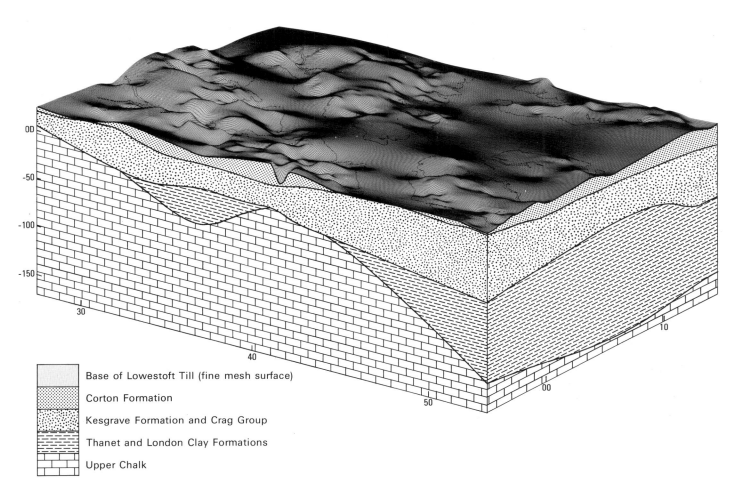

Base of Lowestoft Till (fine mesh surface)

Corton Formation

Kesgrave Formation and Crag Group

Thanet and London Clay Formations

Upper Chalk

Figure 19 Perspective view, from the south-east, of strata in the district; Upper Chalk to the base of the Lowestoft Till (*computer-generated plot derived from the borehole database*).

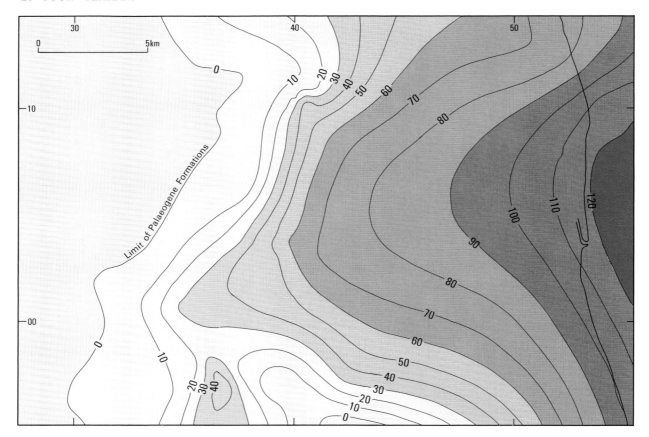

Figure 20 Isopachytes (metres) of the Tertiary clay formations (*computer-generated plot derived from the borehole database*).

tion of 'London Clay' and 'Woolwich and Reading Series' in Norfolk. Later, Boswell (1916, 1920) gave an account of their regional distribution, which included information from additional borehole provings at Cantley (TG 30SE/5), Southwood Oaks (TG 30NE/10) and Wheatacre, and also, in nearby northern Suffolk, the East Anglian Ice Company's boring at Lowestoft (TM 59SW/56, Figure 21, Appendix 2).

Onshore, information sufficiently detailed to permit the subdivison of the Tertiary strata has been obtained only from the Ormesby and Hales boreholes (Figures 21 to 24, Appendix 2; Cox et al., 1985; Knox et al., 1990). Elsewhere onshore, the dearth of recorded detail in the logs of boreholes that have penetrated these strata precludes subdivision and permits the determination of the distribution of these strata only in broad outline. Offshore, the availability of seismic data has allowed a subdivision of the upper, but not the lower part of the sequence.

A perspective view of the base of the Crag is given in Figure 27. It shows that the Palaeogene strata form a prominent buried, north-west-facing escarpment in central and northern parts of the district. Figure 19 is a perspective sectional view showing the form of the Palaeogene beds and their relation to the underlying Chalk.

PALAEOCENE

The Palaeocene strata of the London Basin, comprising the 'Thanet Sands', the 'Woolwich and the Mottled Clays, Sands, and Pebble Beds' (subsequently renamed the 'Woolwich and Reading Series') and the 'Basement Bed of the London Clay', were grouped as the Lower London Tertiaries by Prestwich (1852, 1854). Whitaker (1866) renamed them the Thanet Beds, Woolwich and Reading Beds, and Oldhaven Beds respectively. The Oldhaven Beds included the upper part of Woolwich and Reading Series of Prestwich, and the lower part of his Basement Bed of the London Clay; the upper part of this bed reverted to the London Clay. Cooper (1976) applied the term 'formation' to each of the Thanet, Woolwich and Reading, and Oldhaven beds and referred them formally to the Lower London Tertiary Group. In this district, the Woolwich and Reading Beds and Oldhaven Beds are not represented; the correlative of the Thanet Formation is present and is referred to informally as the Ormesby Clay (Knox et al., 1990).

Table 4 Lithostratigraphical nomenclature and correlation of Palaeogene sequences in the southern North Sea Basin and onshore, in Kent and this district; chronostratigraphical classification is indicated.

	STAGE	NORTH SEA BASIN FORMATIONS	ONSHORE FORMATIONS	DIVISIONS OF ONSHORE FORMATIONS	
				NORFOLK	KENT
EOCENE	Ypresian	Balder Formation	London Clay Formation	Walton Member	Walton Member
				Harwich Member	Oldhaven Beds
		Sele Formation		Hales Clay	
PALAEOCENE	Sparnacian		Woolwich and Reading Beds		Woolwich Shell Bed
					Woolwich Bottom Bed
	Thanetian	Lista Formation	Thanet Formation	Ormesby Clay	Thanet Formation

Thanet Formation

ORMESBY CLAY

The Ormesby Clay, known in detail from the Ormesby (Figures 23 and 24) and Hales (Figures 22 and 24) boreholes, unconformably overlies the Upper Chalk, and is thought to be continuous east of a line between South Walsham and Seething. The boreholes encountered similar lithological sequences, although a facies contrast is apparent in the upper part (Knox et al., 1990). The thicknesses of the Ormesby Clay are 25.5 m

in the Hales Borehole and 27 m in the Ormesby Borehole.

A thin (less than 2 m) bed of green, glauconite-coated flint pebbles and cobbles (the Bullhead or Stone Bed) marks the base of the Ormesby Clay. This is succeeded by a light olive-grey, poorly bedded silty mudstone, that is slightly to highly glauconitic, with many thin (c.2 cm), poorly defined layers of pale green mudstone; glauconite granules and small phosphatic nodules are scattered throughout. There are several thin altered volcanic ash layers, belonging to Phase 1 of the North Atlantic (Faeroe–Greenland province) early Palaeogene pyroclastic activity (Knox and Morton, 1988). The top of this silty mudstone is penetrated by burrows, including *Chondrites*, which are filled with reddish brown clay derived biogenically from the base of the overlying sub-unit. The succeeding sub-unit comprises a distinctive, regionally persistent, pale reddish brown, poorly bedded mudstone (Figures 22 and 24), which passes upwards into a pale grey, bioturbated, slightly calcareous and glauconitic mudstone. This sub-unit is sharply overlain by greyish brown, poorly bedded, calcareous, highly glauconitic mudstone, which becomes siltier and less glauconitic upwards. Unlike the underlying units, the succeeding mudstones exhibit lithological contrasts between the two provings, but generally comprise variegated mudstones with green layers and clasts. The youngest sub-unit of the Thanet Formation is known only from the Hales Borehole; it consists of waxy, dark greyish brown mudstone with abundant arenaceous foraminifers. An altered volcanic ash layer occurs near the base.

EOCENE

The Eocene strata of the London Basin comprise the London Clay Formation, the Claygate Beds and the

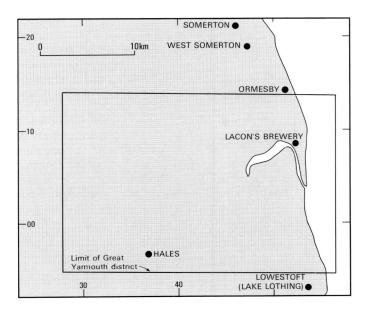

Figure 21 Location of important boreholes penetrating Tertiary strata.

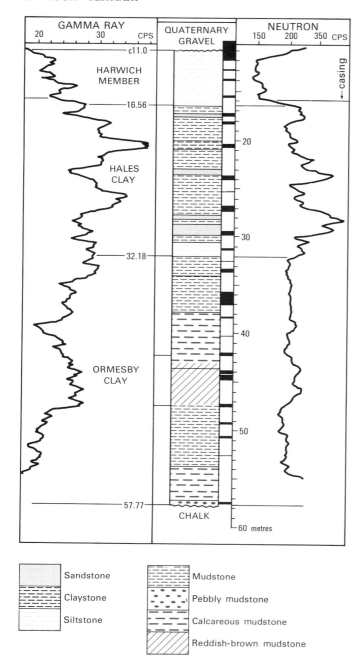

Figure 22 Simplified graphic log and selected geophysical logs of Tertiary strata in the Hales Borehole (from Knox et al., 1990) The column on the right shows core loss in black.

Bagshot Beds (Prestwich, 1847, 1850, 1854). Only the oldest of these, the London Clay Formation, is known to occur within the district.

London Clay Formation

The detailed stratigraphy of the London Clay is known from the Hales and Ormesby boreholes (Figures 22, 23 and 24; Appendix 2), supplemented by coastal site in-

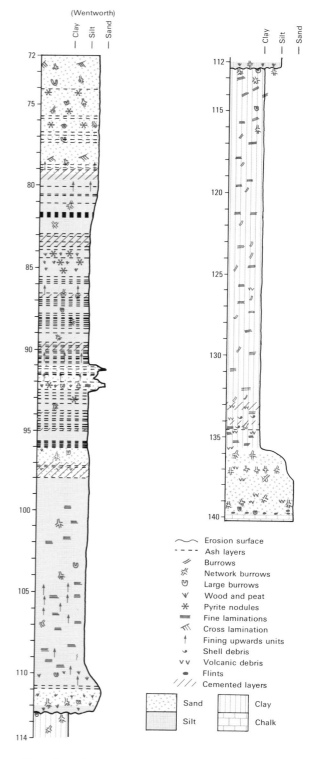

Figure 23 Graphic log showing sedimentological detail of Tertiary strata in the Ormesby Borehole (from Cox et al., 1985).

vestigation data near Great Yarmouth and offshore seismic profiling data. Two distinctive units have been recognised at the base of the formation; the informally named Hales Clay (Knox et al., 1990), succeeded by the

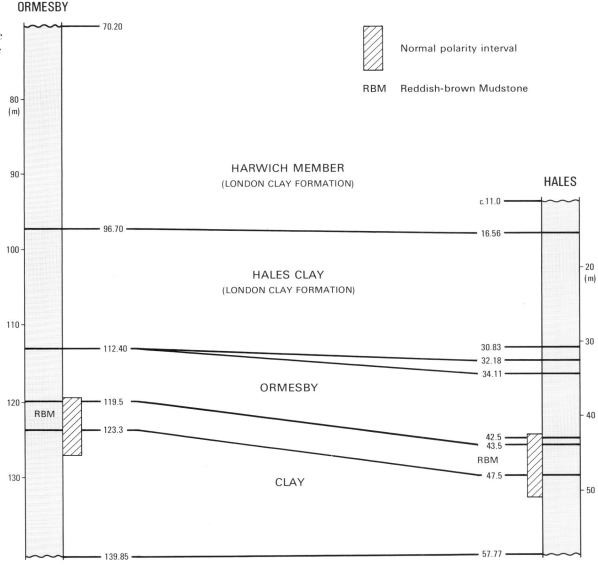

Figure 24 Correlation of early Palaeogene sequences in the Ormesby and Hales boreholes (after Knox et al., 1990).

Harwich Member (King, 1981). The London Clay that succeeds these units is referred to as the Walton Member.

HALES CLAY

The Hales Clay is 15 m thick in the Hales Borehole. It comprises a basal pale brown siltstone (not present in the Ormesby Borehole) and overlying pale greyish brown, silty and sandy mudstones and siltstones. Layers of fine-grained, micaceous, glauconitic sand up to 30 cm thick occur throughout, and four bentonised ash layers belonging to Sub-phase 2a of Knox and Morton (1988) are also present.

HARWICH MEMBER

A full sequence of the Harwich Member, 26.5 m thick, has been recognised in the Ormesby Borehole and the basal part in the Hales Borehole; however, only the uppermost 20 m or so have been distinguished in off-

shore seismic profiles, in which they are defined by a prominent double reflector at the base. This reflector may be the Harwich Stone Band. The Harwich Member is an olive-grey to greyish brown, sandy siltstone with numerous basaltic ash layers (at least 86 in the Ormesby Borehole, Figure 23). These ashes are generally reworked and bioturbated, and belong to Sub-phase 2b of Knox and Morton (1988). The buried escarpment in central parts of the district may be formed by this comparatively resistant member of the London Clay Formation.

WALTON MEMBER

The distribution and thickness of this unit, which overlies the Harwich Member, are known only from offshore seismic profiling data. Borehole information off Great Yarmouth describes the sediments as stiff, brown to blue-grey, laminated silty clay. The clay is locally fissured and contains pyrite nodules and small selenite

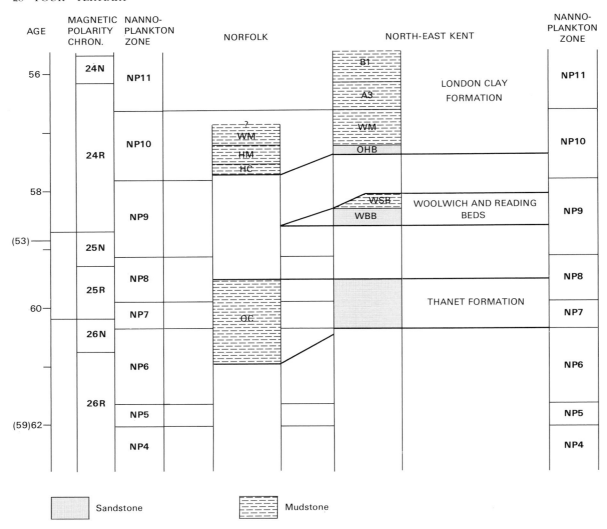

Figure 25 Correlation of Palaeogene sequences in Norfolk and north-east Kent (after Knox 1990). A3, B1, London Clay divisions of King (1981). HC, Hales Clay. HM, Harwich Member. OC Ormesby Clay. OHB, Oldhaven Beds. WBB, Woolwich Bottom Bed. WM, Walton Member. WSB, Woolwich Shell Beds.

crystals. It attains a thickness of about 50 m in the extreme east.

DEPOSITIONAL ENVIRONMENTS

From lithological and faunal indicators, Cox et al. (1985) deduced that, after an initial transgression, deposition of the Ormesby Clay, their 'lower unit', took place in water deepening to over 200 m. By contrast with the Ormesby Clay, Cox et al. (1985) considered the younger Palaeogene mudstones, their 'upper unit', to have accumulated in very shallow brackish water.

Assemblages of benthonic foraminifers in the sediments indicate that the Ormesby Clay accummulated rapidly in deep water, probably at depths similar to those of the outer shelf (200 m) whilst, by contrast, the Eocene sediments were deposited in shallow brackish water (Cox et al., 1985).

REGIONAL PALAEOGENE GEOLOGY

The district lies athwart the northern boundary of the Palaeogene rocks within the London Basin. A regional correlation of the strata is given in Figure 25 and Table 4.

Typically, the Thanet Formation consists mainly of sands; however, in Norfolk these are replaced by a glauconitic mudstone unit, the Ormesby Clay (Cox et al., 1985; Knox et al., 1990). According to Cox et al., this unit contains a benthonic fauna characteristic of NSB 1b of King (1983) and a dinoflagellate cyst flora indicative of the *Alisocysta margarita* informal zone of Knox et al. (1981); it was correlated by them with the Lista Formation of the central North Sea Basin. Although the mudstones are almost barren of calcareous nannofossils (E Steurbaut, personal communication in Knox, 1990) and thus preclude the application of the standard NP zonation, a probable correlation of the Kent and Norfolk sequences is provided by magnetostratigraphy. A well-defined reverse-normal-reverse (R-N-R) magnetic polarity sequence in the Ormesby Borehole indicates that the equivalent of the upper part of the mudstone unit of Norfolk (Cox et al., 1985; Knox, 1990) is the type Thanet Formation, which has a normal-reverse (N-R) magnetic polarity sequence.

The Woolwich and Reading Beds of the London Basin consist of two main facies; a basal bed of green glauconitic sands and an upper bed of brightly variegated clays corresponding, respectively, to the Woolwich Bottom Bed and the Woolwich Shell Bed. Cox et al. (1985) tentatively correlated their Unit 2 (Hales Clay) in the Ormesby sequence with the Woolwich and Reading Beds on incomplete biostratigraphical evidence. They also considered this unit to be the equivalent of a similar facies, named the Sele Formation, described by Lott et al. (1983) in the Southern North Sea Basin. However, Knox et al. (1990) have placed the Hales Clay in the London Clay Formation on lithological and stratigraphical grounds. A confidential borehole some 35 km south of Hales proved a fluviolacustrine facies, not present in Norfolk but typical of the Woolwich and Reading Beds, sharply overlain by mudstones closely similar to the Hales Clay. Knox et al. (1990) have considered the Hales Clay to represent an early phase of the southward transgression of the London Clay sea.

The tuff-rich sandy siltstones overlying the Hales Clay have been assigned by Cox et al. (1985) to the Harwich Member of the London Clay Formation because, despite the lack of a diagnostic fauna and uncertain palaeomagnetic evidence, there is a close lithological similarity between these siltstones, those of the Harwich Member in the Harwich and Sudbury areas, and the widespread main ash marker of the central North Sea within the lower part of the Balder Formation. Correlation of the basaltic ash layer sequences (tephrostratigraphy) within the Palaeogene of the North Sea Basin and adjacent areas (Knox and Morton, 1983; Knox, 1984; Knox and Morton, 1988) supports the conclusion of Cox et al. (1985).

The mudstones with sporadic tuff layers overlying the Harwich Member in the Ormesby and Hales boreholes are lithologically very similar to the London Clay Formation of the London Basin, with which they have been correlated by Cox et al. (1985). These authors gave as supporting evidence the occurrence of the zone fossil *Coscinodiscus sp.* 1 of the NSP4 Zone of King (1981) in the upper part of the sequence, and the presence of dinoflagellate cyst species characteristic of the *Hyperacantha* Zone of Costa and Downie (1976).

CLAY MINERALOGY

Clay fractions (less than 2 μm) from a total of 46 samples from the Tertiary sequence in the Ormesby Borehole

(Appendix 2) were examined by X-ray diffraction analysis. Air dried, glycerol saturated and heated (375°C) preparations were analysed on a Philips PW1130 diffractometer using Ni-filtered CuKα radiation, F 40Kv, 30mA, initially scanning the range 3–35°2σ at 0.5° per minute.

Most of the samples consist of the clay assemblage smectite > illite ≃ kaolinite ± trace chlorite, but considerable variation in the relative proportions of smectite to illite + kaolinite occur through the sequence. Generally, there is an underlying upward trend of increasing illite + kaolinite at the expense of smectite. These changes do not occur as smooth stratigraphical processes, but are the result of lithological variation, particularly the occurrence of sandy and silty mudstones and clays, relatively rich in kaolinite and detrital mica, in the middle and upper parts of the sequence.

The lower part of the Ormesby Clay, below the reddish brown mudstone horizon, is rich in smectite, with minor illite and traces of kaolinite. Minor amounts of zeolite, of the clinoptilolite-heulandite group, and K-feldspar also occur in the lowermost 13 m. Glauconite is common in the basal 3 m, occurring both as pellets and coatings on mineral grains, and typically consists of mixed-layer Fe-rich illite/smectite. Highly glauconitic, fine-grained sands at the base have a green clay matrix which is essentially the same mixed-layer glauconite. The reddish brown mudstone horizon of the Ormesby Clay is characterised by increased proportions of illite, kaolinite and chlorite, at the expense of smectite in the clay assemblages. Proportions of illite and kaolinite decline slightly upwards in the upper part of the Ormesby Clay, but this trend is reversed in the Hales Clay, where kaolinite, illite and traces of chlorite generally increase upwards in the sequence, at the expense of smectite.

The Harwich Member of the London Clay Formation is characterised by a high smectite content throughout, but kaolinite and illite are notably more abundant than in the lower part of the Ormesby Clay. Smectite content is closely related to the occurrence of the ash bands. Between closely spaced ash bands, mudstones are rich in smectite, whereas kaolinite and illite are more abundant in the non-tuffaceous strata. Neither chlorite nor clinoptilolite-heulandite were detected in the Harwich Member.

Clay mineral variations in relation to lithology indicate that the Tertiary strata in the Ormesby Borehole were derived from two sources. A volcanic source was largely responsible for the high smectite content, particularly of the lower part of the Ormesby Clay and the Harwich Member. The presence of glauconitized igneous grains in the basal Ormesby Clay (E58841) and numerous ash bands in the Harwich Member provides a clear link between volcanigenic material and smectite content. A second, non-volcanic source was clearly responsible for much of the terrigenous, fine-grained sand and silt, including detrital muscovite and biotite; this appears to have been the main source of kaolinite, illite and chlorite.

FIVE

Late Tertiary/Quaternary — Pre-Ludhamian to Cromerian

At the beginning of the Pleistocene, the district lay near the western coast of the Southern North Sea Basin. Marine sediments, the Crag Group, accumulated in the district as part of a system of prograding deltas which at that time were forming in the North Sea. During Early Pleistocene times, as a result of a steady regression, the shoreline migrated across the area from west to east (Cameron et al., in press). By the late Early Pleistocene/early Middle Pleistocene much of the district was land; widespread fluviatile sediments, the Kesgrave Formation, were deposited by braided rivers flowing mainly from the southwest. The Yarmouth Roads Formation, comprising mainly nonmarine to intertidal sediments, the partial equivalent of the Kesgrave Formation, was deposited offshore but is not represented in the district, having been eroded from the present-day inshore area by tidal scour.

CRAG GROUP

The late Pliocene and early Pleistocene marine deposits of East Anglia (Figure 26) are collectively known as the Crag, or Crags. These sediments accumulated near the western margin of a rapidly subsiding North Sea sedimentary basin (e.g. Kooi et al., 1989) which, during this period, probably had a geometry and tidal characteristics similar to those of the present day (Anderton et al., 1979). The margin of the basin was a few kilometres to the west of the Great Yarmouth district (Cox et al., 1989).

In East Anglia the Crag does not exceed 70 m in thickness, and the thickest known onshore sequence in and close to the district is 57 m in the Ormesby Borehole (Figures 26 and 28; Appendix 2). However, in the North Sea Basin and the Netherlands, its temporal equivalents are hundreds of metres thick (Caston, 1977; Zagwijn and Doppert, 1978); according to Cameron et al. (1992), up to 350 m occur in the Southern North Sea Basin and 800 m in the central North Sea Basin.

The oldest Crag formation, the Coralline Crag, considered to be of early Pliocene age, is not present within the district.

Nomenclature

'Crag' was originally an East Anglian dialect name for any shelly marine sand. It was later adopted by geologists for the widespread deposits of shelly sands and interbedded clays in Suffolk, Norfolk and Essex.

The literature on the Crag is vast, particularly that written during the 19th century when there was a great deal of scientific interest in these deposits. Lyell (1833) considered the Crag worthy of great attention because the fauna included numerous recent species which were un-

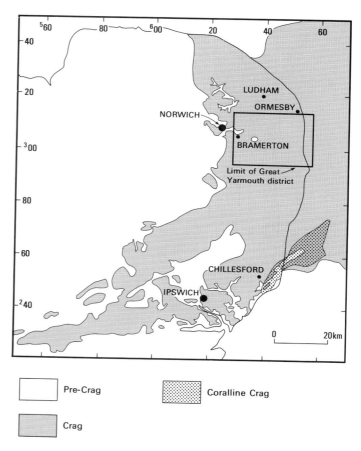

Figure 26   Regional distribution of the Crag Group: the subcrop of the Coralline Crag is shown shaded (after BGS, 1988 and Zalasiewicz et al., 1988).

known from the underlying sedimentary rocks. Reid (1890) gave an exhaustive review of Crag literature. It is not an intention of this account to attempt such a review, but it is considered appropriate to give a résumé of the more seminal works. The stratigraphical nomenclature of the Crag is summarised in Table 5.

The earliest known account of Crag deposits is that by Dale (1704). Shells from the Crag were noted by J Woodward in his 'Catalogue' of 1729, and the deposits were described in the writings of Arderon (1746). Although Parkinson (1811), and Conybeare and Phillips (1822) referred to crag [sic] deposits, Taylor (1824) was the first to apply the name Crag in a strictly geological sense and gave a clear account of sediments exposed at Bramerton. Lyell (1833) referred the Crag to the Pliocene; Conybeare and Phillips (1822) had already placed the crag [sic] as the youngest British Tertiary formation.

Table 5 An outline of recent late Pliocene — early Pleistocene nomenclature of the Crag, with particular relevance to this district.

BRITISH STAGES OF WEST (1961, 1980) FUNNELL (1961) FUNNELL AND WEST (1977) BECK et al. (1972)	LITHOSTRATIGRAPHIC UNITS OF FUNNELL AND WEST (1977)		REVISED STAGES OF ZALASIEWICZ AND GIBBARD (1988) ZALASIEWICZ et al. (in press) GIBBARD et al. (1991)	REVISED STRATIGRAPHY OF THE CHILLESFORD BEDS. ZALASIEWICZ et al. (1991)	UNITS MAPPED IN THIS SURVEY
PASTONIAN	PASTON MEMBER	CROMER FOREST BED FORMATION (part)	PASTONIAN		CRAG GROUP
PRE-PASTONIAN b-d (substages)	SHERINGHAM Mbr.				
PRE-PASTONIAN a (substage)	SIDESTRAND Mbr.		PRE-PASTONIAN/	CHILLESFORD CLAY ? ≡ EASTON BAVENTS CLAY	
BRAMERTONIAN	CHILLESFORD BEDS	NORWICH CRAG FORMATION	BAVENTIAN		
BAVENTIAN	NORWICH MEMBER (inc. Easton Bavents Clay)		BRAMERTONIAN/ ANTIAN	CHILLESFORD SAND	
ANTIAN					
THURNIAN	LUDHAM MEMBER	RED CRAG FORMATION	THURNIAN		
LUDHAMIAN			LUDHAMIAN		
PRE-LUDHAMIAN	RED CRAG MEMBER		PRE-LUDHAMIAN		

Charlesworth (1835) recognised two divisions of the Crag; a Lower, or Coralline Crag and an Upper, or Red Crag. He considered the Crag of Norfolk to be an extension of the Red Crag of Suffolk and Essex. By the following year (published in 1837) he had reversed his earlier opinion and established a third, younger, division for the Norfolk deposits which he named the Mammaliferous Crag. Lyell (1839) referred to the Mammaliferous Crag of Charlesworth as the Norwich or Fluvio-marine Crag; the name Norwich Crag has remained in use to the present day.

In the following decades the relationship of the Red Crag to the Norwich Crag was a subject of much controversy. Deposits of broadly similar aspect to the Crag of Norfolk, the Chillesford Sand and Chillesford Clay, were recorded by Prestwich (1849) overlying the Red Crag at Chillesford in Suffolk In his first paper on the Crag, Wood (1864) suggested that the Fluvio-marine Crag of Norfolk was coeval with the upper part of the Red Crag. Wood and Harmer (1868, 1872) compared the Bramerton and Chillesford sections and observed that the Chillesford Sand and overlying Chillesford Clay overlay the Red Crag at Chillesford, and the Fluvio-marine (or Norwich) Crag at Bramerton. They also noted that *Scrobicularia plana* occurred in the Fluvio-marine Crag and was abundant in the so-called Scrobicularia Crag of Wood (1866), beneath the Chillesford Sand at Chillesford. They concluded, not entirely without reservation, that the Fluvio-marine or Norwich Crag at Bramerton was coeval with the youngest part of the Red Crag.

In his later important contribution, Prestwich (1871a, b, c) declared his conviction that the Chillesford Clay had the same relationship to both the Red and Norwich Crag 'both of which it overlies and with both of which it shows a close relation'. Thus he considered their deposition to have been more or less contemporaneous, but in

basins separated by a ridge of Coralline Crag. The underlying assumption by Prestwich, and Wood and Harmer that the clay beds at Bramerton (and other Norfolk localities) were the correlatives of the Chillesford Clay was later to be much criticised (e.g. Woodward, 1881).

In 1871, Bell and Bell suggested the names Upper, Middle and Lower Crag for the Norwich, Red and Coralline Crags. Woodward (1881) classed all of the deposits below the Lower Boulder Clay (= Norwich Brickearth, Cromer Till, or, in this account, till in the Corton Formation) as Upper Crag, although Wood and Harmer (1868) had excluded from the 'True Crag' what they termed the Pebbly sands and Pebble Beds that overlay the supposed Chillesford Clay in Norfolk.

Harmer (1899, 1900a, b) proposed the name Icenian Crag to replace Norwich Crag. He, like Prestwich (1871c), considered that the Coralline Crag formed a barrier between separate basins of deposition of the Red and Icenian Crags. He established a number of zones and stages based on mollusc assemblages, and concluded that these represented northwards-younging deposits. This stratigraphical scheme remained essentially unchanged until the palynological and foraminiferal work of West (1961) and Funnell (1961).

In 1950 a pilot water supply borehole was sunk at Ludham, 5 km north of the Great Yarmouth district (Figure 26). Funnell (1961) examined the foraminifers in samples of Crag obtained from this borehole. He found that assemblages in the lower part of the sequence resembled those of the Red Crag of Suffolk and differed from all known Icenian assemblages, while those obtained from the upper part of the sequence were more akin to assemblages from surface outcrops of the Norwich Crag. In particular, the highest of the horizons contained fauna resembling that from the upper part of the sequence at Bramerton. In the same paper, Funnell considered the foraminifers of his B II Horizon, which immediately underlies the 'Chillesford Clay' in the Bramerton Common section, to be indicative of a climate too cold to permit correlation with the Chillesford Crag. He concluded that there was at that time no evidence for correlating any clay bed of Norfolk with the Chillesford Clay.

Pollen from samples of Crag from the Royal Society Borehole (Appendix 2) sunk close to the Ludham Pilot Borehole was the subject of an investigation by West (1961). He recognised five climatic stages and named four: the Ludhamian (warm), Thurnian (cold), Antian (warm) and Baventian (cold) (Table 5). West also attempted to correlate these five stages to the foraminiferal horizons of Funnell (1961). The alternation of cold and warm climates indicated by the foraminifera and pollen contrast with the steady decline in temperature that Harmer (1900b, 1902) thought was represented by mollusc assemblages in the Red and Icenian Crags.

In recent years further climatic stages have been introduced (Table 5), for example the cold Pre-Ludhamian (Beck et al., 1972), the warm Bramertonian (Funnell et al., 1979) and the cold Pre-Pastonian *a* sub-stage (West, 1980). However, various workers (e.g. Bowen et al., 1986; Funnell, 1987; Zalasiewicz and Gibbard, 1988; Zalasiewicz et al., 1990; Gibbard et al., 1991) have noted that the relationships between some of the stages are unclear; there may have been duplication of stages.

A lithostratigraphical classification of the Crags (Table 5) was proposed by Funnell and West (1977), although, despite the intensive research and debate of the 19th and early 20th centuries described above, there was no means as yet of mapping the various units. Consequently, Bristow (1983) suggested that the Red and Norwich Crags should be grouped as the Crag Formation, while retaining chronostratigraphical stage names, biozones or other biotic divisions. However, Zalasiewicz and Mathers (1985) and Zalasiewicz et al. (1988, 1991) have shown that in south-eastern Suffolk lithostratigraphical subdivision of the Crag is feasible.

Offshore, just to the east of the district, the sedimentary succession equivalent to the Crag has been divided into seismostratigraphical units; among them the Red Crag Formation, Westkapelle Ground Formation, Smith's Knoll Formation, Winterton Shoal Formation and Yarmouth Roads Formation (Stoker et al., 1983, 1985; Cameron et al., 1984, 1987; Balson and Cameron, 1985). Funnell (1987) has suggested that only high sea-level stands are recorded onshore, represented by the Red Crag, Smith's Knoll and Yarmouth Roads formations. However, in contrast, Cameron et al. (1992) postulate a steady regression throughout the Early Pleistocene, and a shoreline that migrated eastwards across the district. Seimostratigraphical units have been recognised offshore in the district but onshore it has not proved possible to subdivide the Crag lithostratigraphically. In order to accommodate this conclusion, and the recognition of formations defined elsewhere in East Anglia, it is here proposed that these formations and the undivided Crag be referred to collectively as the Crag Group.

Early workers assigned the Crag to the Pliocene. Later, however, on the recommendation of the 28th International Congress (1948) it was placed in the Pleistocene.

Mitchell et al. (1973) referred the Red and Norwich Crags to the Lower Pleistocene, but Funnell (in Curry et al., 1978) recognised that part should be considered to be of Pliocene age, although no sedimentary break or lithological change at the Plio-Pleistocene boundary is recorded in these deposits. Recent practice has been to refer the Pre-Ludhamian and early Ludhamian stages to the late Pliocene, and younger stages to the Pleistocene (Funnell, 1987). However, there is still uncertainty about the position of British stages in relation to the Plio-Pleistocene boundary, and a full account of this is given in Gibbard et al. (1991).

Distribution, stratigraphy and sedimentation

The Crag occurs throughout the district except where cut out by the buried valley beneath the River Yare, and locally in the south-west near Hales Green, where the Hales Borehole (Appendix 2) proved younger deposits resting on London Clay. It unconformably overlies Tertiary strata in the central and eastern parts of the district but oversteps onto the Upper Chalk in the west. In north-central parts, the Crag has completely buried a north-westward-facing escarpment of Tertiary strata, formed largely of London Clay (Figure 27).

The Crag crops out along the lower slopes of most of the valleys west of a line between Langley Green and Pilson Green, but east of this line it crops out only sporadically, for example, at Limpenhoe, Reedham and Stokesby. Crag has also been recorded beneath pre-Anglian and younger deposits in many boreholes throughout the district and identified in seismic profiles offshore.

The base of the Crag is irregular and its thickness variable, the deposits having accumulated thickly in depressions and thinly on the intervening highs. The Ormesby Borehole (Figures 26 and 28; Appendix 2) penetrated 57 m Crag to a depth of 65 m below OD in one such depression; the Royal Society Ludham Borehole (Appendix 2) proved 41 m of Crag overlying London Clay at a depth of 50 m in another. These depressions do not appear to have a structural origin, for there are apparently no faults associated with them. Some authors (e.g. Zalasiewicz and Gibbard, 1988) have suggested that they may be the result of tidal scour. Bristow (1983) considered similar depressions in Suffolk to be fault-bounded but there is no evidence from this survey in support of a structural origin for those in this district.

There is evidence to suggest that some of the Chalk outcrops which underlie the Crag near the Yare Valley at the western margin of the district may be glacially emplaced rafts (Wood, 1988; Cox et al., 1989; Chapter three). It follows that the overlying Crag sediments may not be in situ.

At outcrop, the Crag is generally represented by a sandy loam soil. Augering beneath the soil commonly reveals sediments comprising yellowish brown to reddish brown, micaceous, fine-grained sands with beds of clay. Both the sand and clay are ferruginous, especially at the upper and lower surfaces of clay layers where tabular ferruginous concretions (iron pan) are common. These concretions are often turned up by the plough and are

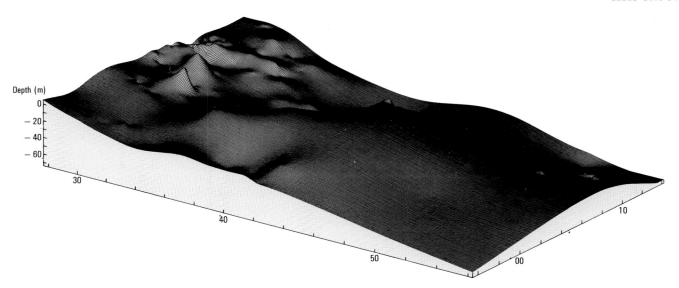

Figure 27   Perspective view, from the south-east, of the basal Crag surface (*computer-generated plot derived from the borehole database*).

found scattered in the soil. In the Panxworth area iron pan is sufficiently abundant at outcrop to have supported a local foundry (Chapter ten).

Certain beds within the overlying Kesgrave Formation resemble parts of the Crag. Where other indicators are absent, it can be difficult to distinguish one from the other. Because of this. it has been accepted that, on the published map, parts of the Kesgrave Formation may have been included within the Crag and vice-versa.

The Bramerton Common section (Figure 26), first described by Taylor (1824) and later to become the type section of the Norwich Crag (Reid, 1890), and Blake's Pit, Bramerton, are the only sizable exposure of Crag recorded in the district. In recent years they have been the subject of detailed investigations and full descriptions have been published (Funnell, 1961; Norton, 1967; Funnell et al., 1979). In summary, the sections comprise a basal bed of flints, overlain by shelly sand with thin clay layers which passes up into sporadically shelly sand with a bed of shelly sand at the top, followed by alternating sand and brownish grey clay beds. It is these clay layers that were thought by many early workers to be the Chillesford Clay. Woodward (1881), the primary survey-or, found that these clays, in the vicinity of Bramerton and Surlingham, were discontinuous lenses at different levels. His conclusions are supported by this survey; thus contiguity with the Chillesford Clay is considered unlikely. However, Funnell et al.(1979) assigned the lower part of the Blake's Pit sequence, which they correlated with the Chillesford Crag, to the Bramertonian Stage and the overlying sediments to the Pre-Pastonian *a* sub-stage: Zalasiewicz et al. (in press) have suggested that the Chillesford Clay correlates in part with Pre-Pastonian *a* deposits, including those at Bramerton.

Many boreholes in the district have proved Crag but, apart from the Ormesby Borehole (Figure 28; Appendix 2), provide little detail. In boreholes where the Crag rests on Upper Chalk a basal bed up to 2 m thick, comprising flint pebbles and cobbles, is commonly recorded. In a borehole (TG 30SW/13) at Rockland St Mary, these flints were coated with glauconite. This stone bed is similar to, and possibly the same as that at the base of the Thanet Formation, albeit reworked; against this the Chalk erosion surface west of the limit of Palaeogene strata is younger than that beneath the Thanet Formation and has a shallower dip (Chapter three). Overlying the basal bed there is generally a sequence of interbedded sands and clays. Where the deposits are unweathered, they have usually been described as 'dark' or 'greenish', or even 'blue' or 'black', a manifestation of the abundance of glauconite. Where they have been weathered, above the water table, the sands have often been described as 'reddish' and the clays 'brownish'. Shelly sands have been noted from some boreholes but are not particularly common. Beds of flint gravel have also been recorded. Correlation of beds between boreholes has not proved possible.

In the Ormesby Borehole, the lower part of the sequence is mainly argillaceous while the upper part is mainly arenaceous (Harland et al., 1991). Four litho-facies units have been recognised. Unit 1 (70.43 to 60.00 m) comprises bioturbated, glauconitic, coarse sand with abundant comminuted shell debris, overlain by olive-grey, finely laminated clay interbedded with cross-bedded, glauconitic shelly sand (Plate 1a). There is a transition to Unit 2 (60.00 to 45.73 m) which is a uniform sequence of finely interlayered sand and mud, and flaser- and lenticular-bedded clay, silt and fine-grained sand (Plate 1b). Glauconite and mica are common. Bioturbation is rare but the clays are burrowed and sand-filled escape burrows are present at the top of the unit. At 45.73 m there is a sharp change to mainly arenaceous sediments. Unit 3 (45.73 to 25.99 m) comprises light olive-grey, well-sorted medium-grained sand with thin clay drapes over ripples. Mica and glau-

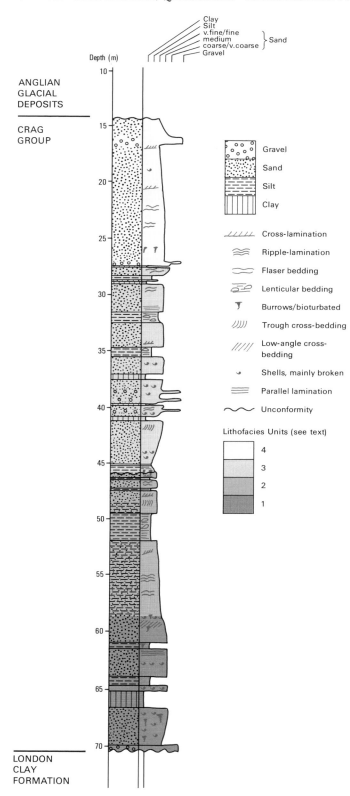

Figure 28 Graphic log of Crag Group strata in the Ormesby Borehole.

conite are present and comminuted shell debris occurs sporadically. Thick beds of flaser- and lenticular-bedded micaceous clay occur at intervals. In Unit 4 (25.99 to 14.36 m) the clay content decreases abruptly until there are only sporadic clay drapes on ripples.

This sequence indicates that the sediments accumulated in a tidal, shallow-shelf environment. Unit 1 may be interpreted as either intertidal, with the shelly sands as deposits within tidal channels, or subtidal (e.g. Reineck and Singh, 1973). Some indicators, such as the extensive bioturbation of the shelly sand by crustaceans, and assemblages of dinoflagellate cysts (Harland et al, 1991), support subtidal deposition. Strikingly similar deposits in the Red Crag of Suffolk, Unit AS-Lith 1 of Zalasiewicz et al. (1988, p. 233, Fig. 6), have also been interpreted as probably subtidal in origin. The sedimentary features of Unit 2 are characteristic of tidal mud flats (e.g. Terwindt, 1971; Reineck and Singh, 1973). The bioturbated top of this unit and the sharp base of Unit 3 indicate a break in sedimentation which is reflected in the dinoflagellate cyst, foraminiferal and pollen evidence (Harland et al., 1991). The mainly sandy sediments of Unit 3 are interpreted as representing a change to a higher energy tidal sand flat environment. The alteration of the sand and clay beds in this unit is probably autocyclic in origin. The presence of reworked pollen spores and pebbles at some horizons, together with decreasing clay and silt content, indicates progressive shallowing and intermittent deposition above the hiatus (Harland et al, 1991). The shallowing-upward sequence of the Ormesby Borehole appears to accord with the regional setting suggested by Cameron et al. (1992) and discussed above.

Offshore stratigraphy

An offshore geophysical survey comprising several seismic reflection profiles (vessel tracks shown on the published map), indicates a Crag succession broadly similar to that proved in the Ormesby Borehole (Figure 28). Interpretation of these profiles has permitted the recognition of seismostratigraphical units with distinct acoustic characters, bounded at top and base by acoustic reflectors interpreted as erosion surfaces.

Unit A has a strong reflector at its base in the offshore seismic profiles which is interpreted as an angular unconformity. The unit is characterised in seismic profiles by distinct subparallel reflectors or by a chaotic configuration of reflectors and can be correlated with Unit 1 of the Ormesby Borehole. The thickness of the unit lies in the range 5 and 50 m, but is generally about 20 to 30 m. Unit B is characterised by weak, parallel or slightly diverging reflectors and has a maximum thickness of 35 m, although it is generally less than 20 m thick. It appears to corresponds to units 2 and 3 of the Ormesby Borehole.

Correlation between onshore and offshore formations

Correlation between the established seismostratigraphical formations of the Southern North Sea Basin, seismostratigraphical units A and B of this district, and the

Plate 1a   Core samples from the Ormesby Borehole (Appendix 2): laminated and bioturbated clays, silts and fine-grained sands formed in intertidal conditions.

lithostratigraphical units identified in the Ormesby Borehole on the coast have proved problematical because of conflicting biostratigraphical and seismostratigraphical interpretations. A background of confused nomenclature has also been a hindrance; for example, there is uncertainty whether the onshore and offshore Red Crag Formations are equivalents (Cameron et al., 1992).

The acoustic character of Unit B, and the lithologies of units 2 and 3 of the Ormesby Borehole, resemble those of the Westkapelle Ground Formation. But the Westkapelle Ground Formation contains a flora of Thurnian aspect (Cameron et al., 1984) whilst, according to Harland et al. 1991, Unit 2 of the Ormesby Borehole can be assigned to the Pre-Ludhamian, and Unit 3 to the Pre-Pastonian. Jeffery and Balson (p.45 and 46 in Gibbard et al., 1991) suggest that, in the Southern North Sea Basin, emphasis should be given to the correlation of sediment bodies rather than stages. However, in this district, the seismic data are sparse, and the sequence in the Ormesby Borehole is not fully represented in the nearshore seismic profiles because of erosion by tidal scour. Acoustic character is a function of lithology, and the lithologies of units 2 and 3 are not unique in the Crag Group. The type locality of the Westkapelle Ground Formation is far removed from the district and seismic profiles in the intervening area are discontinuous. Onshore/offshore correlation in the district by seismic interpretation alone is therefore uncertain.

There are two possible correlations. First, that the seismic evidence is in doubt and that the Westkapelle Ground Formation is not present in the district. In this case units 1 and 2 of Ormesby can be assigned to the Red Crag Formation, albeit a facies variant, and correlated with seismic units A and B. Units 3 and 4 may be ascribed to the Yarmouth Roads Formation. Second, that the seismic evidence is correct. In this case, Unit 1 of Ormesby and seismic Unit A are assigned to the Red Crag Formation. Unit 2 and seismic Unit B are then assigned to the, by implication diachronous, Westkapelle Ground Formation which would be older in this district than at its type site. Units 3 and 4 would also be assigned to the Yarmouth Roads Formation in this interpretation.

Biostratigraphy

A comprehensive account of late Pliocene and Early Pleistocene stages recognised in the marine sediments of the Red and Norwich Crag formations of East Anglia and the adjacent North Sea was given by Funnell (1987). The seven stages, which are all based on pollen assemblage biozones (West, 1961, 1980; Beck et al., 1972; Funnell and West, 1977; Funnell et al., 1979) are included in column 1 of Table 5.

Sediments belonging to the oldest stage, the Pre-Ludhamian, have been identified in the Ormesby Borehole (Harland et al, 1991). The offshore Red Crag Formation has been assigned to this stage on the basis of evidence

Plate 1b   Core samples from the Ormesby Borehole: mostly laminated and burrowed silts and clays with layers and laminae of medium- and coarse-grained sand with shells formed in subtidal conditions.

from a borehole outside the district (Cameron et al., 1984). The Ludhamian, Thurnian, Antian and Baventian stages were defined on the basis of pollen assemblages from the Crag sequence in the Royal Society Borehole at Ludham (Appendix 2; West, 1961). Palynological analysis of the sediments in the Ormesby Borehole indicates that the lower part of the sequence can be referred to the Pre-Ludhamian and Ludhamian stages while the upper part has been assigned to the Pre-Pastonian and Pastonian stages (Harland et al., 1991). Material from boreholes in the south-east of the district has been referred to the Thurnian and Antian stages (Hopson and Bridge, 1987). The Crag at Bramerton includes the type locality of the Bramertonian stage (Funnell et al., 1979).

Details

Rackheath–Blofield

A borehole at Mouseholdheath Farm (TG 31SW/20) proved 21 m of grey and brown sand interbedded with grey clay; the sand was shelly at the base. The Crag here is overlain by 8.5 m of Corton Formation and underlain by Upper Chalk. Another borehole near Witton House (TG 30NW/31, Appendix 2) penetrated 14.3 m of sand, pebbly in part, with thin clay lenses, beneath 7 m of Anglian deposits. A borehole at Manor Farm, Blofield (TG 30NW/32, Appendix 2) proved 16.1 m of sand, partly pebbly, with thin clay lenses, underlying 3.9 m of Corton Formation.

South Walsham–Acle–Halvergate–Limpenhoe

A section in a cutting [3527 1296] carrying the main Acle road out of Panxworth, sampled by augering, comprises some 6 m of strata assigned to the Crag and capped directly by sandy till of the Corton Formation. The lowest beds are interbedded orange-brown, fine-grained sand, silt and clay, as well as some light grey clay and abundant concretionary iron oxide (ironpan); above these are orange fine- and medium-grained sands which become pebbly upwards, including quartz pebbles; and at the top are medium-grained sands with layers of grey silty clay.

In a temporary section at a construction site at a boatyard [3728 1434] near Pilson Green, the top 0.5 m or so of the Crag, underlying some 0.9 m of soil and cover silt and resting on 0.8 m of Kesgrave Formation (medium-grained sand passing down into gravel), was seen to comprise interbedded orange-brown sand, clayey sand and grey clay. Similar lithologies in the uppermost few metres of the Crag are recorded in ditches in the marshland fringe at several localities between Pilson Green and Acle [e.g. 3848 1328 to 3859 1319]; in instances where the deposits remain unweathered, grey, grey-green and khaki colours pertain, as for example [4082 1060] east of Acle. Most of the deeper site investigation boreholes sunk for the Acle By-pass scheme entered the Crag; their logs record sand and pebbly sand, commonly grey or grey-green but orange-brown towards the top, silty in part and interspersed with layers of grey or dark grey clay or silty clay. Scattered to abundant shell debris is recorded in many of the logs. In three of the boreholes to the east of Acle (TG 41SW/106, 107 and 108), the base of the Crag was penetrated and shown to rest on the London Clay Formation (Figure 46). About 1 m of gravel is recorded at the base in TG 41SW/107.

The Crag has discontinuous outcrops along the lower parts of the hillsides adjacent to the marshland between Halvergate and Limpenhoe [e.g. 420 070; 395 038]. The outcrops are mostly obscured by cover silt or hillwash and their limits are proved by augering or, locally in ploughed fields, by a distinct darkening of soil colour (particularly evident around Brickstone Carr [424 025; 404 036]). The sporadic nature of the hillside outcrops may be due in part to irregularities of the Crag surface —probably a consequence of erosion prior to deposition of the overlying Kesgrave Formation and cryoturbation involving both the Crag and the overlying deposits (see main text).

At the base of an overgrown pit in the hillside below Hill Farm [403 031], a recently excavated trench (dug to c.2 m depth) revealed layered, dark orange to yellow, iron oxide-stained, silty, fine- to medium-grained sand interpreted as Crag. Gravels and sands of the overlying Kesgrave Formation and Corton Formation are present in the worked face of the hillside (now obscured).

Within the marshland between Damgate Marshes and Limpenhoe Common [e.g. 4090 0910 to 3970 0360] several ditch sections up to 1 m deep revealed Crag under Holocene peats and silts. In these instances the Crag comprised highly mottled, orange to dark grey-green, interbedded sands (with subordinate gravels), silts and clay and, locally, traces of iron oxide (?ironpan). A drain [3988 0362] dug in the small outcrop of Crag at Limpenhoe revealed 1.5 m of grey sand. A nearby slurry pit [3994 0345] exposed 1.5 m of ferruginous reddish brown medium-grained sand. An augerhole [3999 0345] proved 1.2 m of laminated yellowish brown and grey silty clay.

Bramerton–Brooke–Loddon–Haddiscoe

The famous sections at Bramerton Common [2952 0602] and Blake's Pit [2979 0606], are no longer well exposed. A detailed description of the former was given by Funnell (1961), and in 1975 the latter was described as follows (Dr P E P Norton, written communication, abridged):

	Depth m
Shell deposit, multilayered pavement of broken shells; some stones	0.3
Buff sands and loamy sands with silt layers, and sporadic shell fragments	2.6
Shell deposit at 2.71 to 3.11 m	3.7
Grey and mottled sand; silt layer	4.2
Grey and brown silty sand with some shells, more shells above 4.31 m	4.5
Grey silty clay with shells	4.7
Clay, with flints	4.9

Approximately 6 m of yellowish brown to reddish brown fine- and medium-grained sand with thin clay beds are very poorly exposed in a pit [3085 0694], now a rifle range, north of Surlingham. Between Hill House, Surlingham [3114 0676] and Surlingham Wood [326 053] there are several backfilled pits from which, presumably, Crag clay was worked. The sections that were exposed in these pits during the latter part of the 19th century have been described in detail by Woodward (1881).

Some 4.5 m of greyish orange, thinly interbedded, micaceous clay and sand were seen in a disused pit at Low Common [3203 0363] 3.5 m below 1.5 m of till of the Corton Formation; the intervening strata were obscured by talus. To the south of Hellington a borehole (TG 30SW/12, Appendix 2) proved 7.5 m of interbedded clay and sand at a depth of 23 to 30.5 m, and another, to the north-west of Langley School (TG 30SW/14, Appendix 2), encountered 4.2 m of sporadically shelly sand beneath 23.8 m of younger deposits. To the north of Mundham, strong yellowish brown fine-grained sand interlaminated with grey clay was recorded in several augerholes [329 900].

Stokesby–West Caister

Sands and clays assigned to the Crag are exposed in ditches in the marshland fringe near Billockby [e.g. 4234 1335] and to the north of Stokesby [e.g. 4255 1129]. The typical lithologies recorded are dark orange and khaki sands and clayey sands and light grey clay, the clay occurring as lenses a few centimetres across and as more extensive layers. Augering south-west of Whitegate Farm [e.g. 4306 1151] indicates that the Crag at outcrop there, which is largely clay, forms a structural bulge of a few metres relief, of unknown origin but apparently disrupting the Kesgrave Formation.

Farther east, the top of the Crag is exposed in a drain fringing Walter's Covert [4850 1116 to 4882 1106]; up to about 0.5 m of orange and olive-grey fine- and medium-grained sands containing lenses of light grey clay up to a few centimetres across are exposed at the base of the cut under the Kesgrave Formation (see Chapter six). In another drain nearby [4947 1083] the top of the Crag is represented by aquiferous khaki and grey-green fine- to medium sand that carries a weak ferruginous cement as well as a plexus of iron-pan concretions. Some 0.5 m are exposed under a cover of orange-buff, fine-grained sand and pebbly sand assigned to the Kesgrave Formation; the Crag sand weathers rapidly to an orange-brown colour upon exposure.

Great Yarmouth area

Crag is not exposed in the Great Yarmouth area but is proven in many site investigation borings, mostly as sands and silts underlying the pre-Anglian and Holocene sequences. Generally, the borehole logs provide little lithological detail. The inferred top of the Crag is often poorly defined and pebbly or gravelly; this surface ranges from about 4 m below OD around the South Denes area to approximately 25 m below OD under the North Denes. A group of boreholes whose sites straddle the coast at North Beach, east of Newtown, proved the base of the Crag, resting on the London Clay Formation (Figure 47).

The upper part of the sequence is dominated by fine- and medium-grained sand with thin beds of silty clay, and the lower part by interlaminated clay, silt and sand; shells are present in some layers. Underlying Great Yarmouth, the deposits may exceed 50 m in thickness. An excavation (c.1954) through the spit at South Denes for the outfall of the electricity generating station is described by Green and Hutchinson (1960, pp.132–134). Their section included 'Basal "Red Beds"' and 'probable "Red Beds" not seen in situ'; these comprised 'fine, compact, reddish sands, sometimes containing laminae of silt and grey-green clay'. The upper surface of these deposits ranged between 4 and 10 m below OD and was overlain by Beach deposits (North Denes Formation). In the present account these Basal Red Beds are interpreted as Crag.

Somerleyton–Corton

Crag is not exposed inland from the coast and has not been recognised in the cliff sections. However, sixteen boreholes drilled for the British Geological Survey, primarily to investigate the Middle Pleistocene deposits between Hopton on Sea, Somerleyton and Corton (see Bridge and Hopson, 1985) all proved Crag. The Crag surface is irregular, ranging from above OD between Somerleyton and Blundeston (up to 2 m above OD at Poplar Farm in borehole TM 59NW/23) to 9.3 m below OD (in borehole TM59NW/18) towards the north of the area; the 'high' and 'low' corresponding to Hopson and Bridge's (1987) 'Corton Embayment' and 'Raveningham–Lound Depression' respectively (Figure 30).

Lithological detail from these boreholes shows that the Crag comprises fine- and medium-grained sands, micaceous and shelly in part, with seams and partings of silty clay. Bridge (1985) and Hopson and Bridge (1987) noted that the upper part of the Crag hereabouts may be subdivided into three distinct lithofacies. The lowest, comprising green shelly sands, is overlain by a middle sequence of stiff silts, followed by an uppermost lithofacies consisting of fine- and medium-grained sands interlaminated with clays. Leaching and oxidation of the Crag above the contemporary watertable has resulted in decalcification and removal of shell debris (particularly in the upper part of the sequence), leaving a brown sand containing only thin ironstone bands and concretions. The pebble content is generally less than 5 per cent comprising subrounded black flint.

KESGRAVE FORMATION [1]

Nomenclature and distribution

The Kesgrave Formation (Rose et al., 1985) is a suite of pebbly sands, gravels and silts which unconformably overlies the Crag. The most notable characteristic of the formation is the significant proportion (up to 25 per cent) of rounded quartz and quartzite pebbles in the mainly flint gravel. The Kesgrave Formation includes equivalents of the Kesgrave Sands and Gravels of Suffolk as defined by Rose et al. (1976), and the Ingham Sand and Gravel of Clarke and Auton (1982) which crops out in north-west Suffolk. East Anglian sediments which crop out on the coast and are of broadly similar age were ascribed by Funnell and West (1977) and West (1980) to the Cromer Forest Bed Formation; they have here been included within the Kesgrave Formation. The Kesgrave Formation of Rose et al. is taken to be the terrestrial, or wholly fluviatile equivalent of the partly marine Cromer Forest Beds and the offshore (just outside the district) seismostratigraphical unit known as the Yarmouth Roads Formation which is interpreted as a delta-top sedimentation unit (Cameron et al., 1984; in press). It was not practicable, for this survey, to subdivide systematically the Kesgrave Formation as has been accomplished elsewhere (Hey and Brenchley, 1977; Rose and Allen, 1977; Green and McGregor, 1978; McGregor and Green, 1978, 1983; Hey, 1980; Green et al., 1982; Kemp, 1985; Rose et al., 1985); Bridgland, 1988).

Formerly, the quartz-rich gravels of the district were were variously included in the Bure Valley Beds (Wood, 1866), the Pebbly Sands and Pebble beds (Wood and Harmer, 1868) and the Westleton Sands and Shingle (Prestwich, 1871c). Wood and Harmer were alone in referring these deposits to the 'Glacial series'; all the other authors assigned them to the Crag. A summary of the history of nomenclature of the formation is given in Table 6.

Bowen et al. (1986) considered that the Kesgrave Sands and Gravels of Rose and Allen (1977) accumulated during the Pre-Pastonian (*a* and *c* sub-stages) and Beestonian stages. Their view was on the grounds that the formation rests on Bramertonian sediments at Bramerton (Funnell et al., 1979) and Baventian sediments at Covehithe (Hey, 1976), and is overlain by Cromerian deposits along the Norfolk coast (West, 1980). However, Bowen et al. (1986) retained some caution about correlation because of the evidence for major hiatuses during this period (Mayhew and Stewart, 1986). Funnell and West (1977) referred their Cromer Forest Bed Formation to the Pre-Pastonian *b* to Cromerian. Some authors have informally included deposits assigned to the Pre-

---

1 As this memoir was going to press, two papers were published (Whiteman, 1992; Whiteman and Rose, 1992) in which the status of the formation has been raised to that of a group (Kesgrave Group). The group consists of two formations (Sudbury and Colchester formations, each containing four members) and represent a total of eight pre-Anglian-glaciation Thames terraces. The regional correlations of these terraces have also been substantially revised compared to those given in this memoir.

Plate 2   Kesgrave Formation at Corton Cliffs [54 99] in 1931; peat resting on clay with rootlet traces *(Rootlet Bed)* and overlain by pebbly sand with clay lenses and laminae. A5670.

Pastonian *a* (e.g. Gibbard and Zalasiewicz, 1988) because of evidence for an unconformity beneath sediments of this stage (Mayhew and Stuart, 1986); this practice is adopted in the present account.

The Kesgrave Formation crops out in a more or less continuous belt on the lower slopes of the valleys of the Yare and Bure, and their tributaries, and in patches north of the River Waveney around Blundeston. It locally forms the base of the cliffs between Hopton on Sea and Corton (see Plate 2), but much of this outcrop is concealed by sea defences. Along this stretch of coast during exceptionally low tides the lower part of the formation can be seen on the sea bed; it crops out above 6 m below OD, offshore. Boreholes have proved the formation beneath younger deposits, generally the Corton and Lowestoft Till formations, which form the interfluvial plateaux. The base of the formation is irregular with some evidence of channelling into the underlying sediments of the Crag Group.

Stratigraphy and sedimentology

Rose and Allen (1977) considered that the Kesgrave Sands and Gravels were the sediments of a braided river flowing under periglacial conditions. They postulated that the deposits were part of a proto-Thames braidplain that, during the Beestonian, covered much of East Anglia. Clast analyses by later workers (Hey, 1980; Clarke and Auton, 1982; Hopson and Bridge, 1987) have suggested that the braidplain may also have been supplied by rivers that were contemporaneous with the ancient Thames but which drained a more northerly basin (Figure 29). Rose (1987) has speculated that at least some of the quartzose gravels of northern and central East Anglia were the deposits of an hypothetical pre-Anglian river that drained the outcrop of the Kidderminster Formation, flowed eastwards through the Midlands (near Melton Mowbray), across the area now occupied by the Fenland and along the line of the present River Waveney. Green and McGregor (1990) have suggested that, from the evidence of

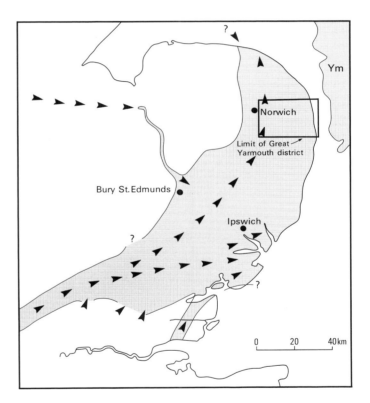

Figure 29   Generalised regional distribution of the Kesgrave Formation and its partial equivalent, the Yarmouth Roads Formation (YM). The arrows show approximate directions of flow of the proto-Thames and its tributaries. N=Norwich, I=Ipswich and B=Bury St Edmunds. (after Rose et al., 1985; Rose, 1987; Bridgland, 1988; Green and McGregor, 1990).

clast-analysis, Pre-Pastonian or older gravels of north Norfolk reached the area via a proto-Thames system, and later 'Midland' gravels of pre-Cromerian to Cromerian–early Anglian age had their origins to the north or north-west.

Table 6   The Kesgrave Formation: its history of nomenclature and its temporal equivalents.

EARLY WORKERS (either included in or equivalent to; age not implied)	BRITISH STAGES	ROSE et al. (1976) ROSE AND ALLEN (1977) (Suffolk)	HEY (1980) (East Anglia)	CLARKE AND AUTON (1982) (Suffolk/Norfolk borders)	KEMP (1985) ROSE et al. (1985) BOWEN et al. (1986)[1] BRIDGLAND (1988)[2]	This survey; GREEN AND McGREGOR (1990)	FUNNELL AND WEST (1977) (Norfolk/Suffolk coast)		CAMERON et al. (1986; 1992)
Bure Valley Beds (Wood, 1866) Pebbly sands and Pebble beds Glacial series (Wood and Harmer, 1868) 'Lower glacial' (Wood, 1870) Westleton Sands and Shingle (Prestwich, 1871)	ANGLIAN	Barham Soil			Lower St. Osyth Gravel[2] (Terrace)	Kesgrave Formation	Cromer Forest Bed Formation	Bacton Mbr. Mundesley Mbr.	Yarmouth Roads Formation (part)
	CROMERIAN ('CROMERIAN COMPLEX')	Valley Farm rubified sol lessivé		Kesgrave Sands and Gravels	Wivenhoe Gravel/Cooks Green Gv.[2] Ardleigh Gravel (Terraces)[2]			West Rinton Mbr.*	
	BEESTONIAN	Kesgrave Sands and Gravels	'Low Level' Gravels		Cooks Green Gravel[1] (Terrace)			Runton Mbr.	
	PASTONIAN			Ingham Sand and Gravel				Paston Mbr.	
	PRE-PASTONIAN d				?				
	c				Waldringfield Gravels[1] (Terrace)			Sheringham Member	
	b								
	a		'High Level' Gravels		Westland Green Gravels[1] Baylham Common Gravels (Terraces)[1]				

*Includes Rootlet Bed of Blake, 1890

Studies of the elevation of bodies of sediment within the Kesgrave Sands and Gravels, supported by lithological analysis and soil stratigraphy, have allowed differentiation of six terrace deposits in southern East Anglia (Table 6; Rose and Allen 1977; Hey, 1980; Allen, 1984; Bridgland, 1988). These deposits probably accumulated during the cold periods of the Pre-Pastonian *a* to early Anglian stages (Bridgland, 1988; Gibbard et al., 1991). In this district the paucity of exposure has not permitted a detailed analysis of the stratigraphy and sedimentology of the formation. The Kesgrave Formation as here defined, as also by Bridgland (1988), includes lithofacies representative of a wider range of environments, and accumulating over a longer period, than those envisaged by Rose et al. (1985). In the western and central parts of the district the formation is wholly fluviatile in character; towards the east the marine influence becomes increasingly important with some facies, for example the Cromer Forest Beds, reflecting an intertidal/estuarine depositional environment.

The formation is typically represented at outcrop by a spread of pebbly or gravelly soil low on the flanks of valleys. Detailed borehole logs are sparse except in the south-east of the district, but from these records it appears that the greater part of the formation comprises pebbly sands and gravel. Thin layers of clay and silt occur locally, and in some boreholes, including Green Lane, Hellington (TG 30SW/12, Appendix 2), 6 km south-east of Norwich, Hales Hall (TM 39NE/6, Appendix 2) and two in the south-east (TM 59NW/26 and 27), biogenic deposits of presumed Cromerian age are recorded. The base of the formation tends to be poorly defined, especially where sands of the Kesgrave Formation rest on sands of the Crag Group; in the absence of clear distinguishing criteria it is accepted that some Crag deposits may have been classified erroneously as Kesgrave Formation, and vice versa.

Blake (1884, 1890) and Reid (1890) recorded the following sequence (with descriptions and thicknesses generalised from their accounts), which they referred to the Cromer Forest-bed Series, at the base of the cliffs between Hopton on Sea and Corton (see Plate 2):

		Thickness m
5	Pebbly quartzose sand, with laminated grey and brown clay	up to 3.0
4	Compressed lignite, with flattened wood and matted reeds	c.0.15
3	The Rootlet Bed comprising greenish and dark bluish grey unstratified clay, with occasional white calcareous concretions ('race'), ferruginous sandy concretions, and abundant rootlets. Some mammallian remains.	up to 2.5
2	Stratified grey and brown clay	up to 1.0
1	Gravels with quartzite pebbles	up to 1.0

More recently West (1980) recorded this, generalised, sequence in boreholes and sections at the base of the cliff between Hopton and Corton:

		Thickness m
i	Pale, fluviatile sand with mud streaks; extensive ice-wedge system	0.5
h	Tidally laminated sand and clay	up to 1.4
g	Iron-stained flint and quartz gravels, and sand; ?beach deposits	up to 0.3
f	A biogenic layer, including much wood	c.0.15
e	Blue-grey clay with rootlets (the Rootlet Bed of Blake); approximately at OD	2.3
d	Detritus sandy mud; freshwater	0.2
c	Iron-stained flint and quartz gravels of possible fluviatile origin	1.5 to 7.8
b	Tidally laminated silts and clay	
	unconformity	1.7

a   Flaser and lenticular-bedded clay and
      sand seen to 8 m below OD

West interpreted the basal bed *a* as representing a tidal-flat environment and assigned it to the Pastonian stage. Beds *b* to *i* he interpreted as representing a complex interplay of marine and fluviatile environments across a low-lying coastline, resulting from many fluctuations in sealevel; these he assigned to the Cromerian. He referred the whole sequence to the Cromer Forest Bed Formation of Funnell and West (1977). Bridge (1985) recorded the following sequence at the base of Corton Cliffs (Figure 38):

		Thickness m
2	Sand and pebbly sand, interbedded with thin clay seams folded and overturned to the south; ice-wedge casts with gravel fill developed locally	1.58
1	Clay, blue grey, sticky, with sand lenses and peat fragments (seen on foreshore) — *Rootlet Bed*	1.21

The ice-wedge casts are attributed to the development of periglacial structures at the onset of the Anglian glaciation (Plate 3; Chapter six). A more complete sequence was recorded by Bridge (1985) in borehole TM 59NW/26.

At least two generations of Kesgrave Formation deposits have been identified within the district. Using data from boreholes in the south-east, between Raveningham and Corton, Hopson and Bridge (1987) were able to subdivide what they termed 'quartzose Pre-Anglian gravels' into two units which occur at different elevations and in separate areas (Figures 30 and 31). The older of these is locally overlain by deposits of Cromerian age and comprises bedded gravels and pebbly sands up to 7 m thick containing pebbles thought to have been derived from

the Kidderminster Formation of the Midlands. The base of this older unit rests on a Crag high, the 'Toft Monks Ridge', at elevations of between 5 and 8 m above OD and has been tentatively correlated with the Ingham Sand and Gravel. The younger unit, confined to the lower-lying 'Corton Embayment' (Figures 30 and 31), was divided by Hopson and Bridge into three subunits: the basal subunit consists of iron-stained, poorly sorted, pebbly sand and gravel up to 5 m thick; this is overlain by up to 2 m of bluish grey silty clay, identified as the Rootlet Bed of Blake (1884, 1890); and this in turn is overlain by up to 5 m of interbedded ferruginous sand, clay, and gravel comprising mainly rounded flint pebbles with a proportion of quartz and quartzite (c. 22 per cent of the +8 mm to −16 mm fraction), and minor constituents of silicified limestone, *Rhaxella* chert and fine-grained mafic volcanics. This younger unit rests on Crag at elevations of between 5 m below and 5 m above OD and was correlated by Hopson and Bridge with the coastal Cromerian deposits described by West (1980).

Details

Acle–Halvergate–Reedham–Limpenhoe

Ditches bordering the marshland between Pilson Green and Acle [e.g. 3862 1287 to 3868 1298] reveal sections up to 1 m of fine- to coarse-grained sand interbedded with gravel (Kesgrave Formation) underlying cover silt, comprising up to 1 m of stony silt with an irregular gravelly base. The Kesgrave deposits are in part leached and, where they rest on clay deposits in the Crag [e.g. 3832 1335 to 3847 1328] they are locally richly ferruginous. Where ferruginous, their distinction from the Crag is commonly unclear, a difficulty that may be compounded by their inclusion of clay lenses [3963 1315].

The Kesgrave Formation has an almost continuous outcrop on the lower hillslopes between Acle and Limpenhoe; it is generally capped by sandy till of the Corton Formation, although, locally, it is overstepped by Lowestoft Till [e g between 400 079

Figure 30   Topography of top of the Crag in the south-eastern part of the district (amended from Hopson and Bridge, 1987); section along line A–B shown in Figure 31.

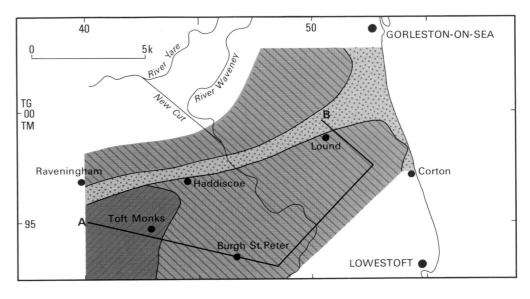

Toft Monks Ridge
> +5m OD

Corton Embayment
+5 to −5m OD

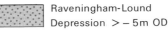

Raveningham-Lound
Depression > −5m OD

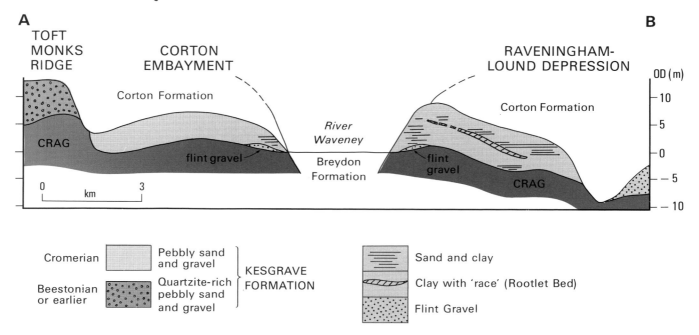

Figure 31   Section along the line indicated in Figure 30 showing the relationships of the 'quartzose pre-Anglian gravels' in the Kesgrave Formation (amended from Hopson and Bridge, 1987).

and 401 074]. The thickness proved at outcrop generally ranges between 3 m and 5 m but exceptionally it is up to an estimated 13 m [376 047] near Swill's Meadow. The base of the outcrop ranges from OD to about 1 m above OD and rests either on an irregular Crag surface [e.g. 425 075] (probably eroded and cryoturbated) or abuts the Holocene deposits of the marshland. For the most part the deposit comprises fine-grained sand and pebbly sand with lenses and layers of quartzite-bearing gravel.

Numerous abandoned shallow workings are evident along the crop [e.g. 418 090; 427 055; 428 054; 416 043; 429 034; 418 026]. These much degraded pits are commonly distinguished by notably pebbly soils comprising abundant quartzite with flint gravel. Locally [e.g. 408 090 and 423 083], where the Kesgrave Formation abuts the marshland, ditch sections up to 1 m deep expose pebbly sands with gravel stringers. Some of the ditch sections are richly ferruginous and include clay seams; in these instances and where the Kesgrave Formation is particularly sandy, the distinction between this formation and the underlying Crag may be uncertain.

East of Reedham, railway cuttings poorly expose up to 6 m of sand and pebbly sand (Kesgrave Formation) underlying sandy till of the Corton Formation. Within Reedham village, up to 2 m of pebbly sand of the Kesgrave Formation is poorly exposed in the overgrown faces of a former pit [420 021], from which the overlying clay of the Corton Formation was formerly worked for brick-making. Close by, a recent face clearance of the railway sidings cutting [416 022] adjacent to Reedham Station showed Kesgrave Formation comprising about 8 m of layered orange-yellow sand with sporadic clay layers and silty partings.

Bramerton–Loddon–Haddiscoe

Exposures in a disused and partly back-filled pit at Langley Street [3655 0195] show pebbly sand in which the pebbles in-

clude mainly flint with some quartz and quartzite, underlying till of the Corton Formation. 1.5 m of sandy gravel are exposed in a small pit [3492 9831] south-east of Sisland. The gravel fraction comprises mainly rounded flint pebbles, with subordinate rounded quartz and quartzite pebbles. A borehole (TG 30SW/12) at Green Lane, Hellington (Appendix 2), penetrated 8.6 m of sand and gravel beneath 20.4 m of glacial deposits. The gravel fraction comprised well-rounded flint and some quartz and quartzite pebbles. The sand and gravel deposit (Kesgrave Formation) included a layer of biogenic deposits between 21.4 and 23.0 m depth, consisting of dark grey to dark ochre brown clay and interbedded peat of presumed Cromerian age. Borehole TM 39NE/6 at Hales Hall, (Appendix 2), penetrated 8 m of pebbly sand and sandy gravel beneath 15.5 m of glacial deposits, the gravel fraction consisting mainly of rounded flint, quartz and quartzite pebbles. A 0.35 m thick layer of dark grey silty clay with sporadic shell fragments, similar to that proved in borehole TG 30SW/12, was encountered within the pebbly sands at 18.05 m depth.

West Caister

Sections of up to 3 m of the Kesgrave Formation, some capped by sandy till of the Corton Formation, were exposed in a freshly excavated drain known as Pickerill Holme [4945 1180 to 5006 1201]. They comprise cross-bedded, light orange-brown, fine- to medium-grained sand and pebbly sand with layers and lenses of gravel especially towards the base; foresets dip generally to between east and south-east. Lenses and flakes of light grey and red mottled clay occur in the basal metre or so in some sections and, in others, gravel-filled ice-wedge cryoturbation structures are preserved. Quartz and quartzite pebbles are conspicuous in the gravels. The basal part of the formation is exposed farther south in Pickerill Holme [4947 1083] and, to the south-west, in a ditch section in Walter's Covert [4845 1107]. In the latter locality it comprises up to about 1 m of light orange-brown fine-to medium-grained sand, capped by cover silt, resting on up to 0.3 m of sandy to clayey medium gravel composed of flint, quartz and quartzite pebbles; the base of the gravel, resting on orange to olive-grey sand with lenses of light grey clay (Crag), is irregular, a consequence not only of erosion preceding the accumulation of the gravel but also cryoturbation involving both the Kesgrave Formation and the top of the Crag.

Corton and Somerleyton

Some 3 m of the Kesgrave Formation are exposed under the Corton Formation at the base of Corton Cliffs and on the adjoining foreshore [5400 9863] (Figures 33 and 38); sand and pebbly sand form a layer 1.6 m thick which rests on 1.2 m of blue-grey clay that is identified as the Rootlet Bed (see also Plate 2). The sands are interbedded with thin seams of clay deformed into folds that are overturned to the south; they include gravel-filled ice-wedge casts (Plate 3). During exceptionally low tides, the lower part of the formation is visible on the sea bed. A disused brickpit at Somerleyton [4795 9667] provides a somewhat poorly exposed section of 6.5 m of pebbly sand of the Kesgrave Formation under a cover of sandy till (Corton Formation); the sand is buff coloured, medium- to coarse-grained and contains abundant well-rounded black flint pebbles.

SIX

Quaternary — Anglian

Deposits of Anglian age form most of the upland terrain of the district, although their outcrops are extensively masked by a veneer of cover silt (see Chapter seven). Only in the west and north-west, and as a fringe around the marshland margin farther east, do older formations emerge from a cover of these deposits. In most of the off-shore area and under most of the marshland, deposits of Anglian age are absent, removed by erosion.

Two glacial formations are formally recognised within these deposits and are indicated by letter symbols on the published map: the older is termed the Corton Forma-tion (new name) and the younger, the Lowestoft Till For-mation. Another formation, the Yare Valley Formation, although regarded as being mainly of Devensian age, may incorporate older deposits including some of Anglian age and is described in Chapter seven. As well as these formal-ly defined units, there are various glaciofluvial deposits that are depicted by graphic symbols on the published map; some specific deposits are distinguished informally by letter superscripts. The formations and their relation-ships with the deposits that are not subject to formal clas-sification are shown schematically as a tablet on the map.

Evidence of the onset of the Anglian cold period is pre-served in the Kesgrave Formation, underneath the An-glian glacial deposits. Vertical to subvertical wedge-shaped structures in the tidal silts, peat and Rootlet Bed at Corton were first noted by Blake (1884), and interpreted as ice-wedge casts by Gardner and West (1975), who recognised that these structures formed a polygonal pattern which had developed in early Anglian times. Rose et al. (1985) noted that the ice wedges were filled with allogenic materi-al, mineralogically different from the host material but similar to the Barham Coversand, which they assigned to the Barham Soil, an early Anglian soil horizon.

CORTON FORMATION

Classification, nomenclature and distribution

A complex unit comprising tills, sands and subordinate gravels, for which the name Corton Formation is intro-duced, overlies the Kesgrave Formation and, in the west, overlaps that formation to rest directly on the Crag; these relationships are illustrated schematically in a tablet on the published map and also in Figure 32. The unit forms the lower part of the Anglian stratotype, which was desig-

Figure 32 Corton Formation: generalised sections form boreholes and coastal cliffs, showing variations in thickness and lithofacies. Depths and heights are given in metres OD.

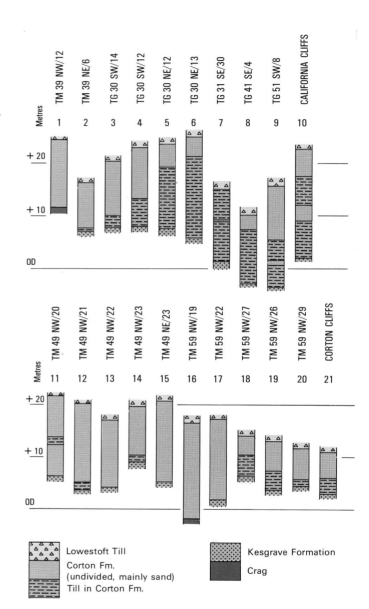

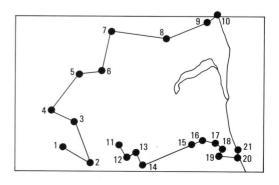

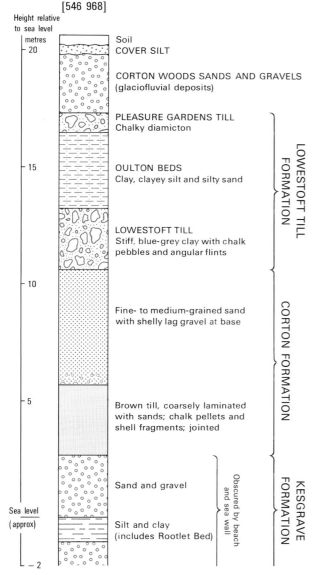

[546 968]

Height relative
to sea level

metres
- 20

Soil
COVER SILT

CORTON WOODS SANDS AND GRAVELS
(glaciofluvial deposits)

PLEASURE GARDENS TILL
Chalky diamicton

- 15

OULTON BEDS
Clay, clayey silt and silty sand

LOWESTOFT TILL
Stiff, blue-grey clay with chalk
pebbles and angular flints

- 10

Fine- to medium-grained sand
with shelly lag gravel at base

- 5

Brown till, coarsely laminated
with sands; chalk pellets and
shell fragments; jointed

Sand and gravel

Obscured by beach
and sea wall

Sea level
(approx)

Silt and clay
(includes Rootlet Bed)

- 2

LOWESTOFT TILL
FORMATION

CORTON FORMATION

KESGRAVE
FORMATION

Figure 33   The generalised succession in the sea-cliffs at Corton, the stratotype for the Anglian Stage (amended from Bridge and Hopson, 1985).

nated by Banham (1971) as a sequence exposed in the sea cliffs at Corton (Figures 33 and 38); the upper part of the stratotype comprises the lithologically contrasting Lowestoft Till Formation, together with other units of local occurrence. The same locality is designated the type section of the Corton Formation in this account.

The history of nomenclature of the deposits that make up the Corton Formation is summarised in Table 7. The formation incorporates the till-dominated units previously identified within the district and termed variously the Lower Glacial (Wood and Harmer, 1868), the Lower Boulder Clay (Gunn, 1867), the Norwich Brickearth (Harmer, 1902), the North Sea Drift (Harmer, 1909b), the Cromer Till (Baden-Powell, 1950) and the First Cromer Till (Banham, 1970); and referred to more re-

gionally, but informally, as the North Sea Drift group by Perrin et al. (1979) on the grounds of a lithological similarity between them. It also includes the sand-dominant deposits that have been previously termed the Middle Glacial (Wood and Harmer, 1868), Corton Beds (Baden-Powell, 1948, 1950; Banham, 1971), and Corton Sands (Baden-Powell, 1950; Bridge and Hopson, 1985; Hopson and Bridge, 1987). The name Corton Formation is synonymous with North Sea Drift Formation (Mathers et al., 1987). The division is equivalent to the Contorted Drift of north-eastern Norfolk (Wood and Harmer, 1868), and is regarded as a product of the Anglian 'Scandinavian ice-sheet' rather than the 'British Eastern ice-sheet', to which the Lowestoft Till Formation is attributed (see Hart et al., 1990).

The Corton Formation is of widespread occurrence in the uplands, the most extensive outcrops (in part masked by cover silt) being those in the Plumstead area in the north-west and in the Filby–Caister-on-Sea area; other outcrops occur around Freethorpe and in the Gorleston-on-Sea–St Olaves area. On the published map, the formation is depicted in an undivided mode where sand is dominant, but units of till within the formation are shown where they are mappable. The till units are regarded as correlatives of the Cromer tills of north-east Norfolk (Banham, 1970), but individual correlations with specific named units in the Cromer sequence are not attempted.

As a mapping expedient throughout the district, the base of the Corton Formation has generally been taken at the base of the lowest, and over wide areas, the only till unit within the succession (Plate 3). Mapping and borehole data show that this unit is locally impersistent, particularly in the southern part of the district (Figures 32 and 38; see Hopson and Bridge, 1987). In such circumstances, the position of the base of the formation within a sequence consisting solely of sands and gravels is difficult to determine either at outcrop or in boreholes; its identification depends on the recognition of igneous indicator pebbles of Scandinavian origin, which are believed to be restricted to the Corton Formation and younger deposits. In some places sands and gravels directly underlying the lowest till may properly belong to the Corton Formation (Bridge and Hopson, 1985; Hopson and Bridge, 1987); however, in the absence of clear criteria by which they may be distinguished, they have been included in the Kesgrave Formation or, if this is absent, the Crag.

A contoured plot showing the relief of the basal surface of the formation based on borehole and mapping data is given in Figure 34; for the sake of continuity the plot incorporates extrapolated contours across the marshland area where the formation is absent, removed by erosion. Compared with the corresponding plot of the basal surface of the overlying Lowestoft Till (Figure 35), this plot represents a surface of low relief and shows no instances of confined, till-filled channels. Another contoured plot (Figure 36), based on the surfaces shown in Figures 34 and 35, shows a reconstruction of the thickness variation of the Corton Formation after the deposition of the Lowestoft Till. Figure 32 illustrates the general lithological variation within the formation across the district.

Table 7 Lithostratigraphical nomenclature adopted in this survey for the Anglian glacial deposits of the district compared with a selection of previous schemes.

THIS SURVEY	HOPSON AND BRIDGE (1987)		BANHAM (1971)	BADEN-POWELL (1948, 1950)	HARMER (1902, 1909b)	WOODWARD (1881) BLAKE (1890)	WOOD AND HARMER (1868) WOOD (1880)
Glaciofluvial deposits	Plateau Gravels					Gravel (Cannon Shot gravel) (Plateau gravel)	
	Valley Flank sands and gravels						
Lowestoft Till Formation including Pleasure Gardens Till and Oulton Beds	Lowestoft Till Group	Pleasure Gardens Till	Pleasure Gardens Till	Lowestoft Boulder Clay		Boulder Clay = Chalky Boulder Clay	Upper Glacial = true Boulder Clay = Chalky Boulder Clay
		Oulton Beds	Oulton Beds				
		Lowestoft Till	Lowestoft Till				
Corton Formation including till layers	North Sea Drift Group	Corton Sands	Corton Beds	Corton Beds = Corton Sands		Sand and gravel	Middle Glacial
		Leet Hill Sands and Gravels					
		North Sea Drift = Norwich Brickearth	First Cromer Till	Cromer Till	Norwich Brickearth = North Sea Drift	Stony Loam = Brickearth = Norwich Brickearth	Lower Glacial

Plate 3 Corton Formation resting on Kesgrave Formation at Corton Cliffs [5401 9864]; red-brown, crudely stratified till overlies sand with clay lenses, disrupted by subvertical ice-wedge casts. The tops of the casts are sheared to the left, indicating the sense of movement of the till-depositing ice sheet. A14197.

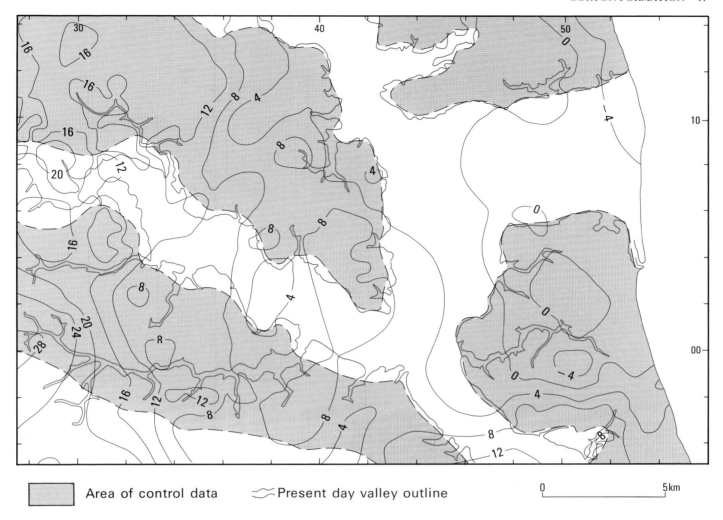

Area of control data   ∽Present day valley outline   0   5km

Figure 34 Contours (metres OD) on the base of the Corton Formation (computer-generated plot derived from mapping and boehole databases; contours extrapolated between areas of occurence, giving a district-wide reconstruction of the penecontemporeous surface, before erosion).

Stratigraphy and sedimentology

The best natural sections in the Corton Formation within the district are those in the sea cliffs between Gorleston-on-Sea and south of Corton, where up to at least 12 m are preserved under the Lowestoft Till. The type section at Corton is typical of the exposed sequences which are bipartite, comprising sand with subordinate gravel overlying till (Figures 33 and 38). In the excellent cliff sections at California Gap (Figure 32, Plate 4), just beyond the northern limit of the district, the exposed sequence, up to 20 m thick, is more complex and comprises two till units (the Lower and Middle tills of Hopson and Bridge, 1987) separated and overlain by sand; the top of the lower till is, in places, an irregular erosion surface, while the overlying sand includes till layers and is locally highly deformed. Whether this deformation is a glacitectonic effect related to an advance of the Scandinavian (Cromer) ice sheet (Banham, 1988; Hart et al., 1990) or

the product of soft sediment slumping (Eyles et al., 1989) is unresolved on the evidence of this survey. A higher till unit, the Upper till of Hopson and Bridge, is here regarded as weathered Lowestoft Till on lithological grounds; it consists of stiff, yellowish brown, sandy clay with angular flint pebbles.

In addition to the sedimentary complexity of the California Gap section, the formation as a whole is folded into a northward-facing, approximately east–west-trending monocline, the folded sequence being overlain unconformably by the Lowestoft Till (Figure 37). This structure is interpreted as a product of proglacial deformation (see Hart et al., 1990), probably due to a readvance of the Scandinavian icesheet from the north rather than to the subsequent advance of the British Eastern (Lowestoft) ice sheet from the north-west. The extent to which the deposits underlying the Corton Formation are involved in this structure is also speculative; it is possible that the clay-

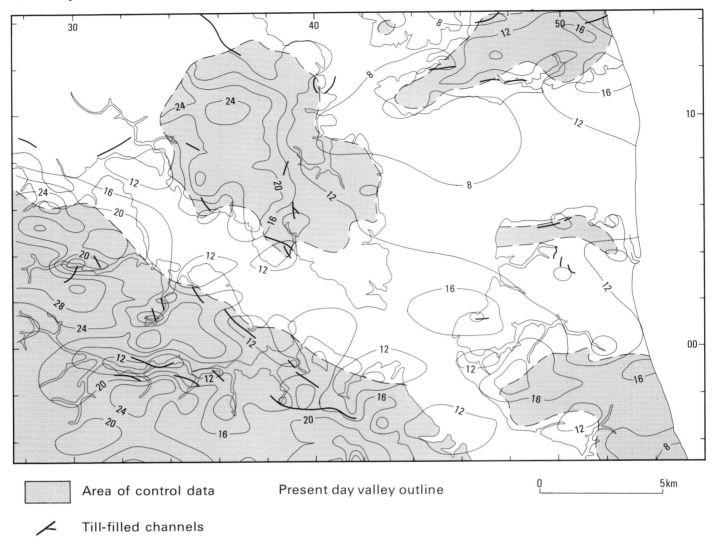

Area of control data	Present day valley outline

⟋ Till-filled channels

0   5km

Figure 35 Contours (metres OD) on the base of the Lowestoft Till and the locations of
elongate till-filled depressions identified in the district (computer-generated plot derived from
mapping and borehole databases; contours extrapolated between areas of occurrence, giving a
district-wide reconstruction of the penecontemporaneous surface, before erosion).

rich 'Rootlet Bed' within the underlying Kesgrave Formation has served as a plane of décollement.

Mapping and boreholes (Figure 32) show that sedimentary complexity similar to that at California Gap extends inland to the Filby and Acle areas, with till commonly present as two leaves and, in a few places, as three.
Such interleaving is also recorded from the Cantley area
and at the Welcome Pit, near Burgh Castle (Figure 39).
In the north-western part of the area the formation preserved under Lowestoft Till is represented almost entirely by till, while south of the River Yare in the Chet valley,
where the preserved thickness is very variable, till forms
only an impersistent basal layer. In the south-east, boreholes show that the till unit at the base of the formation
is absent in a belt extending through Raveningham,
Lound and Hopton, where the formation fills a shallow
trough called the Raveningham–Lound Depression (Fig-

ure 30; Bridge and Hopson, 1985). The offshore extension of this depression, with its fill of Corton Formation,
has been recognised in a shallow seismic profile off
League Hole, Hopton on Sea.

The extent to which the formation is affected by glacitectonic deformation is unclear from the evidence of this
survey. A possible glacitectonic significance may be attached to some of the irregularities affecting the base of
the formation shown in the contoured plot in Figure 34.
However, in the north-west, any irregularities of the base
of the Corton Formation may simply reflect a pre-exist-
ing local relief of the Crag, on which it rests.

The sands, which in the south-east at least make up
most of the formation and which have been referred to either as Corton Beds (Baden-Powell, 1948) or Corton
Sands (Bridge and Hopson, 1985), are well exposed in the
cliff section between Gorleston-on-Sea and Corton (Figure

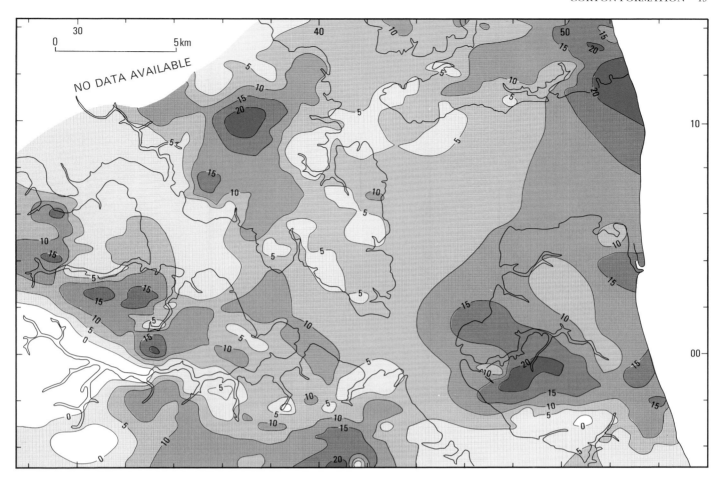

Figure 36   Isopachytes (metres) of the Corton Formation: a district-wide reconstruction at the Lowestoft glaciation (based on the computer-generated surfaces illustrated in Figures 34 and 35).

38); also in a number of sand pits, notably the Welcome Pit (Figure 39, Plates 4 and 5). They are also documented from boreholes, particularly those sunk by the British Geological Survey in 1983 in the Beccles–Corton area, extending into the south-eastern part of the district (Bridge and Hopson, 1985; Hopson and Bridge, 1987). Bridge and Hopson recognised three fining-upwards sedimentary cycles culminating in silt- and clay- grade material within the succession above the basal till (their Norwich Brickearth); they identified a zone of cryoturbation at the junction of their lowest (Cycle 1) and middle (Cycle 2) cycles. The three cycles were correlated with the First, Second and Third Cromer tills of north-east Norfolk (Banham, 1971). The differentiation of individual cycles has not proved feasible in the mapping of the formation.

Where seen in pits and coastal sections, the sands are yellowish buff, commonly cross-bedded and mostly fine grained (Plate 5); chalk grains or larger clasts have been noted in several sections, and in some borehole logs the sands are described in part as chalky. Postdepositional structures have been noted, for example microfaulting in

the Corton cliff section (Plate 6). Sequences are interrupted by thin layers or laminae of silt, clay or pebbly diamicton, typically pink in colour. Lenses of gravel or pebbly sand are exposed in the coastal sections, and were recorded by Woodward (1881) and Blake (1890) from pits now long abandoned and overgrown or backfilled. There are also layers composed largely or wholly of fragmental shell debris. Lists of shell species recovered are given in the memoirs by Woodward and Blake. S V Wood and F W Harmer (in Woodward, 1881) were of the opinion that the species recovered by them in a sand pit at Billockby [4295 1350] were contemporaneous and not derived from the Crag, although the majority of species were common to the Crag.

In the south-east, an impersistent layer of pebbly sands and sandy gravels separates the sand-dominant part of the formation from the basal till. This layer was identified and interpreted as outwash gravels by Bridge and Hopson (1985) and named the Leet Hill Sands and Gravels by Hopson and Bridge (1987). This unit has a maximum recorded thickness of 10 m; it fills what is interpreted as an intraformational erosion hollow trending north-east-

Plate 4 Coastal cliffs in the Corton Formation south of California Gap (North Walsham district) [5196 1453]. A layer of sand, 2 to 3 m thick, forms a ledge separating steep faces of till. The section is capped by dunes of blown sand (unexposed). View to west.

wards through Raveningham, Lound and Hopton, and cutting through the basal till into pre-Anglian deposits (see above; Figures 30 and 31). Similar gravelly deposits, cross-bedded and with an abundance of shell debris, characterise the lower sand unit in the cliff section at California Gap and its correlative in the Ormesby Borehole (Appendix 2), while at Corton Cliffs (Figure 38) the basal till has been locally completely eroded and blocks of it up to 0.5 m across are included within the lowest 2 m or so of the overlying sand. It has not proved feasible to distinguish the Leet Hill Sands and Gravels on the published map; these deposits, together with the Corton Sands, are represented on the map as undivided Corton Formation.

Sporadic calcareous cementation affecting the sands within some 2 m of the top of the formation beneath the Lowestoft Till is a feature of the formation where exposed in the sea cliffs near Corton, and similar cementation has been noted inland at Welcome Pit (Plate 7) and Langley, near Loddon. The occurrence of indurated sands, including doggers, directly under the chalk-rich Lowestoft Till

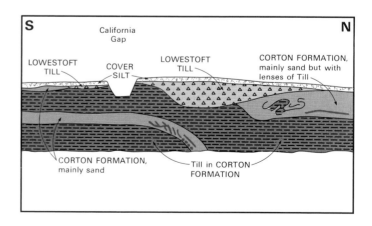

Figure 37 California Cliffs (North Walsham district) [5190 1466 to 5177 1590]: sketch of deformed Corton Formation, and its unconformable relationship to the Lowestoft Till. Cliff height about 15 m, vertical scale exaggerated.

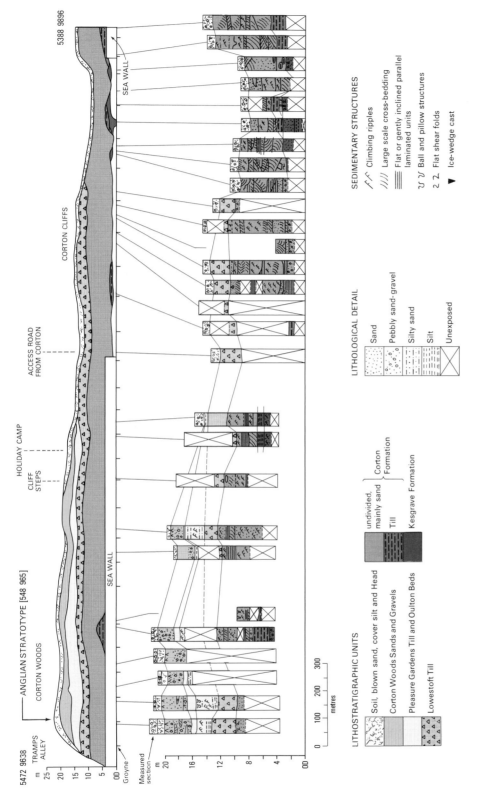

Figure 38 Section of the Anglian deposits in the sea cliffs at Corton.

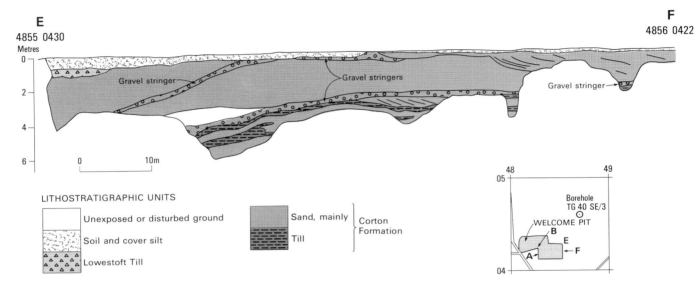

Figure 39 Sections in the Corton Formation at Welcome Pit [482 043], Burgh Castle (based on field sketches by D McC Bridge and P M Hopson).

was well known to the primary surveyors, Woodward (1881) and Blake (1890); Woodward ascribed their existence to calcareous percolation from the overlying till.

The tills within the Corton Formation generally comprise reddish brown or grey diamict of sandy and silty clay or clayey silt with a scatter of pebbles (Plate 8). The proportion of the sand fraction varies both within and between units, and fine sand may occur as lenses or laminae interrupting the diamict and imparting a stratified appearance to sections. Average mechanical composition of till samples from the south-east of the district showed 5 per cent gravel, 52 per cent sand and 43 per cent silt and clay. The tills were formerly extracted for brickmaking, the 'stronger', more clayey varieties being favoured, particularly for the manufacture of pipes and tiles (see Chapter ten).

Where exposed in freshly eroded cliffs, the tills are stiff to very stiff and stand in near-vertical faces; they are cut by steeply inclined fractures which may carry a coating of iron oxides. Where weathered, they range from firm to soft and friable. Some sections show inclusions of chalk of coarse sand or small pebble grade, or of shell fragments, mostly less than 5 mm across. The intraformational erosion of till units has been referred to above. The instability

of the tills during their subsequent burial by sands and gravels is indicated by the intrusion of tongues of till into the overlying sediments, as observed by this survey during the construction of sea defences at Caister-on-Sea (Figure 40). This type of deformation is regarded as a consequence of penecontemporaneous liquifaction under load.

The close association of tills and sands in the Corton Formation suggests that their depositional environments were closely allied, with recurrent widespread subaqueous conditions, regarded by Eyles et al. (1989), following many earlier workers, as glaciomarine. There are no indications that the processes of subglacial piping and tunnel formation (Boulton and Hindmarsh, 1987), apparently a feature of the British Eastern (Lowestoft) ice sheet (see below), were active under the Scandinavian (Corton) ice in this district.

Details

Rackheath–Blofield–Cantley

In a ditch [3305 1025] to the south-west of The Lodge, Blofield, 1.6 m of Corton Formation till, comprising reddish brown sandy, stony clay with flint and quartz pebble clasts, were

Plate 5   Cross-bedded sands and pebbly sands of the Corton Formation at Welcome Pit, Burgh Castle [485 042]; view to east. A15051.

recorded resting on 1 m of pebbly sand underlain by fine-grained yellow sand of the Crag Group. A borehole (TG 30 NW/31) near Witton House (Appendix 2) proved 4 m of till, consisting of greyish brown, sandy, stony clay; the till was underlain by Crag and overlain by 3 m of glaciofluvial deposits. Another borehole (TG 30 NW/32) at Manor Farm, Blofield, (Appendix 2), proved 3.9 m of very sandy, stony clay resting on Crag. At Hassingham, the till within the formation divides into an upper and lower bed, and becomes laterally impersistent; the sand cuts through the till and very slightly into the Kesgrave Formation. West of St Margaret's Church, Cantley, a 500 m-long lens of sand is included within the till.

South Walsham–Acle–Halvergate–Freethorpe

The formation was partially exposed in temporary sections south-west of Acle during the construction of the Acle By-pass; cuttings revealed up to 4 m of pale buff sands resting on reddish brown sandy till, all under and, in places, cut by an irregular drape of Lowestoft Till. The sand is generally fine grained and interrupted by laminae of reddish buff silt and clay; at its base [3930 1012] there is 0.8 m-thick layer of sand and gravel including pebbles of quartz and chalk. An impersistent layer of till within sands is intercepted in a road cutting at Upton [3947 1234]; the section reveals at least 2 m of stiff sandy clay resting on 2 m of fine-grained sand. Generally, the formation is poorly exposed, the best of the sections being those in disused sand-pits, for example one [3777 1045] at Burlingham Lodge Farm and another [3890 1255] near Cargate Green, in which fine-grained sand passes up into some 5 m of laminated clayey sand with scattered stones and silt and clayey silt, under about 1 m of stony cover silt.

Abandoned marl pits in the Lowestoft Till plateau between Tunstall and south of Freethorpe are commonly floored by sands of the Corton Formation. Of these, the largest are at Halvergate, adjacent to Sandhole Lane [4192 0695] and south of Freethorpe, around Brickyard Cottages [4110 0432]. In both, fine-grained, yellow, silty sand up to 5 m is exposed in the sides and floor of the pits.

Bramerton–Brooke–Loddon–Haddiscoe

In a pit [3705 0058] south of Langley Street, 0.4 m of yellow, fine-grained sand, cemented in the upper 0.2 m, were seen beneath 2.5 m of olive chalky clay of the Lowestoft Till Formation. The sand in borehole (TG 30SW/14) at The Grange, Langley (Appendix 2), was also cemented at the top, immediately below the Lowestoft Till. A cutting for a new industrial estate

Plate 6 Microfaulting in sands of the Corton Formation. Cliff section near Corton [5451 9722].

[3699 9791] south-east of Loddon revealed 4.1 m of pale yellow, cross-bedded and cross-laminated, fine-grained sand. Augering at the base of the section proved 0.4 m of ill-sorted gravel comprising pebbles mainly of flint, quartz and quartzite, but with a small percentage of igneous lithologies including rhomb-porphyry; till of the Corton Formation underlies the gravel. In boreholes at Green Lane, Hellington(TG 30SW/12; Appendix 2), and at Hales Hall (TM 39NE/6; Appendix 2), where the till was 5.2 m and 0.6 m thick respectively, it was atypical in that it included clasts of chalk.

The sand in the Hales Hall borehole was silty at the top. East of Raveningham Hall, a section [4006 9682] revealed 4.5 m of pale yellow, very chalky, very fine- to medium-grained sand; some planar and ripple-drift bedding were visible. The sand was overlain by up to 0.4 m of yellowish brown, weathered Lowestoft Till. Borehole TM 49NW/21 at Pockthorpe (Appendix 2), proved 16.5 m of Corton Formation, comprising 1.7 m of

till overlain by 14.8 m of sand. The sand was locally chalky and the basal 1.8 m was pebbly; the pebbles included mainly flint with some quartz and, rarely, some igneous lithologies. The till in borehole TM 49NW/23, at Toft Monks House (Appendix 2), included some shell fragments.

Hey (1967, pp. 437-438) recorded the following (abridged) section in Haddiscoe Old Pit [444 966]:

Bed		*Thickness* m
7	Brown chalky till	1.83+
6	White cross-bedded sand	0.38
5	Brown sand and gravel	0.23
4	Brown clay with flint and rare quartz clasts	0.30
3	Gravelly sand	0.38
2	Brown and grey laminated silt	1.83
1	Pebbly flint gravel	9.81+

Plate 7 Cemented layer at the top of sands of the Corton Formation overlain by Lowestoft Till. Welcome Pit, Burgh Castle [4823 0435]; view to north (photo by P M Hopson).

Hey considered Bed 1 be largely or wholly of post-Baventian age, and believed these gravels to be an outlier of the Westleton Beds. He noted that Bed 4 was lithologically identical to the Norwich Brickearth and remarked on the strong resemblance of beds 5 and 6 to the Corton Beds. Bed 7 he identified as Lowestoft Till. In this account beds 1–3 have been assigned to the Crag Group and Kesgrave Formation, and beds 4–6 to the Corton Formation.

In the adjacent Haddiscoe New Pit, during this survey, up to 10 m of sand of the Corton Formation, comprising pale yellow, fine- and medium-grained sand with rare pebbles, and locally exhibiting small-scale faulting and ice-wedge structures, were recorded beneath up to 5 m of Haddiscoe Sands and Gravels (see below).

Filby–Caister-on-Sea

Boreholes at Runham (TG 41SE/4; Appendix 2) and Nova Scotia Farm (TG 51SW/8; Appendix 2), near Caister-on-Sea, and also the Ormesby Borehole, just beyond the district boundary, penetrated the formation. Apart from coastal sections, the best of the generally poor exposures are those in disused sand or gravel pits, notably those at Billockby [4295 1350] (referred to above), Hillborough Hole [4440 1161] near Winsford Hall, Filby Heath [4890 1303] and Nova Scotia Farm [5087 1341]. The section at Hillborough Hole comprises up to 2.5 m of sand and gravel under up to 1 m of irregularly based sandy till, the whole being draped by up to 1.5 m of cryoturbated stony cover silt. The sand ranges from fine to coarse grained, and is cross-bedded, cross-laminated and locally rich in shell debris; the gravel ranges from fine to coarse grained, with flints up to 0.25 m.

Some 15 m of sands resting on up to 3 m of till were temporarily exposed [5217 1391 to 5222 1373] at the time of survey, during the construction of sea defences at Caister-on-Sea. The sands, capped by cover silt and blown sand, are mainly fine grained but, in the lowest few metres, they are partly gravelly with conspicuous cross-bedding, the foresets inclined mainly to the north; thin layers and laminae of clay and silt, some pebbly, within the sands display a subhorizontal bedding, except towards the southern end of the section. There, the bedding becomes inclined to the south at between 15° and 20°, and the sands are overlain, apparently without angular discordance, by the Lowestoft Till (Figure 40). This deformation is interpreted as a collapse feature related to subglacial piping during the Lowestoft glaciation (see below). The till underlying the sands comprises red-brown sandy, silty clay with scattered pebbles; its upper surface is irregular with a relief of up to 3 m, and lenses of gravel or ferruginous gravel occur in local hollows. Superimposed on this generally irregular relief, there are flame structures of till protruding as tongues into the overlying sands (Figure 40).

There are extensive exposures of the Corton Formation in the sea cliffs south of California Gap, just beyond the northern limit of the district [5207 1433 to 5172 1500] (Plate 4). The section comprises two layers of till (the Lower till and Middle till

Plate 8 Core samples of till from the Corton Formation (on the left) and the Lowestoft Till, showing conspicuous chalk clasts.

of Hopson and Bridge, 1987), separated and overlain by sand-dominant layers. The lower of the two tills is up to at least 7 m thick and comprises red-brown, sandy to very sandy clay with scattered angular clasts and rounded pebbles up to about 20 mm in diameter; it includes shell fragments and is generally layered or laminated by partings of fine-grained sand up to 10 mm thick. Shear planes and joints, cemented with iron oxide, are recorded and the upper surface of the layer is locally irregularly eroded. The succeeding sands, typically about 3 m thick, form a ledge on the cliff face; they comprise fine-, medium- and coarse-grained varieties and are commonly cross-bedded. Towards their base they include lenses of sand and fine gravel composed partly, and in places almost wholly, of shell debris; they include layers and laminae of sandy clay with scattered pebbles. Soft sediment deformation structures including load casts and convolute bedding have been noted. The succeeding till layer, up to at least 5.5 m thick, consists of red-brown sandy,

silty clay with shell fragments and scattered pebbles. The overlying sands, which form a layer up to 5 m thick, are mostly fine grained and, especially towards the base, include laminae and layers of brown silt with scattered pebbles; the sands also include masses of till consisting of red-brown sandy clay and clayey sand with strongly deformed bedding, including recumbent folds. The structure of the formation is gently undulating, except just north of California Gap [5182 1477] (Figure 37), where the tills and sands alike are disposed in a northward-dip-

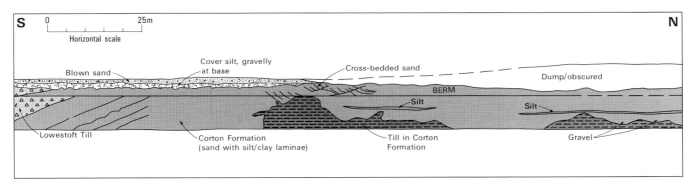

Figure 40 Temporary section at Caister-on-Sea [5222 1373 to 5217 1391]: sketch of the Corton Formation in excavations for sea defences, showing the complex relief of the upper surface of an included till unit. Height of section about 6 m, vertical scale exaggerated; base of section at about OD. The southward continuation of this section is shown in Figure 42.

Plate 9 Post-depositional deformation structures in sand overlying sandy clay till: Corton Formation. Eastern face, Welcome Pit, Burgh Castle [485 042].

Plate 10 Basal till overlain by parallel-bedded sand: Corton Formation. Cliff section [5451 9722] near Corton.

ping, approximately east–west-trending monocline with a maximum dip of about 35°. The age of this monocline predates the Lowestoft glaciation, for the structure does not involve the Lowestoft Till that forms the upper part of the cliff section.

Great Yarmouth–Burgh Castle–Fritton

Numerous boreholes drilled in the conurbation south of Great Yarmouth, including Bradwell and Gorleston-on-Sea, proved Corton Formation (up to 15.7 m in borehole TG 50SW/89), comprising mostly silty, fine-grained sand with sandy clay till lenses and a more persistent basal sandy clay till. Away from the coast, exposed sections are generally shallow and prove only sand or pebbly sand [e.g. 505 028; 503 033].

Several temporary sections excavated for a housing development [508 053] near Gapton Hall showed up to 4 m of cross-bedded, yellow to orange, silty, fine-grained sand with pebbly stringers, capped impersistently by a thin layer of chalky clay (Lowestoft Till). From the top of a disused railway cutting [5215 0410] in Gorleston-on-Sea, the section comprises 1 m of decalcified Lowestoft Till underlain by up to 3 m of layered, pebbly, shelly, yellow, silty, fine-grained sand. Below this to where the face is obscured, a further 1 m sand unit includes several impersistent, thin (c. 0.3 m), silty clay layers.

Welcome Pit [482 043], an active though partially backfilled sand and gravel pit near Burgh Castle, has provided excellent sections of the Corton Formation; the easternmost face, described by Bridge and Hopson (in Gibbard and Zalasiewicz, 1988, pp. 126–128), remains fairly well exposed. From north to south, the eastern section shows a wedge of Lowestoft Till (up to 0.5 m) overlying a complex of subhorizontal to gently northward-inclined sands, gravels and sandy clays (Figure 39, Plates 5, 7 and 9). In detail, these deposits include an upper layer (between 0.4 and 2 m) of well-rounded, coarse-grained, flint gravel, locally heavily stained with iron oxide. Although this upper lithology is atypical of the Corton Formation, it has been mapped as, and is included in the formation; the contemporaneity of these gravels with the adjacent sands is suggested by the recent observation of Lowestoft Till overlying them in a recent face clearance [4854 0424].

Below the gravels lie parallel-, ripple- and cross-bedded, chalky, fine-grained sands up to 3 m thick; these sands include abundant postdepositional deformation structures (including slump structures, convolute bedding, water-escape structures and microfaulting) associated with dewatering and loading of competent and incompetent strata. Locally, this sequence is interbedded with yellow-brown to brown, cross-bedded sandy gravels to pebbly sands with up to three, impersistent, brown, silty, sandy clay till stringers (maximum thickness 0.5 m). Beneath each of these tills, ice-wedge casts have been recorded by Bridge and Hopson (in Gibbard and Zalasiewicz, 1988, p. 127). The base of this sequence (and the Corton Formation) is marked by a persistent sandy, pebbly till up to 1 m thick. Within the pit, this till lies submerged at the lowest level of working; however, its lateral persistence outside the pit is known from borehole TG 40SE/3 [4871 0460] and from records of clay extraction for a former brickworks [475 043] below Cliffe House Farm. In one locality within Welcome Pit [4824 0436] (in the mostly obscured northern face), Lowestoft Till rests on Corton Formation comprising a highly indurated, calcareous sand layer, up to 50 mm thick (Plate 7).

Corton Formation is exposed in a small, partially re-excavated pit [474 013] near Caldecott Hall. Here, several trench sections showed up to 1 m of cover silt overlying traces of stiff, brown, chalky clay (Lowestoft Till), in turn underlain by at least 3 m of yellow, silty, fine-grained sand.

Somerleyton–Blundeston–Gunton

Several disused brickpits in this area provide sections of a basal till in the Corton Formation. Locally, this till layer forms 'highs' free from any overlying sand within the formation. For example, in Somerleyton Brickpit [4795 9702], 6.1 m of unstratified till (Corton Formation), containing subangular flints and quartz pebbles, is directly overlain by Lowestoft Till and rests on pebbly sands of the Kesgrave Formation.

A former pit at Blundeston [5166 9752] exposes 4.6 m of, brown, sandy clay till with small flints and quartz pebbles; this overlies 0.6+ m of buff-white sand of the Kesgrave Formation. Two former pits at Gunton [5330 9630; 5335 9586] show Lowestoft Till overlying Corton Formation till comprising up to 6.4 m of reddish brown, stratified, stone-free, sandy clay; the till is stiff and in part mottled grey.

Gorleston-on-Sea–Corton

The coastal sections between Gorleston-on-Sea and Corton are largely degraded by minor landslips, whilst sea defence emplacements obscure the cliff base between South Pier [535 036] and Gorleston Golf Course [531 020], and at Corton [547 964]. Between Gorleston-on-Sea and Hopton on Sea [e.g. 530 035 to 535 003], the cliff section shows some 10 m of silty, locally shelly, fine-grained sand of the Corton Formation under Corton Woods Sands and Gravels. The sand generally thins southwards against a basal till outcrop.

In the cliffs south of Hopton on Sea to Corton, the Corton Formation includes a basal sandy clay till (Plate 10). A typical section [540 986] shows head on Corton Formation comprising sand and gravel (3.7 to 8.8 m) with a basal till layer (0 to 0.8 m). Locally, the underlying Kesgrave Formation is exposed at the base of the cliffs and on the adjoining foreshore [e.g. 5400 9863]. Farther southwards to Corton Woods [546 966], the Corton Formation ranges between 1.2 and 7.2 m in thickness and includes a basal till which locally exceeds 3.3 m (Figure 38). The Kesgrave Formation, once evident on the foreshore (West, 1980), is now obscured.

LOWESTOFT TILL FORMATION

Classification and nomenclature

The Lowestoft Till Formation crops out in the upper part of the cliff section at Corton (Figures 33 and 38; Banham, 1971). The importance of the Quaternary sedi-

ments at this site has long been recognised (Blake, 1884; Baden-Powell, 1950), and although the cliffs there are now much degraded, the locality has been cited as the type section for the Anglian Glacial Stage and, in particular, the Lowestoftian Stadial (Banham, 1971; Mitchell et al., 1973). This formation has never been formally defined. Its deposits have been referred to in the literature variously as the Lower Erratic Tertiaries–Chalky Jurassic boulder clay of south Norfolk (Trimmer, 1851), the Upper Glacial or true Boulder Clay (Wood and Harmer, 1868), the Upper Glacial or Chalky Boulder Clay (Wood, 1880), Boulder Clay or Chalky Boulder Clay (Woodward, 1881), the Chalky Boulder Clay (Blake, 1884) and, more recently, as the Lowestoft Boulder Clay (Baden-Powell, 1948) and the Lowestoft Till (Banham, 1971, 1975, 1988; Bristow and Cox, 1973; Perrin et al., 1973; Hopson and Bridge, 1987; Rose, 1989) (see Table 7).

This part of the Pleistocene sequence has attracted much scientific interest not least because of the widespread cover of chalky till that extends well beyond the district, over much of eastern Britain. Debate has covered topics including the provenance and relative ages of the various chalky tills (Harmer, 1909b, 1928; Hill, 1902; Hollingworth and Taylor, 1946; Rice, 1968; Horton, 1970; Perrin et al., 1973, 1979); whether the Lowestoft Till and the Cromer Till of north-east Norfolk were products of contemporaneous ice sheets whose ice fronts were vying across north Norfolk (Cox and Nickless, 1972); and whether the Lowestoft Till might be subdivided into an Upper Chalky Boulder Clay (the Gipping Till) and a Lower Chalky Boulder Clay whose accumulations were separated by the Hoxnian Interglacial (Baden-Powell, 1948; West and Donner, 1956; Straw, 1960; West, 1963; Bristow and Cox, 1973). The Lowestoft Till Formation is now regarded as a product of the British Eastern ice sheet (Hart et al., 1990).

Distribution

The Lowestoft Till forms a widespread but extensively dissected, undulating sheet over much of the district. The most continuous outcrops are in the south-west, south of the Yare valley, and north of the Yare around North Burlingham. Fragmentary outcrops are present in the upland areas between Stokesby and Caister-on-Sea, between Gorleston-on-Sea and Burgh Castle, and in the south-east between Lound and the outskirts of Lowestoft. Trimmer (1858) recorded a visit with Rev. Mr Gunn to the 'Gorlston Cliffs' [sic] where they apparently observed '..Upper and Lower Boulder-Clays..'; the upper boulder clay was described as characterised by an abundance of oolitic detritus. This observation was cited by later workers as being relevant to the present Gorleston Cliffs (e.g. Harmer, 1909b). However, Gunn (1867) clarified his observation by recording '...in the cliffs of Corton and Hopton, near Gorleston...'. Neither Blake (1890), nor the present survey found evidence of the existence of the Lowestoft Till in Gorleston Cliffs.

Plate 11 Lowestoft till overlying sand of Corton Formation. The sharp contact between the till and the sand suggests that the underlying sands were probably frozen during the advance of the till; contorted lower sands layers are the result of post-depositional loading. Cliff section [5458 9689] south of Corton.

Although absent from the north-west, the regional distribution of the Lowestoft Till suggests that it formerly covered the entire district; its present fragmentary distribution is the result of episodes of erosion over the last 300 000 years or so. Its discordant relationship with the glaciofluvial deposits (see below), themselves considered to be of Anglian age, implies that the major dissection of the till sheet was initiated during the period of retreat of the Lowestoft ice sheet.

The mapping of the plateau outcrops of Lowestoft Till shows that the upper surface of the deposit is generally a smooth, gently undulating surface. Except in the south-west, the till plateaux are draped by a veneer of cover silt (not mapped; see Chapter seven) usually between 0.5 and 1.5 m thick; locally, especially in the south-east and west, they are overlain by spreads of glaciofluvial deposits.

The Lowestoft Till forms an irregular sheet that rests generally on the Corton Formation (Plate 11), except in the south-east around Blundeston, where it lies directly

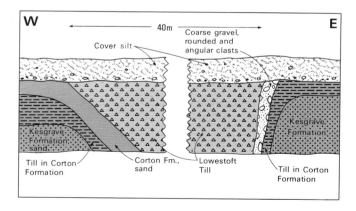

Figure 41 Temporary section at Acle [398 101]: sketch of excavation for Acle By-pass showing Lowestoft Till filling a depression in the Corton and Kesgrave formations. Height of section about 2.5 m.

on the Kesgrave Formation (Figure 19). The base is considerably more irregular than that of the Corton Formation (Figures 34 and 35). Locally, the Lowestoft Till extends below the general sheet, filling or partially filling channel-like depressions. Some of the depressions are confined within the Corton Formation; others cut through the Corton deposits and penetrate the Kesgrave Formation and even the Crag. Where the till sheet has been removed by erosion, these depressions are manifest in impersistent ribbon-like outcrops of Lowestoft Till. Notable examples occur at South Walsham, Acle, Cantley and near Heckingham (Figures 35, 41 and 46).

The till-filled depressions are mostly less than 200 m wide and may extend more than 20 m below the general level of the base of the till sheet, in a few cases below Ordnance Datum. They have a dominant north-west–south-east elongation with undulating thalwegs. Information from other parts of East Anglia suggests that these buried channels are a general feature at the base of this formation (Boswell, 1914; Woodland, 1970; Cox, 1985a, 1985b; Mathers and Zalasiewicz, 1986). Woodland (1970) considered them to have been eroded subglacially by water flowing under hydrostatic pressure, and he likened them to subglacial tunnel-valleys in Denmark (tunneldale) and northern Germany (rinnentäler). However, most of Woodland's examples are considerably larger and more extensive than those mapped in this district and underlie present-day river valleys (Woodland, 1970, pl. 28). One such buried valley, known from a borehole [253 084] in the Yare valley at Thorpe St Andrew and regarded by Woodland (1970) as part of his Tas buried tunnel-valley, is inferred to extend eastwards into this district as a trench in the Chalk.

The Lowestoft Till, with its high chalk content, has been extensively excavated mainly for use as agricultural marl over several centuries (Chapter ten). These marl pits are commonly sited on the fringes of individual outcrops; they may exceed 4 m in depth and many are floored by the Corton Formation whose sands afford free drainage. Many pits remain as surface depressions whilst some have been used for landfill. Elsewhere, the till has been excavated to make water reservoirs, generally for agricultural supply, and excavated till has been used as a puddling clay for ponds and reservoirs on more permeable materials. In the neighbourhoods of Burgh Castle and Freethorpe, till from this formation (as well as the underlying Corton Formation) was formerly dug for brickmaking (Chapter ten).

Lithostratigraphy

The typical lithology of unweathered Lowestoft Till is olive-grey (dark olive-grey when wet), sandy, silty clay with scattered lithic clasts. The matrix consists largely of reconstituted Kimmeridge Clay and other Mesozoic argillaceous rocks (Perrin et al., 1973, 1979). The lithic component is dominated by subangular to subrounded fragments of chalk, between 56 and 84 per cent, (Perrin et al., 1973), but includes a wide range of other lithologies including older Mesozoic limestones and sandstones, flint and derived fossils; in addition, quartz and quartzite pebbles, and fragments of iron-pan may occur, derived from the Kesgrave Formation and the Crag. The clasts are illsorted and range from sand through to blocks more than 2 m across; empirically, the modal size is between 25 to 35 mm. Chalk comprises the bulk of the smaller clasts (Plate 8) whilst flint commonly form those which exceed 40 mm.

Analyses of the derived fossil content (Woodward, 1881, p.115; Blake, 1890, p. 53) indicate that amongst the more common species observed are: *Gryphaea arcuata* (Lower Lias), *Gryphaea dilatata* (Oxford Clay); ammonites from the Lias, Kimmeridge Clay and Oxford Clay; and *Pachyteuthis abbreviatas* (Corallian and Oxford Clay).

In its unweathered state, the Lowestoft Till is cohesive, with a low permeability. Where weathered, the till is rust-brown, and is generally more friable and permeable than the unweathered till. Depending on the degree of weathering, the till may be completely decalcified, the chalk having been removed by solution; where this is the case, the dominant clasts are flints or flint fragments. The depth of weathering is variable, with profiles extending to as much as 3 m below its top. Where the Lowestoft Till is extensively decalcified and directly overlies the till in the Corton Formation, some difficulty may be experienced in distinguishing between the two, as in the Surlingham, Lingwood and Freethorpe areas.

The provenance of the constituent material, coupled with measurements of the included pebble fabrics (West and Donner, 1956), and the regional trends observed within the composition of the matrix (Perrin et al., 1979), indicate that the Lowestoft Till was the subglacial product of a mass of ice probably originating in the North Sea. One of the simpler explanations (Perrin et al., 1979) is that the 'Lowestoft' ice stream moved southwards across the western North Sea Basin. En route this sheet accumulated chalk and oolite and limonite-bearing Jurassic debris off the coast of Yorkshire, overran the Cretaceous escarpments in Lincolnshire and Norfolk, and excavated the Jurassic clays of the Wash–Fenland basin. Subsequently, the sheet fanned out radially with lobes spreading eastwards and south-eastwards or, according to Hart (1987), eastwards then northwards, across the district.

Most of the Lowestoft Till is probably a lodgement till (Woodward, 1881, p. 115; Harmer, 1909b; Perrin et al., 1973; Bridge and Hopson, 1985), although other processes of till formation, including deformation, flow or meltout are likely to have contributed.

At Strumpshaw Hill, gravel and subordinate sand, included by Woodward (1881 p.129) within his glacial gravel (Cannon Shot Gravel), are closely associated with the till, being present either within or overlying it; their outcrop is distinguished from that of the undivided formation on the published map. They comprise deposits of crudely stratified, ill-sorted, mainly angular coarse flint, locally up to 15 m thick; the deposit occurs around 30 to 40 m above OD on the till plateau.

At the Anglian type-section in the cliffs south of Corton, Banham (1971) described glacial deposits overlying the Lowestoft Till as comprising up to 4 m of bedded clays and sands, the Oulton Beds, overlain by up to 3 m of another chalky till (the Pleasure Gardens Till) (Plate

Plate 12 Laminated silts and clays of the Oulton Beds overlain by Pleasure Gardens Till (of the Lowestoft Till Formation) in the Anglian stratotype in the coastal cliffs at Corton [5468 9652]; view to the north-west.

12). Pointon (1978) further described these beds, including details on fabric analysis. Both these authors, and Bridge and Hopson (1985), commented on the lack of evidence for the lateral persistence of these deposits inland. However, Banham noted several sections (not confirmed during this survey) within a few kilometres of Corton, described by Blake (1890, pp.56–57 and pp.60–61), that reportedly exposed laminated clays overlying Lowestoft Till. Bridge and Hopson (1985) confirmed that both the Oulton Beds and the Pleasure Gardens Till are mineralogically similar to the Lowestoft Till; they supported the view that the Oulton Beds are lacustrine-proglacial deposits and that the Pleasure Gardens Till represents a flow till, both units being products of a wast-

ing Lowestoft ice sheet. In this account, both units are included in the Lowestoft Till Formation. The gravels and sands (Corton Woods Sands and Gravels) that cap this succession at Corton are described and their affinities discussed later in this chapter.

Structure

No evidence of glacitectonic deformation has been recognised within the Lowestoft Till of the district; the present disposition of the till that fills the various buried channels or depressions, such as those recorded at Acle (Figure 41) and Caister-on-Sea (Figure 42), may be a product of penecontemporaneous collapse related to subglacial pip-

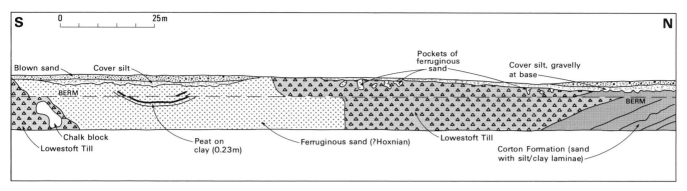

Figure 42 Temporary section at Caister-on-Sea [5226 1359 to 5221 1376]: sketch of excavations for sea defences exposing a depression in the Corton Formation filled with Lowestoft Till and sands of possible Hoxnian age. Height of section about 6 m, vertical scale exaggerated; base of section about OD. The northward continuation of this section is shown in Figure 40.

ing and erosion of the substrate (see Boulton and Hindmarsh, 1987; also Corton Formation details above).

Details

Rackheath–Brundall–Acle–Freethorpe

North of Whitlingham Marshes [2797 0876], a till-filled channel has cut through the Crag and into the underlying Upper Chalk. A large body of till has cut down well into the Crag to the west of Brundall.

Lowestoft Till is preserved in a string of ribbon outcrops through South Walsham [3542 1411 to 3624 1298], the remains of the fill of a buried channel-like depression cut into the Crag; the channel trends north-west–south-east and has an irregular thalweg that is locally overdeepened to a level below OD. Farther south, till forms an extensive, though locally dissected plateau giving generally heavy land characterised by marl pits; one of these, at The Dell [361 107] near Burlingham Green, extends to some 11 m below the surrounding ground surface, an estimated 100 000 m³ of material having been excavated, probably including some sand from the underlying Corton Formation.

South of Burlingham, the till forming the plateau is thin and weathered; a trench [3797 0992] dug for the Acle by-pass exposed up to 1.7 m of stiff, yellowish brown, stony clay with pods of olive-brown chalky clay, overlying 0.5 m of silty sand of the Corton Formation.

Depressions in the Corton and Kesgrave formations and the Crag, filled with Lowestoft Till, were proved in boreholes and exposed in excavations for the Acle by-pass. Boreholes sited on the marshland to the east of the village encountered the till beneath Breydon Formation, extending into the Crag to depths of at least 15.4 m below OD (TG 41SW/15, Figure 46). In a cutting to the south of the village [3978 1008], Lowestoft Till fills a steep-walled depression in the Kesgrave Formation, lined on its flanks by selvages of sand on till, apparently the extruded representatives of the Corton Formation (Figure 41).

Between Cucumber Corner and Southwood, bifurcated till-filled channels cut down deeply. At Buckenham and south-east of Strumpshaw Hill, the till cuts down into the Kesgrave Formation. At Strumpshaw Hill, gravel associated with the till is up to 12 m thick; it is ill sorted, coarse, poorly bedded and comprises mainly flint. A section showed folded and faulted, bedded

sands and gravels with blocks of chalk marl. South of Manor Farm, Cantley, a till-filled channel cuts down from 20 m above OD to OD over a distance of 3 km.

Bramerton–Brooke–Loddon–Haddiscoe

Lowestoft Till forms a plateau more than 20 m above OD; on the valley flanks below this level it infills discontinuous, narrow, ribbon-like channels with undulating thalwegs. Some of these channel fills are isolated from the plateau till, as at Sisland, while the outcrops of others traverse valleys and rise to coalesce with the plateau till. Of the latter type, the longest stretches from a point [348 027] north-east of Carlton St Peter to just north of Hardley Marshes [374 003]; another begins on the opposite side of the Chet valley at Heckingham and stretches to Norton Subcourse.

There are numerous small pits in the Lowestoft Till, particularly within the outcrops of the till-filled channels. Most are degraded, with very poor exposures of till. Up to 2.5 m of olive-grey silty clay with flint and abundant chalk clasts were recorded overlying Corton Formation sand in a pit [3705 0058] south of Langley. A section in a pit west of Loddon Hall showed 3 m of yellowish brown silty clay with clasts of flint and chalk, resting on 1 m of sand of the Corton Formation. Approximately 5 m of yellowish brown and olive-brown stony clay with abundant chalk pebbles, angular flint pebbles and cobbles were underlain by about 3 m of Corton Formation sand in a pit [3923 9694] near The Orchards, Raveningham. A pit [3952 9863] to the southwest of Beacon Hill, dug in a till-filled channel, revealed 5 m of chalky till resting on sand of the Corton Formation.

Boreholes TM 49NW/22, south-east of Thurlton (Appendix 2), and TM 49NW/23, at Toft Monks (Appendix 2), penetrated 1.2 m and 2.1 m respectively of pale yellow, laminated, silty clay and chalky sand within the Lowestoft Till Formation.

Filby–Caister-on-Sea

A temporary section recorded during the construction of sea defences at Caister-on-Sea [5220 1374 to 5226 1359] revealed the Lowestoft Till filling a depression in the Corton Formation to a depth below OD (Figure 42). The till comprised stiff, olive-grey, sandy clay with abundant clasts, mostly of chalk ranging in size from sand grade to a block some 2 m across. Its base was exposed only on the northern flank of the depression; there, the till rests on sands of the Corton Formation that dip southwards at 15° to 20° with no discernable angular discordance. In part of the section, the Lowestoft Till is disrupted by a sharply defined, steep-walled channel filled with ferruginous sand, possibly of Hoxnian age (see Chapter seven), and similar sand fills irregular pockets and pipes down to 1.5 m below the top of the till to the north of the channel. The topmost 1 to 3 m of the till are weathered brown, and are distinguished by conspicuous flints and an upwards reduction in chalk content. The section is capped throughout by an irregularly based layer of cover silt (Chapter seven), and this in turn by blown sand.

Great Yarmouth–Burgh Castle

South of Great Yarmouth and westwards towards Burgh Castle, Lowestoft Till occurs as discrete patches [e.g. 5180 0490; 5200 0400] and as dislocated, lobate outcrops [e.g. 5085 0540]; these strings may be infills of former channels cut into the underlying Corton Formation. The formation is generally overlain by up to 1 m of cover silt and has been proved mostly by augering, by the rare section and by the chance observation of heavy soil or chalky clay fragments overturned in ploughed ground.

The Welcome Pit [482 043] provides the best section. The northern face and the northernmost corner of the eastern face show up to 2 m of stiff, dark grey to brown (weathered), clast-rich clay. The clasts range from sand grade to boulders; they comprise a high proportion of chalk but include other minor components such as flint, derived fossils and fragments of Mesozoic limestones and sandstones. In the environs of the pit, the till directly overlies Corton Formation, in most instances resting on fine-grained, chalky sand or pebbly sand. However, locally [4824 0436], the till rests on a highly indurated, calcareous-cemented sand layer (up to 50 mm thick). Elsewhere in the pit [4854 0424], Lowestoft Till overlies strongly iron-stained, rounded flint gravels regarded as atypical Corton Formation.

Somerleyton–Corton

Between Somerleyton and Corton, the Lowestoft Till is the principal deposit capping the plateau areas between the major valleys. The deposit is thin (less than 5 m over much of the area) and preserved as fragmentary outcrops; their widespread occurrence implies a formerly extensive, perhaps continuous sheet. Generally, the base of the till ranges between 12 and 18 m above OD, although there is considerable local variation. Isolated patches of till have been augered at about 5 m above OD around Flixton Decoy [5144 9533]; elongate till lenses are also known more than 10 m below OD within the 'Raveningham–Lound Depression' (Figure 31; Hopson and Bridge, 1987) and eastwards to League Hole [537 997]. The Lowestoft Till Formation is exposed in the cliffs at Corton [5457 9704 to 5409 9842] (Figure 38; Plates 11–13). These cliffs include the type locality for the formation.

GLACIOFLUVIAL DEPOSITS OF PRESUMED ANGLIAN AGE

Classification and nomenclature

Glaciofluvial deposits, overlying and distinct from the Lowestoft Till Formation, have been referred to in the literature variously as 'older Post-glacial' (Wood, in Woodward, 1881, p.128), 'Glacial Gravel' and 'Cannon Shot Gravel' (Woodward, 1881), 'Plateau Gravel' (Blake, 1890), 'Cannon-shot Gravels' (Solomon, 1932b), 'Plateau Gravels' and 'Valley Flank sands and gravels' (Bridge and Hopson, 1985) and 'Lowestoft Till Outwash' (Cox et al., 1989). On the published map, two classes of these deposits are distinguished informally by symbols on the basis of their lithology and geomorphology, namely the Corton Woods Sands and Gravels, and the Haddiscoe Sands and Gravels; a third class, undifferentiated glaciofluvial deposits, embraces the remaining deposits, which occur in a number of different modes across the district. In some instances, the designation of these deposits in the field is unclear. The ages and origins of these classes remain uncertain, but, in the absence of any clear indications to the contrary, all three are depicted on the published map as glaciofluvial deposits of Anglian age.

Distribution and lithology

Harmer (1909b) regarded his Plateau gravels (Corton Woods Sands and Gravels) and his lower-level gravels (Haddiscoe Sands and Gravels) as being closely related, and part of the same regime of ice wasting. The present survey has not established the true relationship between the Corton Woods and Haddiscoe deposits, and nowhere have the two deposits been recorded in the same section. The mapping indicates that the deposits represent two contrasting depositional episodes. In each case, the deposits rest on an erosion surface cutting into or through the Lowestoft Till; the erosion surface under the Haddiscoe deposits forms major incisions broadly coinciding with the present Waveney valley and some of its tributaries, while that under the Corton Woods deposits is an even plateau surface sloping gently to the north.

CORTON WOODS SANDS AND GRAVELS

The Corton Woods Sands and Gravels are restricted to the plateau tops in the south-east, the base of the deposits lying generally in the range of 10 to 20 m above OD and resting on what is here interpreted as an erosion surface in either the Lowestoft Till Formation or the sands of the Corton Formation. Although not shown on the published map, they are locally present as patches of gravel as far north as Welcome Pit, near Burgh Castle; the section there showed up to 1.2 m of well-rounded, coarse flint gravel with coarse-grained quartz and flint sand, and a clast of Lowestoft Till, resting on sand of the Corton Formation.

Some 7 m of these deposits were recorded in a borehole [4814 9946] near Herringfleet Hall, but the mapping evidence suggests that the deposits generally form a layer up to about 4 m thick which drapes downslope at the outcrop margins. The deposits are broadly equivalent to the Plateau Gravel mapped by Blake (1890), and include the quartz- and quartzite-bearing flint gravels and sands that cap the Anglian type section at Corton (Figures 33 and 38). Pointon (1978) interpreted these deposits in the Corton section as outwash from the Lowestoft ice sheet and considered them to be stratigraphically conformable with the underlying beds. However, Bridge and Hopson (1985), demonstrated that these gravels have no

Plate 13 Gravel of the Corton Woods Sands and Gravels resting on the Pleasure Gardens Till (with chalk fragments) and the Oulton Beds (at hammer) of the Lowestoft Till Formation in coastal cliffs at Corton [5468 9652]. View to north-west. A14181.

mineralogical affinity with the Lowestoft Till sediments, and that they appear to rest on an erosion surface.

The Corton Woods Sands and Gravels exposed in the cliffs at Corton Woods [type locality 5467 9653], south of Corton, show a succession of medium gravels (in the +8 to −16 mm range), with fine- to medium-grained sands up to 4.3 m thick (Plate 13). The gravels comprise mainly flint (66 per cent), with subordinate quartz (18 per cent) and quartzite (7 per cent). The gravels are strongly imbricated but with a variety of modal directions; a good proportion of the flints are well rounded. They rest on the Pleasure Gardens Till (Lowestoft Till Formation), but in adjacent cliff sections [5464 9660; 5468 9652] a layer of black clayey silt up to 0.4 m thick intervenes.

Inland, there are few exposures, but the deposit appears to consist largely of pebbly, well-rounded, medium-grained sands. Where the deposit overlies sands of the Corton Formation, its presence is commonly indicated by the presence of pebbles and a strong orange-brown colour. At a landfill site off Longfulans Lane [5290 9928], near Hopton on Sea, the sands and gravels are cryoturbated and contain lenses of Lowestoft Till.

HADDISCOE SANDS AND GRAVELS

The Haddiscoe Sands and Gravels occur on the south-western flanks of the Yare and Waveney valleys, south-east of Nogdam End [398 004]. There are also isolated deposits on the northern flank of the Waveney valley near Somerleyton. They are the Valley Flank sands and gravels of Bridge and Hopson (1985), which crop out up to about 20 m above OD and extend below the present valley floor. Thicknesses of up to about 15 m are recorded in elongate gravel mounds abutting the floodplain; elsewhere, spreads of between 2 and 5 m are recorded, for example in disused pits [413 994; 402 996] north of Norton Subcourse. Locally, where these deposits occur in juxtaposition with those of the Kesgrave Formation, the field distinction between the two may be unclear. At Haddiscoe Pit [type locality 445 963], the deposit comprises an upper, black, well-rounded, fine to coarse gravel, mainly of flint, overlying sand of the Corton Formation (Plate 14). Woodward (1881, p.85; 1882, pp. 455–456) believed that the 'pebble-gravel of Haddiscoe is Glacial, and distinct from the ... Crag'; furthermore, by inference he correlated the deposit with '... the pebble beds of Halesworth, Hensham, and Westleton ...' to the south of the district. However, the deposits at Westleton are regarded by Hey (1967, p. 436) as '... somewhere within the time interval represented by sub-zone L4c, Zone L5 and the whole of the Beestonian and Cromerian Stages.' i.e. pre-Anglian in age. This survey has demonstrated that the Haddiscoe Sands and Gravels overlie and cut the Lowestoft Till, implying that their age is late Anglian or younger. Hey (1967, p.438) described a section (see Corton Formation details above) in Haddiscoe Old Pit where he recorded over 9.8 m of pebbly flint gravel, which he believed to be of post-Baventian age, beneath Lowestoft Till and Corton Formation deposits. He considered this deposit of flint grav-

Plate 14 Haddiscoe Sands and Gravels (glaciofluvial deposits) overlie sands of the Corton Formation in a disused pit at Haddiscoe [445 963]. (Photo by P M Hopson).

el to be an outlier of the Westleton Beds. It appears that two gravel deposits of similar aspect occur at Haddiscoe: one, the Haddiscoe Sands and Gravels, is younger than the Lowestoft Till, while the other, Hey's 'Westleton Beds', underlies the Anglian deposits. The Corton Formation sand at Haddiscoe Pit shows small-scale faulting and some ice-wedge structures, whilst the overlying Haddiscoe Sands and Gravels has been cryoturbated. These structures indicate periglacial influences possibly during its deposition or later, during the Devensian. A heavy mineral analysis (P M Hopson, oral communication, 1990) shows that the deposit is low in opaque iron minerals but high in rutile and zircon. Elsewhere, for example at Nogdam End, the Haddiscoe Sands and Gravels comprise interbedded pebbly, fine-grained sands and fine- to coarse-grained sands.

GLACIOFLUVIAL DEPOSITS (UNDIFFERENTIATED)

Undifferentiated glaciofluvial deposits occur as localised sand and gravel deposits, cropping out from the west of the district to the south-east of the district. These outcrops are differentiated geographically for the purposes of this account.

In the north-west (Rackheath–Beighton), the deposits occur on plateau tops mostly higher than 30 m above OD, overlying either Lowestoft Till or, more commonly, till within the Corton Formation. Those deposits around Rackheath, towards Great Plumstead, were included by Woodward (1881) within his Middle Glacial, that is older than the Lowestoft Till but younger than the Norwich Brickearth (Table 7); and classified by Cox et al. (1989) as Corton Sands. The deposits range from medium-grained, rusty brown sand with scattered angular flints in the Rackheath area to mainly flint pebble gravel with minor sand near Salhouse Station; their thickness is generally in the range 0 to 3 m. Deposits mapped south-east of Beighton may be a basal gravelly facies, commonly associated with cryoturbated cover silt.

South of the River Yare, from Yelverton to Maypole Green, the deposits mostly overlie either Lowestoft Till or sand of the Corton Formation. They occur variously on the upland plateaux at over 40 m above OD and on lower ground, down to positions low on the valley slope.

In the south-east, the outcrops are few and isolated; the most extensive occur around Flixton Decoy and along part of the northern flank of the River Waveney.

Blake (1890) included these sediments within his 'Pebbly Series', which would imply a pre-Anglian age (Table 6). However, it can be demonstrated locally that they are underlain by Lowestoft Till.

Details

Bramerton–Brooke–Loddon–Haddiscoe

A pit [2828 0044] in undifferentiated glaciofluvial deposits west of Welbeck Farm revealed the following section:

	Depth m
Medium flint gravel	2.74
Fine sand and gravel	3.2
Fine gravel	4.57
Medium sand	5.18
Gravel	5.49

Two pits [3010 0024; 3051 0012] near Hillside Farm exposed 5 m and 2 m respectively of coarse, ill-sorted gravel comprising angular flints and rounded flint pebbles and cobbles, with some quartz and quartzite pebbles, channelled into planar-bedded, medium-grained sand.

A 1.4 m section of crudely bedded, ill-sorted gravel with lenses of orange medium-grained sand was recorded at the top of a 9 m deep pit [3860 0003] near Hardley Hall; the gravel comprised mainly angular and rounded flint up to boulder size, with some pebbles of quartz and quartzite. The glaciofluvial sand and gravel had cut deeply (at least 7.5 m) into the till of the Corton Formation. The lower part of the pit was overgrown at the time of survey, but a description is given by Hey (1967).

At Hill House, Heckingham [3967 9956], 5 m of crudely bedded gravel were exposed. The gravel comprised mainly flint pebbles, most of which were well rounded, with some quartz, quartzite and chert (J Sinclair, written communication). Woodward (1881) was uncertain of the stratigraphical position of these gravels, but Hey (1967) considered them to be Westleton Beds. However, this survey has shown that the gravels at Hill House overlie till of the Corton Formation; they have been classified as Haddiscoe Sands and Gravels.

In the Haddiscoe Old Pit [444 966], which is degraded and overgrown, several small exposures showed clast-supported, well-rounded flint gravel, with some thin stringers of medium- to coarse-grained sand. In the nearby Haddiscoe New Pit [445 963], up to 5 m of similar gravel, the upper 1.5 m of which are cryoturbated and illuviated with clay, overlie up to 10 m of sand of the Corton Formation.

SEVEN

Quaternary — ?Hoxnian to Devensian

Of the Pleistocene stages following the Anglian, only the Devensian is considered to be represented by widespread deposits within the district, though none of these is shown on the face of the published map. The Devensian deposits comprise the veneer of cover silt in the uplands; at least part of the Yare Valley Formation, consisting of sand and gravel in the floors of a buried valley system that underlies most of the marshland, and the main river valleys; and accumulations of Head in tributary valleys and on the flanks of the main valleys. The only other post-Anglian Pleistocene deposits known within the district are sands and organic silts and clays of possible Hoxnian age that fill a buried channel in Anglian deposits at Caister-on-Sea. With the exception of the Yare Valley Formation, which is represented on the published map by a letter symbol, these classes are shown by graphic symbols.

DEPOSITS OF POSSIBLE HOXNIAN AGE

Sands including a layer of organic silt and clay with peat were temporarily exposed in an excavation for new sea defences at Caister-on-Sea (Figure 42). The deposits fill a channel some 60 m wide cut into the Lowestoft Till; they are overlain by mottled stony silt (cover silt). The channel is aligned WSW–ENE. Its walls are steep, in places near vertical; its floor was unexposed but probably lies below Ordnance Datum. The landward extension of the channel remains unproved and the distribution of the deposits shown on the map is speculative. No other similar deposit has been identified within the district.

The sequence recorded near the midline of the channel [5224 1362] is

	Thickness m
Cover silt	
Sand, orange, fine- to medium-grained, ferruginous, without apparent structure	c.2.0
Interlaminated silt, brown, with plant fragments, part sandy, and sand, orange, fine- to medium-grained, subangular to subrounded, rather poorly sorted	0.06
Silt and silty clay, laminated, dark brown to orange-brown; microfaulted	0.04
Peat, dark brown, non-fibrous; crudely laminated towards base	0.5
Interlaminated peat, dark brown, non-fibrous, and silty clay, grey-brown; microfaulted	0.08
Sand, orange, fine- to medium-grained, ferruginous to strongly ferruginous, without apparent structure	c.3.0

The contact between the channel-fill sand and the host sediments is sharp; no trace of reworked or collapsed till was observed in the sand. The organic layer has a dished form, inclined at some 30° to the north against the southern margin of the channel. This form is interpreted as a consolidation effect and may indicate the existence of organic sediments at depth, within the concealed part of the channel fill. Orange sand, apparently identical to that filling the channel, fills pockets and pipes in the uppermost 1.5 m or so of the Lowestoft Till up to 60 m north of the northern margin of the channel.

The origin and age of these deposits are speculative. The distribution of the sand-filled pipes suggests that the host till had been eroded to near its present profile before the piping episode. Six samples from the organic sediments were examined for pollen by the Department of Botany at the University of Cambridge, but all proved barren (written communication, Prof. R G West).

COVER SILT

Much of the upland area of the district, with the exception of the south-west, carries a drape of silt or fine-grained sand that masks many of the outcrops that are depicted on the face of the published map. Indeed the mapping of much of the upland geology necessitated the use of hand augers to penetrate the drape and identify the underlying materials. The deposit is referred to in this account as cover silt. It forms part of a regionally extensive spread of silt and sand called Coverloam (Catt et al., 1971), Cover Loam (Corbett and Tatler, 1974) and Loess (Corbett, 1977). It is probably broadly analogous to the Cover Sand of the Bury St Edmunds district (Bristow, 1990a).

Thicknesses for the cover silt proved by augering range up to 1.5 m. Thicker deposits may occur locally, while elsewhere the silt may be completely absent, either through nondeposition or by erosion of a once more extensive cover. The thickest sequences tend to have been recorded towards the base of concave slopes. While silt is the main component, fine- to medium-grained sand also occurs, giving a distinct bimodal distribution as noted by Catt et al. (1971) and Perrin et al. (1974). In many augerholes, and in natural and temporary sections, angular to subangular flint stones were found to be scattered throughout the deposit. The sand fraction commonly includes well-rounded grains.

The cover silt, where proved in many augerholes, tends to be mixed with soil, a result of deep ploughing, cryogenic or biogenic processes; these processes may also account for the scattered distribution of stones within the silt. In some holes, however, the material recovered by the auger is a buff to light buff silt that may be mottled tan or reddish brown and may include concretions of brown iron oxide. The deposit commonly becomes more sandy and stony with depth, such that penetration by the auger proves impossible.

The temporary section [5226 1359 to 5217 1391] exposed during the construction of sea defences at Caister-on-Sea provided an excellent exposure of the cover silt (Figure 42). There, the deposit forms a layer 1 to 1.5 m thick under vegetated topsoil or blown sand at 5 to 6 m above OD. Silt, about 1 m thick with sparsely scattered stones, mostly angular flints, rests on up to 0.5 m of sandy gravel. The silt carries weak red mottling towards the base, where it is sandy and includes ferruginous concretions. The underlying gravel is also sandy and ferruginous, and laterally impersistent, resting on an irregular erosion surface that includes Cromer Formation, Lowestoft Till and channel-fill sands of possible Hoxnian age. The gravel clasts comprise well-rounded quartz and quartzite, and flints that are mostly angular, though some are very angular and unpatinated, probably the products of shattering by frost with little subsequent transport. The gravel is thickest where it fills shallow gullies in the erosion surface. Cryoturbation structures, characteristic of the sandy cover deposits elsewhere in eastern England were not recorded in this coastal section; however, such structures were noted in the very stony basal part of the 1.5 m-thick cover silt at Hillborough Hole [4441 1165], near Stokesby, and in cover silt in the cliff section north of Hopton on Sea [5330 0085].

No direct evidence for the age of the cover silt has been established within the district. Its accumulation postdates the formation of the contemporary upland topography. However, the deposit does not cover the Flandrian Breydon Formation and there is no evidence that its accumulation accompanied that of the Breydon Formation.

A wind-blown origin for the silty deposits that cover much of north Norfolk was suggested by Catt et al. (1971). A similar origin, with modification by frost heaving and biological mixing, was deduced for both the sandy and the silty cover deposits of eastern England by Perrin et al. (1974). These authors identified separate phases of deposition, sand followed by silt, and concluded that the sandy cover of eastern England accumulated before or during the last intense periglaciation in the Devensian. A date of 19 500 ± 650 years BP for the cover sands resting on the youngest (First) terrace of the rivers Ouse, Cam and Lark in the Ely and Bury St Edmunds districts to the south-west was reported by Godwin and Willis (1964). Thus the bulk of the cover silt is considered to have accumulated during an interval of some ten thousand years that preceded the Flandrian marine transgression into the district, an age range consistent with the suggestion of Catt et al. (1971) that the silt was derived by deflation from Devensian glacial outwash sediments.

YARE VALLEY FORMATION

This previously unnamed formation of gravel and subordinate sand is recognised only from boreholes and, tentatively, in shallow seismic profiles offshore. Onshore, it underlies the Breydon Formation (in many instances the Basal Peat) and occupies the floor of a buried valley system underlying the marshland and the major valleys of the present day (Figure 43 and see Chapter eight). Over most of its distribution within the district it rests on the Crag, though many borehole records, for example in the Acle area (Figure 46), are interpreted as indicating the existence of intervening deposits of head. In the western part of the Yare valley, the formation rests on older formations including the London Clay and the Upper Chalk. Offshore, gravelly sediments, assigned to the Yare Valley Formation, have been recorded in boreholes east of Newtown, Great Yarmouth, resting on Crag and covered variously by Breydon Formation and Recent marine sand (Figure 47).

The deposits comprise gravel ranging from fine to coarse, with variable amounts of fine- to coarse-grained sand; the gravel is mostly flint. Silty gravel is recorded in some boreholes, as are shell fragments and chalk cobbles. The Yare Valley Formation is formally defined in terms of its occurrence in Runham/Yare Borehole 8 (TG 50NW/480) adjacent to the banks of the River Yare outflow from Breydon Water (Appendix 2). The formation there is 5.2 m thick and rests on Crag at 24.0 m below OD. It comprises grey, silty, fine to coarse gravel passing in the topmost metre to grey-brown, gravelly, medium-grained sand; it is overlain by dark brown, sandy peat (Basal Peat) of the Breydon Formation.

The distribution of boreholes penetrating the Yare Valley Formation is shown in Figure 43. In the Waveney valley, up to 7.5 m have been proved at Haddiscoe Marshes and, near Great Yarmouth, thicknesses up to 11 m are recorded. Previous studies of the sediments infilling the buried valley system (Marriott and Gribble, 1904; Pallis, 1911; Jennings, 1952; Lambert and Jennings, 1960; Coles, 1977; Coxon, 1979; Coles and Funnell, 1981; Alderton, 1983) noted the existence of gravel or sandy gravel underlying the marshland silts, clays and peats; but no detailed accounts are published. Funnell (1958) gave a brief description of 'Valley Gravel' underlying alluvium in the Yare valley to the west of the district. Coxon (1979, p.20), referred to 'the sands and gravels of the Waveney Floodplain and the associated alluvial sediments that cover these'; elsewhere (p.186), he described the Waveney floodplain as 'a valley fill of sand and gravel overlain by ... organic mud and clay'. Alderton (1983, pp.74–75), in particular, made reference to these basal gravelly deposits in descriptions of transects across the marshland between the upper Waveney and the lower Yare at Great Yarmouth. Cox et al. (1989, pp.25–26) referred to 'sub-alluvial gravels' and noted that 'alluvium.... is commonly underlain by gravels'.

No direct evidence for the age of the Yare Valley Formation has been established. Coxon (1979, p.20) referred to these deposits as Devensian; Cox et al. (1989) suggested that their deposition may have begun in the late Devensian. It is reasonable to suppose that at least some of the formation consists of fluvial sediments of late Devensian and early Flandrian age, deposited by rivers flowing within the (now buried) valley system and draining central parts of East Anglia to the contemporary

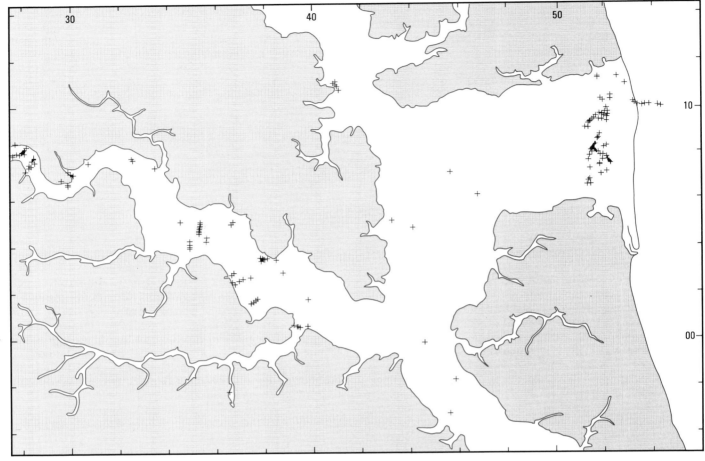

Figure 43   Locations of boreholes in which Yare Valley Formation has been identified.

Southern North Sea Basin. The maximum age of the formation is more speculative. Funnell (oral communication, 1990) has argued that the general characteristics of the deposits imply a late Anglian age. The formation demonstrably postdates much of the Anglian succession, but it is possible that it includes glaciofluvial deposits of late Anglian age (see Chapter six). The formation occurs below the river terrace deposits around Postwick in the Yare valley; also below terraces of the upper Waveney (outside the district), regarded by Coxon (1979) as either Anglian or Wolstonian. In view of the uncertainty over its age, the chronostratigraphical classification of this formation is shown simply as ?Devensian on the published map.

RIVER TERRACE DEPOSITS (UNDIFFERENTIATED)

River terrace deposits have been mapped in the River Yare south of Postwick and east of Surlingham. Less extensive terraces were mapped abutting Strumpshaw Marsh and along Run Dike, a tributary of the Yare flowing through Brundall.

The terraces form flattish or gently sloping features, generally 1 to 3 m above the alluvium but sometimes rising to 8 m above, as at Postwick. There are no recent ex-

posures of the deposits, but in the 19th century '7 feet of gravel' were recorded near Postwick Hall; 'half a mile east of Postwick Church a gravel pit showed irregularly stratified sand and gravel resting on sands (? Crag)' (Woodward, 1881).

The surface of the terraces is littered with subangular flints and some quartz and quartzite pebbles; large cobbles of flint and quartz are common. The 19th century surveyors found it difficult to distinguish the river terrace deposits (which they termed Valley gravel) from the 'pebbly gravel of the Crag Series' (now included in the Kesgrave Formation) (Woodward, 1881), a problem shared by the present-day surveyors. Thus some 'Valley gravel' shown on the 1885 map, for example at Langley Abbey, is now classified as Kesgrave Formation.

The age of the river terrace deposits is uncertain. Cox et al. (1989) thought there was some evidence that terrace deposits to the west of the district might be of late Hoxnian age, but admitted that this evidence was equivocal.

HEAD

Head comprises poorly sorted and poorly stratified deposits formed by the mass movement of superficial materials on sloping ground. The mass movement processes include hillwash and soil creep as well as solifluction, an important mode of sediment transport in periglacial conditions. The deposits mapped or identified in boreholes within the district have not been dated with any accuracy, but it is likely that most were formed during the periglacial conditions of the Late Devensian, with minor accumulation extending through the Flandrian.

Head occurs as a veneer up to a metre or so thick lining the floors and/or lower flanks of the tributary valleys of the district; it is mainly overlapped by, though to some extent intercalates with peat of the Breydon Formation. Elsewhere, for example near Blundeston in the southeast, it passes laterally into undifferentiated alluvium. Whilst head deposits are common, only those considered to exceed 1 m in thickness are shown on the published map. Head up to about 1.5 m thick has been mapped in the upper reaches of small tributary valleys draining the plateau, for example south and east of Fritton Decoy. Thicker deposits, estimated to be up to 3.5 m east of Gillingham Hall and near Beech Farm, Burgh St Peter, occur towards the lower ends of the tributary valleys. Head also occurs on the flanks of the major valleys fringing the marshland, as, for example, adjacent to Langley and Hardley marshes; and in isolated depressions within the outcrop of the Corton Formation between Lound and Corton Cliffs.

In the south-east, head deposits are thicker in southward-draining valleys than in their northward-draining counterparts, and thicker accumulations occur where the hill slopes are entirely of till. Where the valley sides comprise till overlying sand, or are entirely of sand, it seems that any surface runoff was more readily absorbed, with a consequent reduction in downslope soil movement (P M Hopson, oral communication, 1990).

Head is a polygenetic deposit, its lithology generally reflecting the materials upslope from which it was derived. It ranges from yellow-brown to dark brown to grey-black and comprises mainly sand with varying proportions of clay, silt, gravel of pebble grade (mostly flint) and sporadic larger rock clasts.

Deposits interpreted as head have been identified tentatively in boreholes penetrating the base of the Breydon Formation on the flanks of the (now buried) valley system underlying the marshland. These deposits are mainly clayey and pebbly, and appear to form a sheet on the buried valley flanks, draping an undulating surface composed mainly of Crag. The relationships of the head deposits to the Yare Valley Formation and the cover silt remain to be demonstrated. Comparison of borehole sequences in the Acle area suggests that the head there may merge with gravel of the Yare Valley Formation in the floor of the buried valley (Figure 46). It is possible that the irregular, poorly sorted sandy gravel deposits forming the basal part of the cover silt that occurs on gentle slopes are themselves head deposits of the same general age and genesis as the deposits described above.

EIGHT

Quaternary — Flandrian

Deposits of Flandrian age form the marshland that makes up some 25 per cent of the land area of the district; they also form the coastal barrier that extends southwards from Caister-on-Sea to Gorleston-on-Sea, protecting the marshland from direct marine inundation (Frontispiece). The Recent marine deposits of sand and subordinate gravel that occur at the shoreface and on much of the sea bed are also included in this category.

Most of the onshore Flandrian deposits are classified into two formal lithostratigraphical units, the Breydon Formation and the North Denes Formation. Deposits identified offshore from Newtown, Great Yarmouth (Figure 54) may also belong to the Breydon Formation. Other offshore deposits and those onshore deposits that are not included in the formal classification are depicted on the published map by graphic symbols.

BREYDON FORMATION

The fill of the buried valley system that underlies the marshland (Figure 44) is composed largely of Breydon Formation (Figure 45). The formation is dominated by silt and clay and includes a shelly marine fauna. Sand is generally a minor component, though in the Newtown area of Great Yarmouth substantial sand bodies interrupt the argillaceous succession. Peat of freshwater and brackish origins is a major component adjacent to much of the marshland margin and particularly in the valleys of the River Yare and many tributary streams; it also occurs as widespread though locally impersistent layers both at the base of the formation and within it, as well as one of more limited distribution at the top, mainly in the marshland fringe.

The Breydon Formation is up to 22 m thick but thins out altogether at the margins of the marshland. The buried valley system which it occupies is cut through the

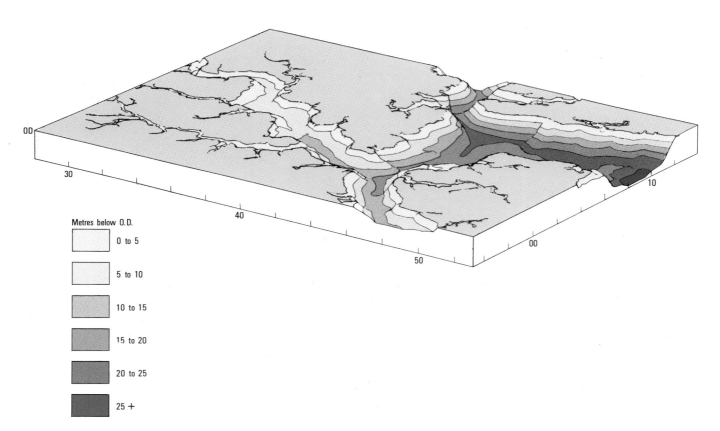

OD

30

40

50

00

10

Metres below O.D.

0 to 5

5 to 10

10 to 15

15 to 20

20 to 25

25 +

Figure 44 Perspective view, from the south-east, of the valley system under central Broadland that has been buried by the Breydon Formation; contours in metres OD, interfluve uplands reduced to zero OD (computer-generated plot derived from the borehole database).

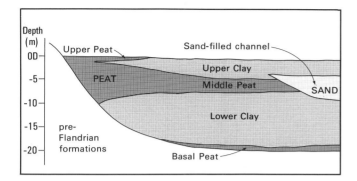

Figure 45   Generalised sequence of deposits making up the Breydon Formation.

Anglian deposits and the pre-Anglian Kesgrave Formation into the Crag; and, in the landward part of the Yare valley, through the Crag into the London Clay Formation and Upper Chalk. It overlies and overlaps the Yare Valley Formation which forms the buried valley floor. The Breydon Formation fills the valley system to within a metre or so of Ordnance Datum, exceeding that level in places, particularly in some of the tributary valleys. Locally, where peat has been extracted from the uppermost few metres of the formation, it has become draped with deposits of nekron and calcareous lacustrine muds (see below), the latter themselves in places masked by an overgrowth of peat.

The general relationship between the Breydon Formation and the North Denes Formation in the coastal zone at Great Yarmouth is illustrated in Figure 56. The main body of the North Denes Formation is banked against an eastward-facing, inclined erosional truncation surface of Breydon Formation. Where the buried valley intersects the coast at Great Yarmouth, only the lowest few metres of the formation are preserved under the North Denes Formation. Farther offshore, deposits which appear to belong to the Breydon Formation have been sampled by vibracore and identified in shallow seismic profiles, and are interpreted as remnants of the fill of a former eastward extension of the buried valley beyond the present coast (Figure 54, Plate 15). Between Caister-on-Sea and Great Yarmouth, the Breydon Formation is overlapped westwards by North Denes sands, while southwards from the outflow of Breydon Water, silts and clays of the Breydon Formation themselves overlap North Denes sands. The relationship of the Newtown sand bodies within the Breydon Formation, referred to above, to the North Denes Formation is unclear from present evidence.

Plate 15   Vibrocore sample taken at the sea bed off Great Yarmouth; some 0.3 m of gravelly to clayey sand (Recent marine deposits) rests on sand with silty and clayey layers capped by laminated silt and clay (presumed sandy facies of the Breydon Formation).

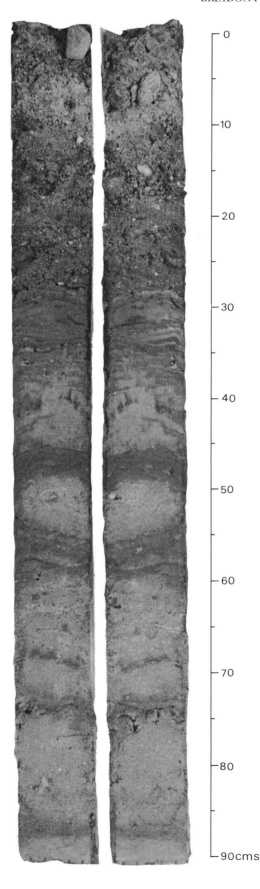

The Breydon Formation is defined formally in terms of its occurrence in North Crains Borehole 208 (TG 50 NW/417) [5156 0782], sited on the southern shore of the eastern end of Breydon Water (Appendix 2), where it is 19.4 m thick and rests on sand and gravel of the Yare Valley Formation (TG 51SW/31) [5184 1082] at 19.15 m below OD. Representative reference sections are provided by a borehole at the waste disposal site, West Caister, 2.5 km to the north near North Denes Aerodrome, and by a borehole on the Acle Bypass (TG 41SW/27) [4117 1061] in the Bure valley (Appendix 2). The locations of these boreholes are shown in Figure 48.

Its deposits were classified by Blake (1890) simply as alluvium, and are shown as such on the Old Series One-inch geological maps covering the district. The first detailed study of the deposits to be published was that of Jennings (1952, 1955), and this was followed by the seminal account of Lambert and Jennings (1960). These workers established the essential stratigraphy, recognising two main argillaceous divisions, the Upper Clay and Lower Clay, separated by the Middle Peat. Another peat, underlying the Lower Clay and forming the base of the succession, was termed the Basal Peat, and a further one, locally capping the Upper Clay, the Upper Peat (Figure 45). This formal five-fold division of the succession was accepted by Coles (1977) and Funnell (1979), but these authors subsequently (Coles and Funnell, 1981) relegated this nomenclature to an informal status, replacing the term Basal Peat by Lower Peat. Saunders (1979) used the names Upper Breydon Clay and Lower Breydon Clay for the main argillaceous units at Great Yarmouth and Alderton (1983) proposed a new nomenclature in terms of named beds for the succession in the Waveney valley, defined in two boreholes in the adjoining Lowestoft district.

This account follows Coles and Funnell (1981) in an informal usage of the Lambert and Jennings (1960) nomenclature, but reverts to Lambert and Jennings' Basal Peat. However, field distinction between the divisions becomes difficult or impractical in places adjacent to the marshland margin and in the more confined valleys, due largely to a coalescence of the otherwise discrete peat units. Peat deposits and sand bodies within the Breydon Formation are distinguished on the published map by lithology, while the remainder of the formation is shown undivided.

Sequences of the Breydon Formation are known or have been inferred from site investigation boreholes and cone penetrometer holes, mostly sited in the environs of Acle and Great Yarmouth (Figures 46 and 47). Detailed sedimentological and stratigraphical data have accrued from augerholes drilled for research projects by the universities of Cambridge and East Anglia (Coles 1977; Alderton, 1983; B M Funnell, written communication, 1990), and for a national lowland peat survey carried out by the Soil Survey of England and Wales (Burton and Hodgson, 1987); these data also include the results of some 360 continuously sampled gouge augerholes (many to a depth of about 4 m and the deepest to about 7 m below ground level), sunk as part of this survey. A plot showing the distribution of borehole and augerhole data is given in Figure 48. Additional field data has been gathered from observations in the network of drainage ditches (dykes) that characterises the marshland, some of which have been cut as much as 3 m below the general ground surface. Geotechnical data for the Breydon Formation are given in Chapter eleven.

Silt and clay

Silt and clay, formed in estuarine conditions, dominate the succession of the Breydon Formation under most of the marshland.

The Lower Clay is 0 to 15 m thick, the unit thinning out towards the buried valley margins. It is nowhere exposed and little sedimentological detail is available. It is a soft, grey-black, silty clay which becomes firm with depth. In some augerholes, traces of bioturbation were recorded; in others, laminae or thin beds of silt and fine-grained sand were identified, usually between depths of 11 and 15 m.

The Upper Clay is typically 4 to 6 m thick. It includes a weathered layer at its top, generally between 0.7 and 1.8 m thick (including some 0.3 m of topsoil), except where it is covered by peat (Upper Peat). This weathered layer, or ripened soil crust, comprises firm to very stiff, silty to very silty clay, light grey in colour but with tan mottling; it includes concretions of brown iron oxide and, commonly, traces of gypsum. It may include traces of plant fragments and rootlets, particularly towards its base; also the chalky remains of gastropod and bivalve shells. The base of the layer is irregular, with the tan colouration penetrating along rootlet traces, worm burrows or fissures in the underlying silty clay. No other weathered layer is known at lower levels in the formation. The soil ripening process appears to be at least in part a consequence of artificial drainage, with irreversible shrinkage leading to the development of a strong, coarse prismatic structure, grading to blocky as ripening proceeds (Dent et al., 1976); it may be accompanied by the development of acid sulphate conditions (see Chapter eleven).

Beneath the weathered layer in the Upper Clay, two conspicuously different sedimentary facies are recorded. One is a mainly soft, light to medium grey, silty clay rich in plant material, which occurs as roots of the reed *Phragmites* in growth position, as scattered spongy fragments, or as comminuted debris imparting a distinct, bedding-parallel lamination on which the sediment may be physically parted with ease; this facies includes sparse bivalve and gastropod shells. The other facies (commonly underlying that described above) constitutes most of the formation down to the top of the Middle Peat layer over wide areas; this is a soft to very soft, dark bluish or brownish grey to black silty clay. It may be bioturbated and, typically, it includes interlaminated silt and clay, and fine-grained sand in sharp-based laminae or thin beds. The black coloration, due to finely disseminated iron pyrite (FeS_2), occurs as diffuse layers, mottles and flecks, the pyrite having been formed diagenetically by the reduction of marine-derived dissolved sulphates by micro-

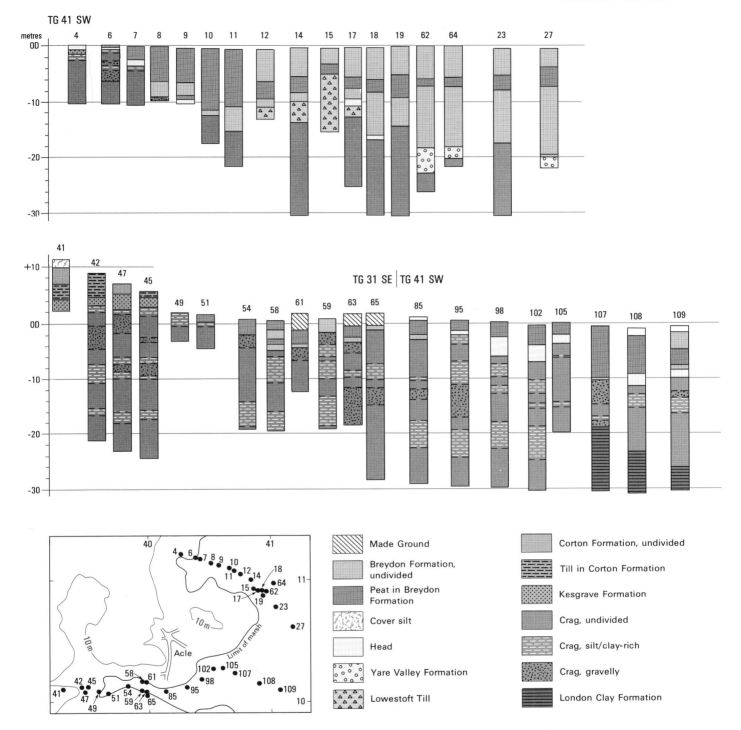

Figure 46 Selected generalised borehole sections at Acle. Borehole numbers are those of the Survey's registration system and refer to the 1:10 000 sheet indicated. Borehole information is published by permission of Norfolk County Council and Department of Transport.

organisms (including *Desulphoribic desulphuricans*) in anaerobic conditions (Price, 1980). Shells are locally common to abundant and include gastropods, thin-shelled bivalves including *Scrobicularia plana* and the common cockle, *Cerastoderma edule*. Disseminated plant debris is recorded, mostly as partings in laminated sedi-

ments, but is generally not conspicuous. From observations in ditch sections, the lamination tends to be even, with individual laminae extending over several tens of metres in some instances; gently inclined lamination traces have also been noted. A layer of fine-grained sand (or locally, at the marsh margins, gravel), a few centime-

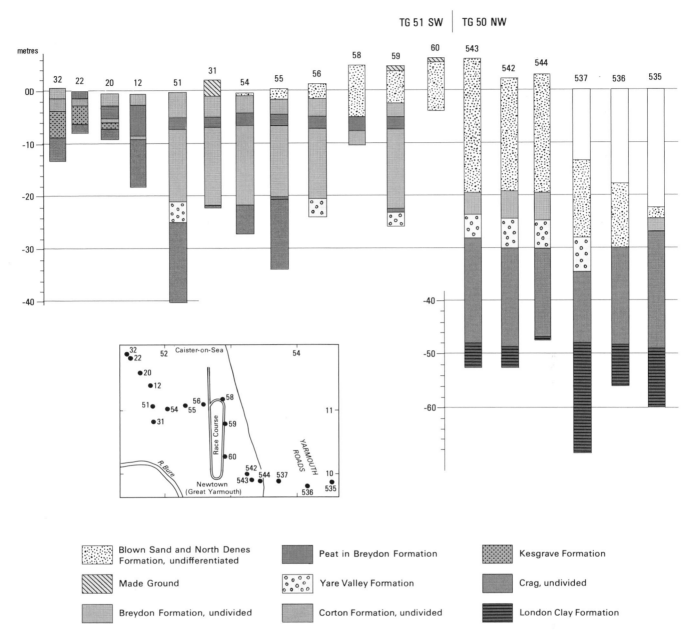

Figure 47 Selected generalised borehole sections between Caister-on-Sea and northern Great Yarmouth. Legend as for Figure 46. Borehole information is published by permission of Norfolk County Council and Anglian Water Services Ltd.

tres thick, directly overlies the Middle Peat in many recorded sections; the sand may be shelly and in some cases includes peat fragments. Some ditch sections in the marshland fringe show that this sandy layer is impersistent and that the underlying peat has an irregular and erosional surface (see below).

Courses of abandoned drainage channels are characteristic of the marshland surface where this is formed of the Upper Clay; these channels are apparent on aerial photographs and their patterns of occurrence, variously indicating salt-marsh and intertidal regimes, were illus-

trated by Coles and Funnell (1981). Augerhole data (J Hazelden, personal communication, 1989) indicates that silt is the main deposit within these channels.

Peat

The distribution of peat within the Breydon Formation is illustrated by sections on the published map and in Figures 46 and 47. The bounding surfaces of the peat bodies as mapped or shown on sections are diachronous and, as noted above, their upper surfaces are, at least in

Figure 48 Locations of boreholes and augerholes in the Breydon and North Denes formations referred to in the text.

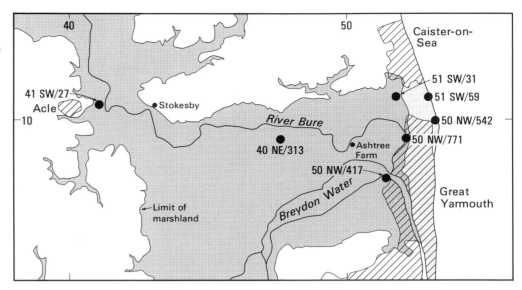

part, erosional. The stratigraphy of these units may be further complicated by substantial consolidation of the peat following burial (Chapter eleven).

Two main types of peat were documented by Coles (1977) and Coles and Funnell (1981); brushwood peat, formed in a freshwater environment, and *Phragmites* reed peat, formed in brackish conditions. Coles and Funnell (1981) recognised salt-marsh peat as a variant of the *Phragmites* facies, and structureless peat and fibrous peat with wood fragments as variants of the brushwood facies. According to Burton and Hodgson (1987), the peat generally accumulated under eutrophic conditions; they noted that it is commonly humified and woody, but, where there is a transition to estuarine clay, sedges and reeds dominate a more fibrous peat which accumulated in fens and reed swamps associated with periods of higher watertable.

Evidence for the existence of the Basal Peat comes largely from boreholes in the Acle and Great Yarmouth areas (Figures 46 and 47); also from augerholes in the Bure (Jennings, 1952; Lambert and Jennings, 1960), Yare (Coles, 1977; W M Corbett, written communication 1987) and Waveney (the Barnby Peat Bed of Alderton, 1983) valleys. The borehole data indicate that this peat occurs as an impersistent layer up to about 2 m thick, the deepest proving being at about 23 m below OD in a borehole (TG 51SW/59) [5292 1078]. In the Bure valley at Ranworth, just beyond the northern margin of the district, the Basal Peat and the Lower Clay overlying it are confined to a channel incised in the main valley floor (Jennings, 1952). The ^{14}C date given by Coles and Funnell (1981) for a sample of salt-marsh peat between 19.3 and 19.5 m below OD in a borehole sited on Acle Marshes near Great Yarmouth (TG 40NE/313; Figure 48) is 7580 ± 90 years BP (HAR 2535). Dates given by Alderton (1983) for the equivalent peat in the Waveney valley [TM 4890 9258, in the Lowestoft district] are 6305 ± 55 years BP (Q-2091) for the top of the unit at 8.6 m below OD, and 7750 ± 55 years BP (Q-2092) at 9 m below OD. The impersistent nature of this layer may be a consequence

of erosion following deposition, as noted in the Yare valley by Coles and Funnell (1981); there, the Basal Peat is of the *Phragmites* facies and occurs between 8.0 and 13.0 m below OD.

The Middle Peat has been penetrated, or its top surface reached (Figure 49) by boreholes and augerholes in most parts of the marshland; it is also exposed in drainage ditches in several places in the marshland fringe. It forms a layer generally 2 to 4 m thick, although records from the Great Yarmouth environs suggest that the layer there may be split into two or more leaves. Coles and Funnell (1981) described the layer in the Halvergate Marshes as comprising structureless peat, which is replaced up the Yare valley by fibrous peat with wood fragments and in turn by brushwood peat. Under the open marshland, the top of the Middle Peat occurs within the range 4 to 9 m below OD but, in the marsh fringe and in the upper parts of the Yare valley, its top may lie as high as Ordnance Datum. In this marginal zone and in the upper parts of the Yare valley, the field recognition of the Middle Peat as distinct from the Basal or the Upper Peat may not be feasible due to a coalescence of the layers.

The top of the Middle Peat is generally a sharply defined boundary; sections in ditches [4463 1220; 4490 1216] near Thrigby and [3814 1414] near Pilson Green show that, at least locally, this boundary is an irregular erosion surface with a relief of up to about 1 m; fine-grained sand has been recorded as filling fissures and hollows in the surface of the peat, and, at the extreme marshland fringe [4238 1361] north-east of Acle, a layer of gravel rests on an irregular erosion surface of the peat. Local erosion on the top of this unit was noted by Coles and Funnell (1981) in the Yare valley, as was the existence also in the Yare valley of a channel incised completely through the peat and now filled with clay. The presence of similar buried channels cutting out at least most of the Middle Peat near to the River Bure at Stokesby is inferred from an augerhole [4146 1361] sunk during this survey, while farther downstream, at Ashtree Farm to the north of Breydon Water, the existence of in-

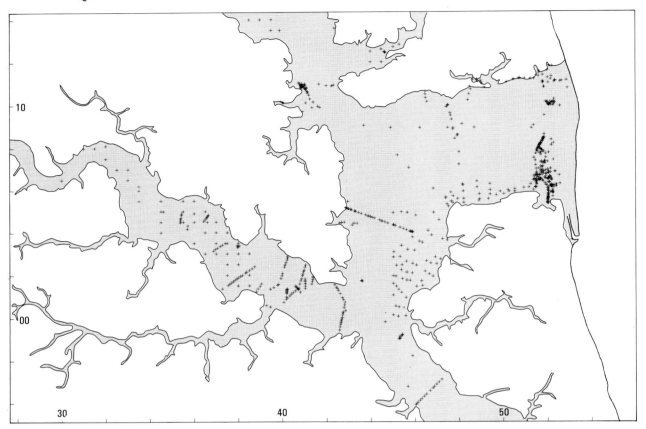

Figure 49 Boreholes and augerholes penetrating the Middle Peat in the Breydon Formation.

traformational channels cut through this part of the succession is interpreted from shallow seismic reflection data (Figure 50). The impersistent occurrence of the Middle Peat as indicated by borehole logs in the Newtown area of Great Yarmouth may similarly be a result of erosion by channelling (see below). A ^{14}C date given by Alderton (1983) for the base of this peat unit (her Burgh Peat Bed) in the Waveney valley [4890 9258, in the Lowestoft District] is 4700 ± 55 years BP (Q-2090), and one for the top of the unit is 2170 ± 55 years BP (Q-2086). A date given by Coles and Funnell (1981) for the top of this peat near Cantley is 1973 ± 50 years BP (SRR 573).

Compared with the Middle Peat, the Upper Peat is much less extensive and is mostly confined to discontinuous outcrops at the marshland fringe. Its certain recognition depends upon the existence of underlying Upper Clay; where that clay is absent, no criteria have been established in this survey for distinguishing between the Upper and Middle peats where these both occur. The peat is well developed in many embayments at the marshland fringe, for example The Doles near Cargate Green and at Southtown, Great Yarmouth; it also occurs as patches separated from the marginal outcrops, for example at Wigg's Carr near Wickhampton, at Norton Marshes near Nogdam End and within Upton Marshes north of Acle Bridge. There is evidence of a former more widespread cover on the marshland at Cobholm Island,

at the eastern end of Breydon Water, where peaty material is recorded at the top of the formation in several borehole logs, for example, North Crains Borehole 208 (TG 50NW/417; Appendix 2). Many factors have contributed to the depletion of the deposit; of these, human activities since Medieval times have had a significant impact (see Chapter ten).

Peat formed by the overgrowth by vegetation of flooded, abandoned peat workings (now broads) has been described by Lambert and Jennings (1960, p.21); these authors regarded this peat as distinct from the Upper Peat. It is described in this chapter in the section dealing with lacustrine mud.

The Upper Peat comprises mostly compact reed (*Phragmites*) and sedge (*Carex* and *Cladium*) remains with some brushwood peat accumulated under generally eutrophic (nutrient-rich) conditions (Lambert and Jennings, 1960; Burton and Hodgson, 1987); thicknesses up to 2 m have been recorded. Lambert and Jennings (1960, p.56) have noted the existence of a 30 to 40 cm-thick highly humified layer (rich in humic acid produced by slow oxidation) at the top of the Upper Peat in the Yare and Bure valleys and have suggested that the humification may indicate degradation of the surface deposits during a period of less waterlogged conditions.

The marginal accumulation of peat in the Breydon Formation appears to have been favoured at sites of sub-

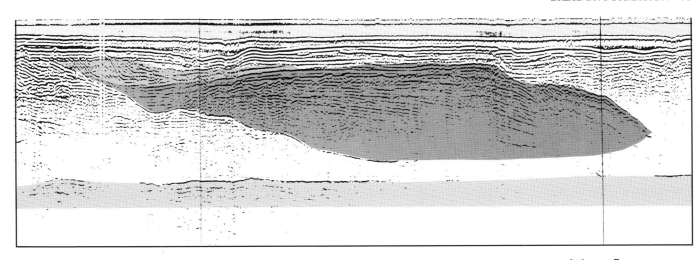

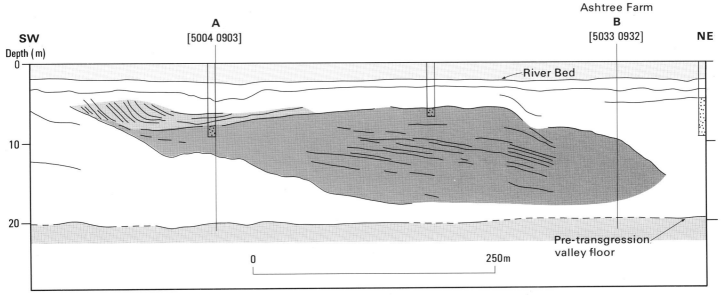

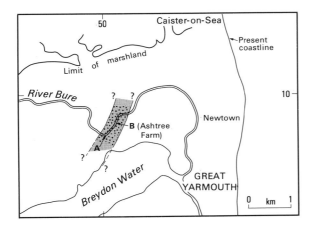

Figure 50   a. Seismic profile (surface tow boomer) along the River Bure at Ashtree Farm, some 2 km west of Great Yarmouth.   b. Interpretation showing Breydon Formation, comprising former channel deposits cutting down through tidal flat sediments, which rest on a subhorizontal surface of Crag and/or Yare Valley Formation. Augerholes by University of East Anglia (sited on adjoining marshland) proving sand (stippled). Location of profile shown in Figure 50c.   c. Course of channel within the Breydon Formation at Ashtree Farm, interpreted from seismic data.

stantial groundwater discharge from the flanking uplands, as for example at The Doles [392 137], near Cargate Green, where springs from the Kesgrave Formation and the Crag feed the adjoining marshland carrs, and near Southtown [523 060] where groundwater flows from sands in the Corton Formation (Chapter ten). At Wigg's Carr, near Wickhampton, groundwater discharges with artesian flow from isolated patches of Upper Peat; it is supposed that the groundwater is derived indirectly from the Kesgrave Formation via the Middle Peat, from which it erupts through the Upper Clay. These peat patches are raised above the general marshland surface by a metre or so; some are characterised by *Sphagnum,* indicating that the deposits may still be forming. Based on a ^{14}C dating of the feather-edge of the underlying Upper Clay (Coles and Funnell, 1981), the Upper Peat is known to have developed sometime after 1609 years BP. A date given by Alderton (1983) for the base of the equivalent peat in the Waveney valley [4404 9298] in the Lowestoft district is 1755 ± 40 years BP (Q-2183).

Sand

Besides its occurrence as laminae and thin beds within the laminated facies of the silt and clay dominated parts of the Breydon Formation, sand also forms a complex of more substantial bodies within the formation in the Newtown area of Great Yarmouth and adjoining parts of the marshland. Boreholes there show, besides an impersistence of the Middle Peat, that the silty clay of the Upper Clay is interrupted by layers of sand and, according to some records, pebbly sand or gravel. In some boreholes, sand dominates the sequence down to as much as 22 m below OD (TG 50NW/771) [5221 0936], with no trace of the Middle Peat. The present borehole data are inadequate to allow confident interpretation of the depositional environment of this sand complex; however, it seems likely that the sands are related to one or more channelling events that postdated the accumulation of the Middle Peat. Augerholes by the University of East Anglia indicate that the intraformational buried channels identified on seismic survey traces from the River Bure at Ashtree Farm, north of Breydon Water, are at least partly filled with sand (Figures 48 and 50).

A small sand body of a contrasting origin overlies the Upper Clay at the surface of the Breydon Formation at the marshland fringe [4774 1035] near Runham; in this case the sand deposit is interpreted as having formed as an estuarine spit extending from a valleyside promontory.

NORTH DENES FORMATION

The North Denes Formation comprises the deposits of a coastal barrier that extends in a tract up to about one kilometre wide between Caister-on-Sea and Gorleston-on-Sea, a distance of some eight kilometres. It consists of sand and subordinate gravel, and flanks the eastern limits of the Breydon Formation. Seawards, the formation extends to an arbitrary limit taken at the present coastline, where it is flanked by shoreface and beach sands (Recent marine deposits, Figures 47 and 54).

Knowledge of the stratigraphy of the North Denes Formation is based largely on borehole and temporary section data. The formation is defined in terms of its occurrence in Marine Outfall Borehole 8 (TG 50NW/542), on North Beach, Great Yarmouth (Figure 48, Appendix 2) , where it is 25.2 m thick (probably including some blown sand at the top) and rests on the Lower Clay of the Breydon Formation at 20.4 m below OD. The sequence there comprises sand and gravel including a layer of cobbles and, towards the base, a thin layer of silty clay. Sequences documented in other borehole logs show considerable variation in the distribution of sand and gravel. However, the specific designation of sand or gravel in these logs may well be unreliable in view of the difficulties usually encountered in the recovery of representative samples of these materials from boreholes.

The North Denes Formation occurs as an elongate, wedge-shaped body that rests unconformably mostly on Breydon Formation, but also, in southern Great Yarmouth and at its northern limit at Caister-on-Sea, on the Crag and to a lesser extent on the Kesgrave and Corton formations. It is largely concealed by blown sand, its most extensive crop being in the Newtown–Caister-on-Sea area where it overlaps the Breydon Formation.

From the Newtown area of Great Yarmouth northwards to Caister-on-Sea, the North Denes Formation rests on a seaward-sloping erosion surface that truncates the Breydon Formation succession (see sections on the published map and Figure 54). The erosion surface does not crop out, but is concealed by an overlap of North Denes sand which thins out westwards within a few hundred metres; this overlap, only a metre or two thick over much of its extent, is interpreted as an apron of washover deposits that accumulated in the lee of the barrier beach at an early stage in its development. In the Newtown and north-central areas of Great Yarmouth, the Breydon Formation that adjoins the North Denes Formation includes substantial sand bodies; as noted above, the relationship between these sands and those of the North Denes Formation is unclear.

Along its western boundary, through central and parts of southern Great Yarmouth, the outcrop of the sand and gravel is overlapped by silts and clays of the Breydon Formation. However, the detailed nature of this overlap is unclear, partly due to the disturbance of these superficial deposits by constructional activities in these quayside areas.

The age range of the North Denes Formation is constrained by its relationship to the Breydon Formation (described above); also by the recovery of dateable artifacts and by historical records. Documentary evidence supports the existence during the 5th century AD of a sandbank known as the Cerdic Sand or Cerdic Shore at the mouth of the Yare estuary, where Great Yarmouth now stands (Figure 55; Press, 1956). A channel into the estuary at the northern end of this sandbank between

Caister and Great Yarmouth, named Grubb's Haven or Cockle Water, became choked with sand soon after the time of the Norman Conquest (see Taylor, 1827; Woodward, 1881). During the early Middle Ages, this coastal barrier extended southwards as a spit which, by the reign of King John (1199–1216), had grown to a point close to Lowestoft (Green and Hutchinson, 1960), thus separating the erstwhile estuary from the open sea by a channel some 15 km long.

The basal North Denes Formation in southern Great Yarmouth accumulated some 800 years ago. A temporary section at the South Denes Power Station recorded by Green and Hutchinson (1960, pp. 131–134) exposed the basal deposits resting unconformably, at depths down to 5.3 m below OD, on an undulating surface of reddish sands, in part with laminae of silt and grey-green clay, and interpreted here as Crag. These basal North Denes sediments comprised a layer of beach ballast (sand and shingle) including potsherds of the 13th century AD. The top surface of this layer carried colonies of acorn barnacle (*Balanus balanoides*). The ballast layer was overlain by dark brown, silty, clayey sand including a mussel bed and further 13th century potsherds, and this in turn by beach extending to about 3.3 m above OD.

Several attempts were made to construct artificial navigation channels through the spit (see Blake 1890; Press, 1956). The last of these, directed by the Dutch engineer Joas Johnson (Joyse Jensen), was successful, and the channel that he created at Gorleston-on-Sea known as the Seventh Haven, was completed in 1613 and remains as the entrance to the port of Great Yarmouth to this day (Figure 55). Since the construction of the Seventh Haven, that part of the spit which lay to the south of the haven mouth, has been removed by marine erosion. North of the haven mouth, the form of the barrier deposits that make up the North Denes Formation has probably changed little since Medieval times, but for some seaward accretion and the accumulation of capping deposits of blown sand.

RECENT MARINE DEPOSITS

The deposits that have formed in the present-day sedimentary regime on the sea bed (including those of the beach and shoreface) and on the beds of tidal rivers and creeks, comprising sand, gravel and mud (silt and clay), are differentiated lithologically by colour on the published map. They are further classified according to their mode of occurrence; the classes are used in the following account.

The topography of the offshore area within, and adjoining the district, is dominated by a complex of coast-parallel sandbanks separated by narrow channels (Figure 51). The channels are floored by a veneer of gravelly or sandy sediments, resting on a substrate mainly of Crag. The crest of the largest of the banks in this complex, Middle Scroby, is exposed at low tides, the highest point being approximately at OD. The other banks may be covered by only a metre or two of water at their highest point at such times. The innermost nearshore channel,

Caister–Yarmouth–Gorleston–Corton Roads, reaches depths of about 25 m below OD. Farther offshore, Barley Picle, which separates Middle Scroby from South Cross Sand and Middle Cross Sand, reaches almost 50 m below OD.

Tidal currents are very strong. In Yarmouth Road, surface spring tidal velocities are around 1.1 m s^{-1}. Farther offshore, to the east of the banks, surface velocities reach 1.7 m s^{-1} (Admiralty Chart, No. 1536). As a result of these powerful currents, the seawater is turbid with suspended sediment. On the sea bed, sediment transport rates are high, as evidenced by the presence of sandwaves and by the observed changes in bank configuration in historical times.

The data on which this account is based were acquired largely from a marine geophysical survey run by the British Geological Survey in 1988. The survey comprised shallow seismic reflection profiling using Boomer equipment, side scan sonar and echo sounding.

Deposits of tidal rivers and creeks

Deposits of silt and clay are forming at the present-day on the reed bed flood plains flanking the tidal rivers that cross the marshland, constrained by manmade flood defence banks or levees. Sections observed in river banks mostly consist of well-laminated silt, which may be charged with plant debris. Some augerholes, bored to depths of a metre or so, show plant-rich clayey deposits; others penetrate peat.

By far the largest area of these deposits is that of Breydon Water, within the flood defence embankments known as the Breydon Wall. Sequences penetrated in augerholes there comprise silts and clays that are indistinguishable from those of the directly underlying Breydon Formation; the junction between them is arbitrary. Both in Breydon Water and on the floodplains of the marshland rivers, the present level of sedimentation lies up to 1.5 m above the general surface level of the adjoining marshland.

Shoreface and beach deposits

The present-day deposits of the foreshore along the entire coastline comprise sand and pebbly sand, and subordinate gravel; those of the backshore may intercalate with blown sand. Deposition is ephemeral, periods of sediment accretion being interrupted by storm events which result in the major seaward removal of sediment. The deposits are flanked to the west, at an arbitrary divide taken at the present limit of marine influence, by the North Denes Formation (Figures 47 and 54).

The relative proportions of sand and gravel on the foreshore differ from place to place, and also with time. Typical foreshore profiles are sand-dominated in their upper parts, with gravel increasing towards the low-water mark, commonly forming shallow cusps flanked by pebbly sand. The gravel is of fine to medium grade and is dominated by subrounded to rounded flint pebbles, although rounded quartz and quartzite pebbles are common. The foreshore sediments themselves are subject to an overall wave-induced southerly migration (longshore drift). In historical times this process has been responsible for the southward deflection of the River Yare by the accumulation of the spit sediments classified as North Denes Formation. At the present time, longshore drift plays an important role in beach formation or decay.

The principal source for the beach material lies in the cliffs to the north of this district. Between Weybourne and Happisburgh they are receding at around 0.9 m years $^{-1}$ (Clayton, 1989). Sediment derived from this erosion is transported along the beaches away from the eroding cliffs by the process of longshore drift, most being transported to the south-east. A coarsening of the sand grain-size in the direction of transport has been noted by McCave (1978) and interpreted as the result of winnowing of finer sand from the beaches by wave action and the subsequent transport of sediment into the nearshore zone, where it is removed by tidal currents. The rate of southward transport along the beaches varies both spatially and temporally and may result in areas of sediment accretion which form the blunt headlands or nesses which characterise the East Anglian coast. For example, Caister Ness, a promontory on North Beach, Great Yarmouth, has prograded at a rate of 4 to 6 m years $^{-1}$ in recent times (Clayton et al., 1983) but was not depicted on the Ordnance Survey map of 1903 (Robinson, 1966). Since that time the ness feature has grown and has migrated first southwards and then northwards again. North of Caister Ness the coast is sheltered from the effects of waves from the south-east by Caister Shoal (Figure 51) and consequently the rate of southward transport is high (Vincent, 1979).

South of Caister Ness the coast is increasingly protected from incoming waves in all directions by the offshore bank complex and, consequently, the rate of beach sediment transport is reduced. Indeed, coastal erosion is not currently a serious problem in this district, although most of the coastline has some degree of sea defence, either in the form of sea walls or groynes. Gorleston Beach, however, has steadily been losing volume since the piers at the mouth of the River Yare were extended in the early 1960s (Clayton et al., 1983). Much of the southward drift of sediment is now deflected offshore and bypasses Gorleston Beach before rejoining the coast a little to the south. Thus the erosion here may be ascribed to human agency. Any future coastal defence policy must, however, take into account the need to ensure a continued supply of sediment from the Norfolk cliffs to the beaches on this very active stretch of coastline (Clayton, 1980, 1989).

Tabular and sheet deposits

The sea bed between the offshore bank deposits is covered by a variety of recent sediments. Medium- and coarse-grained quartz sands and gravelly sands with up to about 10 per cent of broken shell debris form a veneer commonly between 0.25 and 0.6 m in thickness, and locally less than 0.1 m. These thin deposits are not shown on the published map except on the floor of Caister–Yarmouth Roads (Figure 51), where they may exceed 1 m in thickness and include gravels composed mainly of flint with small proportions of quartz and quartzite pebbles. Mr D J Harrison reports that, where the flint gravels are exposed at the sea bed, they are characteristically brown, rounded to subrounded and encrusted with marine organisms. By contrast, the subsurface gravels are black and subrounded to subangular. Cobble-sized clasts of flint are rare and most of the gravel is of fine pebble size (+5 mm −16 mm).

Muddy sediments are found on the sea bed between water depths of 5 and 13 m, on the landward side of the nearshore channel of Caister–Yarmouth–Gorleston–Corton Roads. Sea-bed sediments here include samples with up to 50 per cent mud content (McCave, 1981), but their thickness is unknown. The reason for mud deposition within this channel is unclear. The River Yare has only a small discharge, and the fluvial input of mud is minimal. According to McCave (1981), the turbidity maximum of the River Yare oscillates in and out of the river and may influence the coastal zone; mud deposition is facilitated by the reduction of wave energy through the sheltering influence of the nearshore banks. Alternatively, the mud may originate from the erosion of sea bed exposures of the Breydon Formation off the northern part of Great Yarmouth (Figure 52).

Bank deposits

A conspicuous feature of the offshore topography is the presence of a number of more or less coast-parallel sandbanks (Figures 51 and 53). The largest of the sandbanks, Scroby Sands, is approximately 14 km long and 2 km wide. The banks form a general sigmoidal or parabolic pattern, and are separated by narrow channels, which shallow where the banks coalesce. Caister Shoal is attached to the shoreline and connected to North Scroby at its northern end. The nearshore banks are slightly asymmetrical with steeper western slopes of about 2° to 3° and eastern slopes of about 0.5°. This form contrasts with the more offshore Norfolk Banks (off north-east Norfolk) which may have faces sloping at up to 7° (Caston, 1972).

The sediments that constitute the banks consist mainly of fine- to medium-grained sand, but little is known in detail of their granulometry. Caister Shoal is composed almost entirely of medium-grained sand according to Robinson (1966). Records from shallow seismic profiling across the northern end of South Cross Sand have shown the presence of internal northward-dipping reflectors, subparallel to the surface of the bank. These reflectors have an apparent dip to the north of about 2° and reflect the northward migration of the bank. A comparison of bathymetric charts surveyed between 1866 and 1970 (Craig-Smith, 1972, map 20) has revealed a general northward migration of this bank of several hundred metres in that time. Scroby Sand had extended over 1 km north during the same interval, whilst Corton Sand was found to have migrated 1 km to

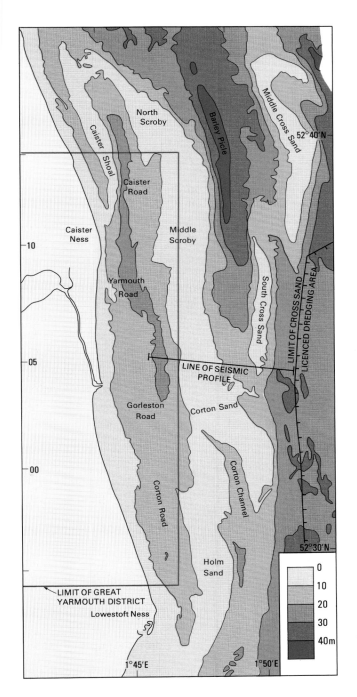

Figure 51 Bathymetry of sea bed (metres below OD) off Great Yarmouth, showing the principal named channels and banks; the line of the seismic profile shown in Figure 53 is indicated.

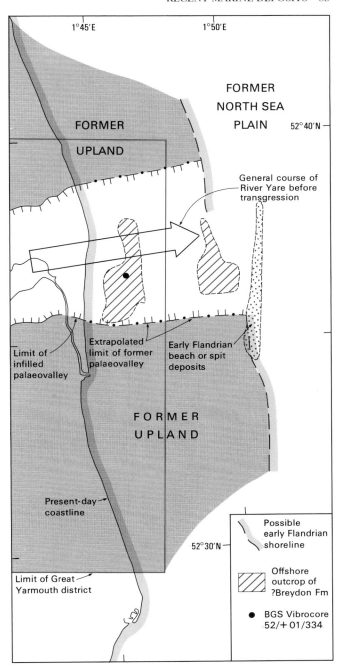

Figure 52 Reconstruction of the early Flandrian palaeogeography offshore Great Yarmouth; the probable extent of preserved Breydon Formation is indicated.

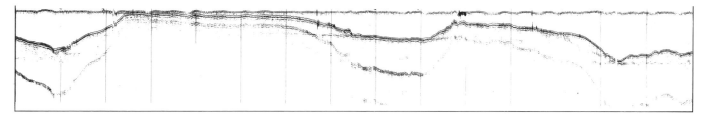

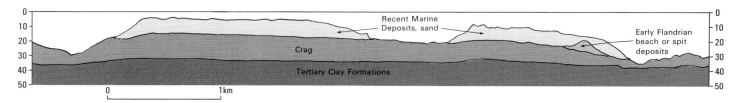

Figure 53   a. Seismic profile (surface tow boomer) along the survey line shown in Figure 51, b. Interpretation showing the blank deposits and the form of the surface of pre-Flandrian formations.

the south. In general terms, Craig-Smith found major movements to have been parallel to the coast with virtually no lateral movement. This contrasts strongly with the situation for the Norfolk Banks; these asymmetric sandbanks lie further offshore and have their steep faces oriented to the north-east, away from the coastline. Their internal-dipping reflectors indicate migration offshore, at right-angles to their long axes (Houbolt, 1968; Stride, 1988).

Sandwaves are generally associated with the sandbanks and may cover their flanks, and, where water depths are sufficient, their tops as well. On the shallowest parts of the banks, sandwaves are not developed due to interference from wave action. Winter storms have a seasonal effect on sandwave distribution in shallow water. The sand waves are commonly 0.3 to 0.5 m high on the flanks of the banks but, in deeper water near the foot of the bank slopes they may be between 3 and 4 m high. Within the area shown by Figure 51, the largest sandwaves, up to 8 m high, are on the seaward side of North Scroby. The migration of the sandwaves, as indicated by the facing direction of their steeper sides, is generally in accordance with residual current directions in the area shown by Robinson (1966, fig. 3), although variations from this simple pattern exist. For instance, in the channel shoreward of Caister Shoal, southward-migrating sandwaves occur in the southern part while northward migration is indicated for sandwaves in the northern part of the channel.

The bank system is believed to be largely supplied with sand which escapes into the offshore area from the headlands of Caister Ness and Lowestoft Ness (McCave, 1978). Ultimately, this sand may pass from this nearshore bank system to feed the more offshore Norfolk Banks to the north of the district (Stride, 1988), a direct distance

of about 100 km, although the actual transport path length may be greater.

LACUSTRINE MUD

Lacustrine mud comprises the deposits of silt and clay, including the nekron and calcareous muds, proved by augering (Jennings, 1952; Lambert and Jennings, 1960, p.55) to line the floors of the Broadland lakes, formed by the flooding of abandoned peat workings (Chapter ten). (Nekron muds are organic and rich in mineral nutrients.)

The limits of the lacustrine mud are imperfectly known and its boundaries as depicted on the published map are generalised. It generally occurs under open water up to 4 m deep. Auger borings indicate that the deposit may be up to 4 m thick, as at the south-western end of Filby Broad (Lambert and Jennings, 1960, p.55). Locally, it may intercalate with alluvium or head. It overlies a range of disturbed substrates (Lambert and Jennings, 1960); this disturbance is cited as evidence in support of the artificial origin of the broads (see Chapter ten). The underlying material comprises peat or clay, or the sand and gravel that forms the floor of the confining valley. The substrate surface is generally uneven and may consist of partially extracted Upper Peat or Middle Peat, the lacustrine mud locally abutting steep-sided peat balks (also cited as artifacts) or overlying flanges of clay (Upper Clay). The clay of these flanges was referred to by Lambert and Jennings as 'primary mud', as distinct from the unconformable 'secondary mud' (lacustrine mud) of the floor of the broad.

Locally, the lacustrine mud may be masked by rafted peat (not depicted on the published map) extending from the margins of the broad. Such peat developed where the waters at the margins were shallow, to produce a hydrosere representing a progression from reed beds through to sallow and alder woods (Jennings, 1952 pp.7–8). They were recognised by Lambert and Jennings (1960, p.21) as being distinct from the Upper Peat.

ALLUVIUM (UNDIFFERENTIATED)

Occurrences of undifferentiated alluvium are distinguished on the published map; in the upper reaches of confined tributary valleys, for example south of Bramerton, near Bloodman's Corner (Hopton on Sea) and south of Blundeston.

This detrital deposit comprises mainly unconsolidated layers of sand and silt but includes material ranging from organic clays through to coarse gravel derived from nearby sources. Downstream, it may be interbedded with peat or merge into and contribute to submerged lacustrine mud lining Fritton and Flixton Decoys. Upstream, the alluvium is usually intercalated with head; locally, where drainage is impeded (as near Bloodman's Corner), it adjoins peat. The alluvium ranges up to 1.5 m in thickness.

BLOWN SAND

Sand of wind-blown origin, locally perhaps as much as 5 m thick, occurs at the surface in the coastal belt, particularly between Caister-on-Sea and Gorleston-on-Sea, and forms the foundation for much of the older part of the town of Great Yarmouth. Away from urban development, dune landforms are preserved, as at the Racecourse and Golf Course at North Denes, where they are largely fixed by grasses, and on North Beach where they are mostly migratory. In their main development, the dunes attain heights of about 7 m above OD, but north of Caister and at Gunton the deposit occurs in cliff-top settings at more than 15 m and 20 m above OD respectively. The deposit has been exploited as a source of aggregate, historically as ballast for ships.

The blown sand rests largely on the sands and gravels of the North Denes Formation, but also on Anglian glacial deposits at Caister-on-Sea and to the south of Corton. The sand is typically buff in colour and mainly fine-grained; it may be distinguished from North Denes Formation sands by the absence of pebbles, though in many borehole logs such a distinction is not feasible. In the urban areas especially, the dunes have been landscaped and some mixing with the North Denes sands may have occurred.

MADE GROUND AND LANDFILL

Made ground falls broadly into two categories: that created for constructional purposes and that which results from the disposal of waste materials. The former occurs mainly in the marshland where it forms artificial levees and provides firm foundations for railways, roads and buildings. It consists variously of loose sand and gravel, rubble and, notably in levees, clay. Ash, clinker, cinders, coal and inorganic and organic rubbish are also found. Thicknesses of this category of made ground, based on borehole and trial pit data, range up to 6 m but are usually less than 4 m.

The waste category can itself be divided into two types: landfill and landraising. Certain localities in the district have been made available by the Norfolk County Council for waste disposal, the largest landfill sites being at Strumpshaw and Bergh Apton (Figure 57). Both are now inactive, but Strumpshaw took about 1 000 000 m³ of waste and Bergh Apton some 700 000 m³. Caister Road (Great Yarmouth) and Cobholm Island are the main landraised waste disposal sites; like the large landfill sites both are now inactive. Figures for the volume of waste at each site are not available, but Caister Road occupies about 10 hectares and Cobholm about 30. Although there are many small waste disposal sites, some of which are active, the bulk of Great Yarmouth's waste is now deposited outside the district at Aldeby.

Because of its proximity to major water abstraction bores, Strumpshaw Pit is carefully monitored for possible contamination of groundwater; none has been detected. However, one problem at Strumpshaw has been the accumulation of methane. This is now burnt off, having been collected via a radial system of pipework within the pit. Plans are in hand to use the heat produced from burning the methane to generate electricity. It is estimated that a 1500 kw generator can be operated for up to eight years. A portable methane burner was temporarily installed at Bergh Apton, but methane has not been a problem there.

LANDSLIPS

Minor landslips have been recorded in the cliff sections between Corton Woods [545 965] and Gorleston Golf Course [530 015]. The areas prone to slippage are generally minor promontaries in an otherwise straight coastline, for example, opposite Long Lane [5460 9698]. The slips are most prevalent where the lower part of the cliff comprises sand of the Corton Formation; they have been arrested in part by the construction of sea defences either on the foreshore or at the cliff base. Aspects of coastal erosion are considered in Chapter ten.

FLANDRIAN EROSIONAL AND SEDIMENTARY HISTORY

The Flandrian stage embraces most of the period of eustatic rise in sea level that followed the Late Devensian glacial maximum, when the sea level fell to as much as 120 m below its present level (Cronin, 1983). Offshore data (Eisma et al., 1981; Jelgersma, 1979) show that the earliest marine incursion into the southern North Sea occurred before 8700 years BP. The Flandrian transgressive sea first entered the region from the English Channel through the Straits of Dover, and, around 8300 years BP, the southern and northern (north of the Dogger Bank) North Sea became connected.

A suggested reconstruction of the coastal land surface in this district at the onset of transgression is illustrated in Figures 52 and 55. It is probable that the uplands of Flegg and Lothingland extended, with undulating landforms similar to those preserved today, to a position some 7 km east of the present coastline. There, they flanked a plain that extended over much of the Southern North Sea area at levels in the range 30 to 40 m below OD. The low relief of this plain farther to the east may be deduced from sections shown on the Quaternary edition of the 1:250K Flemish Bight Sheet (British Geological Survey, 1984). The extended uplands of Flegg and Lothingland were separated, as their remnants are today, by a major valley cut into the Crag, perhaps lined with sands and gravels of the Yare Valley Formation. The course of that valley between Great Yarmouth, where its floor lay at about 23 m below OD, and its point of debouchment onto the North Sea plain is indicated on Figure 52.

The transgression resulted not only in major sedimentary accumulation, notably the Breydon and North Denes formations and the marine sandbank deposits, but also in marine erosion that volumetrically probably far exceeded sedimentation within the district. This erosion has taken several forms, the most important of which has been that at the cliff line, leading to coastal recession. As transgression proceeded, so the heights of the cliffs generally reduced and the stratigraphical composition of the cliffs changed from one dominated by the Crag to one dominated, as in the present day, by Anglian glacial deposits.

Besides the marine erosion of the uplands at the cliffline, it is likely that the weak cementation of much of the Crag rendered that formation prone to further erosion by wave action in the foreshore and nearshore zones. Also in the nearshore zone, the Crag has been further eroded by scouring by strong tidal currents flowing between sandbanks (Figures 51, 53 and 54); as far as is known, this process was restricted to the later stages of the transgression. Probably throughout most of the transgression in the district, marine erosion also resulted in the truncation or channelling of earlier-formed estuarine deposits (Breydon Formation) that had formed in the tidal inlet occupying the former river valley.

The Breydon and North Denes formations provide a sedimentary record of the period during which sea level rose from some 20 m below OD (about 7500 years BP) to its present position. During this period the rate of sea-level rise has not been constant. Based on her work in the Waveney valley, Alderton (1983) has identified alternating positive and negative tendencies of sea-level movement, but whether there was any true regressive episode is controversial.

The base of the Breydon Formation is diachronous, the Basal Peat of the deeper and more seaward part of the buried valley system near Great Yarmouth being older than the shallower occurrences of Basal Peat up-valley to the west (Coles, 1977). The transgression effected a marked change in depositional environment from a river plain in the Yare Valley Formation, firstly to a salt

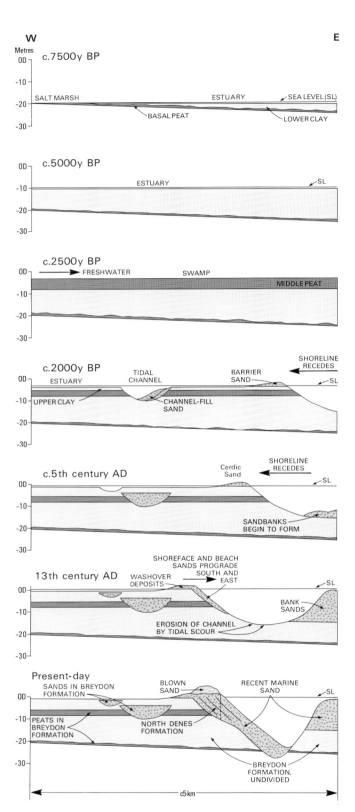

Figure 54 The Flandrian marine transgression, Newtown area, Great Yarmouth: serial schematic sections drawn west–east illustrating the interpreted sequence of events and environments up to the present day.

marsh or brackish swamp (Basal Peat), then, in response to a rapid and uninterrupted rise in sea level, to mudflats with tidal channels and creeks (Lower Clay). The relief of the valley flanks became progressively subdued as a result of the continuing accumulation of the Breydon Formation, with the estuary itself covering an ever larger area inshore of Great Yarmouth.

A change to freshwater conditions occurred in this district at about 4700 years BP, when sea level had risen to about 7 m below OD (Figure 55). The marine influence was temporarily expelled and a floodplain swamp became established, leading to the accumulation of the Middle Peat. This change may have been a consequence of the growth of a sand barrier across the mouth of the estuary (Coles and Funnell, 1981); however, studies of analogous successions in the German Bight indicate that peat accumulation may have replaced mud deposition in some estuaries simply in response to a slowing in the rate of sea-level rise between 6500 and 2600 years BP (Ludwig et al., 1981). The return to the marine mudflat and tidal channel environment represented by the Upper Clay occurred about 2200 years BP. In the marshland fringe at least, this return was preceded by partial erosion of the Middle Peat. The controls on the marine flooding of the Middle Peat are unclear. There is no regional evidence to support an increase in the rate of sea-level rise. However, the dished form of the upper surface of the Middle Peat is interpreted largely as the product of consolidation not only of the peat but also of the underlying Breydon Formation deposits. It is possible that the widespread lowering of the Middle Peat surface implicit in such consolidation may have facilitated marine re-invasion. Climatic control may also have played a part, with a change in the prevailing wind direction or a reduction in the freshwater feed to the estuary. The Upper Clay mudflats extended to the estuary margins except where a substantial feed of freshwater from landstreams or groundwater seepage favoured the accumulation of Upper Peat in fringing swamps (carrs).

The sand bodies that characterise the Upper Clay and fill channels cut through the Middle Peat into the Lower Clay in the vicinity of Great Yarmouth (Figure 54), reflect a significant increase in the tidal current energy affecting this part of the estuary compared with the conditions in which the underlying Lower Clay accumulated. Such an increase would be expected from the relative proximity of the open sea, which, by the onset of Upper Clay deposition, may have extended to within a kilometre of the present-day coastline. The accumulation of at least some of the major sandbanks appears to have commenced late in the transgression, following the marine erosion that formed the broad shelf of Crag at about 10 m below OD in the inshore part of the nearshore zone (see below).

The growth of the existing barrier sand and gravel deposits (the North Denes Formation) across the tidal inlet between Caister-on-Sea and Gorleston-on-Sea is a subject of historical record. During the first few centuries AD, a sandbank known as the Cerdic Sand or Cerdic Shore was in existence at the mouth of the estuary where Great Yarmouth now stands (Press, 1956), with channels feed-

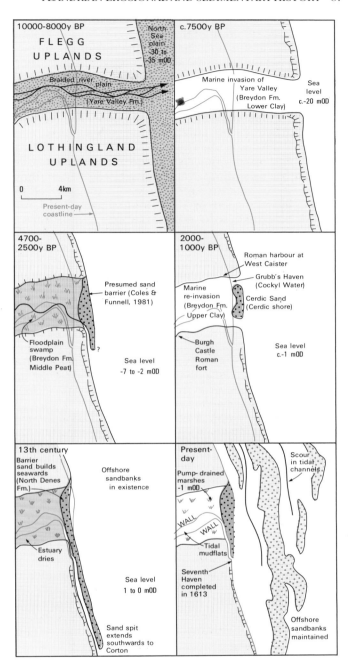

Figure 55   The Flandrian marine transgression: interpreted palaeogeographical evolution of the coastal zone.

ing and flushing the estuary both to north and south. The northern channel (Grubb's Haven) served as the approach to a Roman harbour at West Caister (Green and Hutchinson, 1960); it is likely that this channel remained open until the early Middle Ages (Figure 55).

An extract from an essay by J W Robberds, quoted by Blake (1890), lists the locations of saltworks mentioned in the Domesday Book in the year 1086 around what are now the margins of the marshland. The sites included

South Walsham and Halvergate, but most were situated on the northern shore of the estuary at Runham, Mautby and Caister-on-Sea, an indication that this shore received a regular influx of sea water at that time. Taylor (1827) noted that there were no records of saltworks in existence after the reign of Edward the Confessor, and commented that the demise of the industry was probably a consequence of the 'silting up' of the northern entrance to the estuary. Taylor (1827) further noted that as soon as the tidal ingress was limited to one narrow and obstructed inlet (the southern entrance) its effect was so reduced that, according to ancient records, 'many thousand acres became dry, and in time good pasturage for cattle'. By the reign of King John (1199–1216), the southward extension of the barrier spit had reached a point close to Lowestoft (Smith, 1960). The age of the basal deposits of this barrier at South Denes, Great Yarmouth, has been dated through the recovery of potsherds as 13th century AD (Green and Hutchinson, 1960).

The natural draining of the estuary in the early Middle Ages (Figure 55) led not only to the end of Upper Clay deposition but also to a lowering of the watertable in the peat carrs and peat-filled side-valleys. It was at this time that the major extraction of peat from the Breydon Formation took place, the so-called 'critical period' in the 13th and 14th centuries referred to by Smith (1960). Episodic flooding by marine inundation from the late 13th century onwards resulted in the abandonment of the 'turf pits' or their transformation firstly into fisheries, and then, from the 16th century, into the broads, much as they are known today (Smith, 1960). This flooding affected the marshland in general and, in order to protect the grazing land, flood defence embankments were constructed around Breydon Water (Breydon Wall) and along the marshland rivers (Press, 1956; Green and Hutchinson, 1960); by the 17th century AD, drainage of the marshland by pumping mills was commenced.

Both during and after estuarine sedimentation, the marshland surface has suffered differential subsidence. This effect is conspicuous at the marsh margin near Mautby, where the formation laps into the shallow embayment, of Pickerill Holme, north of the general marshland fringe. At the mouth of this embayment the marshland surface, formed of Upper Clay, is displaced vertically down to the south by about 1.5 m. This displacement is regarded as being due mainly to differential compression in response to the progressive natural loading of the Breydon Formation sediments, especially the Middle Peat (see Smith, 1985); but also in part to consolidation resulting from the dewatering of the uppermost few metres of the formation. This dewatering is a consequence of the programme of pumped drainage of the marshland (see Dent et al., 1976) which has continued to the present day.

The nearshore sandbanks

It is a matter of speculation as to when the nearshore banks were formed. They are separated from one another by channels shown in shallow seismic reflection profiles to have been incised into older formations (mainly the Crag Group) beneath the base level of the bank sediments themselves, as for example the northern part of Barley Picle (Figure 51). The base of the bank deposits forms a surface which dips gently (about 0.1°) the east. In profiles across South Cross Sand, the outermost bank in this area, a sharp break of slope is seen on the profiles; this break may be traced between seismic traverses and runs generally north–south beneath the bank, parallel to and approximately 8 km distant from the present-day coastline. A small body of sediment may be present at this position (see Figure 52), the age of which is unknown, but it is possible that it represents an early Holocene linear coastal shoal, which served as a nucleus for subsequent sandbank growth. The break of slope represented by the crest of the pre-bank sediment body occurs at approximately 22 m below OD on the section shown in Figure 53. The basal Holocene surface dips steeply eastwards to flatten off again at a level some 9 m lower. It continues eastwards at this lower level, 30 to 40 m below OD, over much of the Southern North Sea (British Geological Survey and Rijks Geologische Dienst, 1984).

It is conceivable that this linear feature reflects an early Holocene coastline, when sea level was 20 to 30 m lower than at the present day, predating the formation of these nearshore banks, which lie almost entirely to landward. The precise causes of the initial formation of sandbanks during a marine transgression are unknown, but the availability of sand-size sediment is of fundamental importance. This sand may have come from the reworking of sediments on the seafloor, including glacigenic materials left behind after ice retreat, or from the erosion of older formations. Coastal erosion may have played an important part in the supply of sediments in the early development of the banks, as indeed it does today. This sediment is presently supplied mainly by the erosion of glacigenic sediments in the cliffs between Weybourne and Happisburgh to the north of the district. Retreat rates here are presently approximately 0.9 m years[-1] and it is believed that this rate has been typical for the last 5000 years, (Clayton, 1989). The volume of the banks is of the same order as the total volume of sand released from the Norfolk cliffs during the last 5000 years, assuming this annual retreat rate remained constant (Clayton, 1989).

Sand is lost from the coastline mainly at the locations of the nesses. Within the district, Caister Shoal, a shoreface-attached sandbank, is evidence of offshore sediment transport at this point. The southernmost of this nearshore complex of banks corresponds with the location of Lowestoft Ness to the south of the district.

The origin of the banks in this area was thought by Swift (1975) to be related to the retreat path of a headland across the continental shelf (a shoal retreat massif) during the late Holocene.

Once the banks had become established, they served to protect the coastline from direct storm wave attack from certain directions. This would consequently have reduced coastal erosion, and thus the sediment input to the system. The great mobility of these nearshore banks and the fluxes of sediment passing through the system even within the last century or so make it difficult to speculate on their earlier development. Thus their apparent east–west stability may be only a modern feature. However, this lateral stability seems inevitable because the banks are partially separated by incised channels, as mentioned above. Landward migration of Middle Scroby, for instance, would require the infilling of the nearshore channel of Yarmouth Road. The absence of infilled former channels beneath the present bank sediments (e.g. Figure 53) implies that this process has not previously occurred. Therefore, it is suggested that, once the banks had formed, the closely constrained tidal currents might be responsible for sea-bed scouring between the banks. This would have resulted in the overdeepening of the channels, serving to stabilise the positions of the banks into a coast- and tidal current-parallel orientation. Most subsequent changes would have occurred at the ends of the banks where they are linked to their neighbours and where the thickness of sediment may fluctuate, but the underlying formations (mainly Crag Group) have not been exposed to tidal scour.

SOIL DEVELOPMENT ON THE BREYDON FORMATION

The soil types recorded on the Breydon Formation span a range of parent lithologies from peat of freshwater origin to silts and clays formed in an estuarine environment. Those soils developed on the well-established peat carrs of the marshland fringes are classified by the Soil Survey as the Adventurer's Series; where the peat thins or has mineral layers within it there are also the Prickwillow Series and the acid Mendham Series; whilst those within predominantly estuarine clay areas include the Waveney, Newchurch and Wallasea series (Corbett and Tatler, 1970; Soil Survey of England and Wales, 1986; Burton and Hodgson, 1987; Hazelden, 1989).

As noted in Chapter eight much of the marshland has been subjected to a succession of drainage schemes, mostly associated with flood prevention and/or land reclamation for agricultural purposes. As a result, most of the carrs and marshes have been converted to high water table (between 25 and 40 cm below the surface in winter, lower in summer) grazing marsh that is pump- or gravity-drained through a network of ditches (dykes) to major drainage channels (O'Riordan, 1980); in parts of the marshland, including much of that flanking the River Bure, the water table has been further lowered (generally below 1 m) to allow arable cropping.

For the most part, the reclaimed marshland initially provides good quality agricultural land. However, the quality of the soils may deteriorate due to acidification, ochre accumulation and structural alteration due to a large sodium content. Soil ripening is an important pedological process noted within exposed Upper Clay. As water drains from the formerly thixotropic sediments, irreversible shrinkage and fissuring of the uppermost 0.7 to 1.8 m occurs. The effect is seen as a strong iron-oxide mottling, a change to a more open soil structure, improving soil drainage (Dent et al., 1976), and an increase in the load-bearing capacity of the ground. This process makes non-acid soils suitable for cereals (Broads Authority, 1981). However, the soil ripening may be accompanied by leaching, and a reduction in organic matter; also the soils are naturally low in phosphate (Corbett and Tatler, 1970). This survey has commonly noted a thinning of the ripened crust towards the marsh margins and a complete thinning out against outcrops of Upper Peat; in these circumstances, the load-bearing strength of the surface of the Upper Clay may be much reduced, causing problems for heavy machinery.

Acid sulphate conditions (actual or potential upon future drainage) are common in both peat and clay soils; the most severely affected soils are those around the edge of the marsh where the peat is adjacent to estuarine-derived clays (Burton and Hodgson, 1987). Commonly, acid sulphate horizons are characterised by a yellow mottling of jarosite ($KFe_3(SO_4)_2(OH)_6$) (Dent et al., 1976). The acidification results from the oxidation of pyrite in the sediment, releasing sulphuric acid and thus lowering the pH of the surrounding soil (Price, 1980). A systematic soil survey in the Halvergate area (Hazelden, 1989) identified several localities where extremely acid soils are present (or potentially present); these include Tunstall, Beighton and Norton marshes. Where pyrite is accompanied by calcium carbonate (from shell inclusions in the clays), the sulphuric acid reacts to form gypsum (Price, 1980). The aeration and resulting acidification of pyrite-rich sediments may also lead to the bacterial precipitation of ochre within drains (Bloomfield, 1972). In some places, acidification may result from sulphate-enriched groundwater seeping from older pyrite-bearing rocks (Burton and Hodgson, 1987). Ochre development in marshland drains adjoining outcrops of the Crag and the Kesgrave Formation has been noted in this survey, as, for example, [409 091] near Tunstall.

A decrease in salinity with time is common within drained marshland as the salts in soil solution are leached out. The drainage of unstable sodium-rich clay soils leads to deflocculation, movement and redeposition of clay minerals, blocking drains and the fissures and pore spaces in the soils. This results in drainage failure and surface ponding, and reduces crop yields (J Hazelden, written communication, 1990). Locally, in fields adjacent to former saltmarsh creeks, saline recharge may occur in areas subject to tidal influence. The marshland north of Runham at the eastern end of Breydon Water has atypically high salinities within the top metre or so (J Hazelden, oral communication, 1989) which are interpreted as the result of saline recharge from sand bodies present within the Upper Clay of the Breydon Formation in the Newtown area (see Figure 50).

NINE

Structure

The structure of the concealed Palaeozoic and Mesozoic rocks within the district is described by reference to structure contour maps (Chapters two, three and four), to Section 2 of the published 1:50 000 map and to interpretations of the Bouguer gravity and aeromagnetic anomaly maps shown on the margin of the map. The structure contour maps are generalised from regional studies of seismic data, calibrated against boreholes outside the district (Figure 2) and omitting features of commercial sensitivity.

THE LONDON–BRABANT MASSIF

The district lies at the northern margin of the London–Brabant Massif (Wills, 1978). To the north lies the Eastern England Shelf, with its succession of Mesozoic sedimentary rocks of generally simple structure extending to the Market Weighton Block in south Yorkshire. To the north-east and east is the southern North Sea Basin, a major Mesozoic and Tertiary sedimentary basin. The massif comprises folded and low-grade regionally metamorphosed Precambrian and Lower Palaeozoic rocks which form part of the concealed Caledonide fold belt of eastern England (Chapter two; Allsop, 1987; Pharaoh et al., 1987). The massif acted as a buoyant structural feature through much of Upper Palaeozoic and Mesozoic times, exerting a large control upon the structural and stratigraphical development of the region.

The surface of the platform dips gently to the north-east within the district, from about 400 m below OD in the south-east to about 900 m below OD in the north-east (Figure 3). A north-easterly increase of slope is seen within the district and is related to increased subsidence peripheral to the southern North Sea Basin. This line of increased tilting is approximately coincident with the surface extrapolation of a major upper crustal feature observed on seismic reflection data to the north of Great Yarmouth. The feature is imaged as a strong seismic reflection at between 1.2 and 1.7 seconds two way travel time (TWTT), corresponding to a depth of about 2.2 to 3.5 km, striking north-north-west and dipping at about 15° to the north-east. Seismic reflection data along strike, off the north Norfolk coast, show a similar north-easterly dipping seismic reflection in the upper crust (Reston and Blundell, 1987; Cameron et al., 1992), and it is possible that these features are related.

The reflection indicates the presence of a strong acoustic impedance contrast in the subsurface, normally associated with the contact of different rock types. Cameron et al. (1992) have suggested that it represents the transition from metasedimentary rocks to Caledonian volcanic rocks off the North Norfolk coast. However, aeromagnetic data in the district indicate that vol-

canic or crystalline rocks lie deeper than the reflection (see below) and it is thought more likely that the latter represents a major thrust of ?Caledonian age. This lineament appears to mark the hinge line between the relatively stable platform and the rapidly subsiding Southern North Sea Basin. To the south-west of the feature the available evidence indicates a largely unfaulted platform with a preserved sequence of thin Triassic or younger rocks. To the north-east, there is increased faulting, depositional thickening and a fuller Carboniferous, Permian and Mesozoic succession (Figure 56).

The internal structure of the massif is largely conjectural, and is based on interpretation of regional geophysical data (Chroston and Sola, 1982; Allsop, 1984, 1987; Evans and Allsop, 1987; Lee et al., 1990) and limited borehole records (Pharaoh et al., 1987). Regional interpretation of aeromagnetic data indicates a depth to magnetic basement within the district of the order of 3 to 4 km (Allsop, 1984, fig. 7), suggesting that a thick sequence of Lower Palaeozoic (?Silurian) sedimentary rocks (see Chapter two) is present above crystalline basement. A major granitic body has been postulated from gravity and seismic refraction evidence running from the Wash to Saxthorpe along a west-north-west trend (Chroston et al., 1987). This postulated granite approaches the north-west of the district and, between Saxthorpe and Norwich, is interpreted as being as little as 3.5 km below OD (Chroston et al., 1987). The application of image analysis methods to the British Geological Survey Gravity and Magnetic databases has shown the dominance of north-west to south-east, eastern England Caledonide trends within the basement of the region (Lee et al., 1990). This trend is also dominant in the faulting which affects the Carboniferous and Mesozoic rocks of the district and the adjacent offshore areas (e.g. Hewett Fault Zone), strongly suggesting the possibility of reactivation of basement features during later phases of deformation. Some faults in the region show evidence of lateral displacement, further supporting the idea of basement reactivation under later stress.

A period of flexuring, uplift and erosion related to the Caledonian orogenic episode occurred during early to mid Devonian, Acadian times movements (Soper et al., 1987), and is inferred to have affected the Lower Palaeozoic and Precambrian rocks of the region. It was responsible for the major post-Caledonian unconformity separating massif rocks from later sequences, as, for example, at Somerton. The pattern of progressive south-westerly overlap of later rocks (see Section 2 on the published map) shows that the massif maintained persistent structural stability as a relative high from this time until the early Cretaceous, in contrast to the recurrent subsidence implicit in the stratigraphy of the adjoining parts of the Southern North Sea Basin.

Figure 56 Section showing the principal unconformities affecting the Palaeozoic and Mesozoic sequences within the district (not to scale).

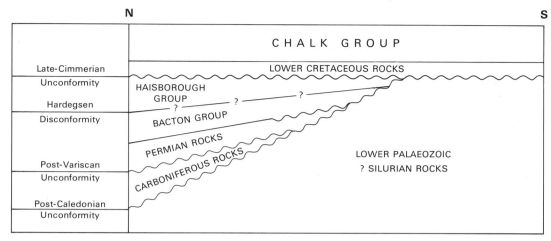

CARBONIFEROUS–EARLY MESOZOIC TECTONISM

Carboniferous rocks are confined to the north-east of the district (Figure 5), where they thin onto the eroded basement. The massif at this time formed part of a land mass stretching from Belgium to Ireland, known as St George's Land (Anderton et al., 1979). A further period of deformation during late Westphalian and early Permian times, related to north–south compression during the Variscan orogeny, resulted in folding and faulting of the Carboniferous sequence. Subsequent erosion, evidenced by the post-Variscan unconformity (Figures 6 and 56), has truncated the Carboniferous strata in the district, removing much of the Dinantian sequence and any Westphalian rocks originally deposited. The nature of this unconformity at the margins of the London–Brabant Massif offshore is illustrated by Tubb et al. (1986).

Active subsidence and sedimentation in the Southern North Sea Basin commenced during early Permian times in response to the initiation of a broadly east–west tensional stress regime and subsequent crustal extension. It is likely that Permo-Triassic subsidence within the district was due to thermal relaxation effects following this earlier rifting. The gradual encroachment of sedimentation onto the London–Brabant Massif during Permian and Triassic times forms part of the 'steers horn' profile (cf. Dewey, 1982) at the margin of the basin. Generalised structure contour maps of the top of the Plattendolomit (Brotherton [Magnesian Limestone] Formation) (Figure 7), the top of the Hewett Sandstone Member (Figure 10) and the top of the Bacton (Sherwood Sandstone) Group (Figure 11) illustrate the present north-easterly dip of the Permian and Triassic sequences, and the associated flexuring which is commonly associated with minor faulting. Southerly thinning of Triassic sediments onto the platform is illustrated by isopachytes for the Bacton (Sherwood Sandstone) Group (Figure 9) and Haisborough (Mercia Mudstone) Group (Figure 12).

Another major episode of uplift and consequent erosion during late Jurassic and early Cretaceous times resulted in the formation of the late-Cimmerian unconformity (Fyfe et al., 1981; Ziegler, 1981). This uplift was probably related to a combination of eustatic sea-level rise and post-extensional isostatic re-equilibration, following the major extensional phase in the North Sea Basin (Chadwick, 1985a). The removal by erosion of any Jurassic rocks deposited within the district is likely to have occurred at this time; also the removal of Triassic rocks from the south of the district (Figures 9 and 12). The present configuration of Permian and Triassic strata within the district results from a combination of south and south-westerly depositional attenuation related to the structural stability of the London–Brabant Massif, coupled with the effects of late-Cimmerian erosion.

CRETACEOUS AND LATER TECTONIC EVENTS

A period of regional subsidence related to thermal relaxation effects (Chadwick, 1985b) started during Barremian–Albian times, resulting in complete overstep of the London–Brabant Platform by the Gault in Albian times (Owen, 1971; Rawson et al., 1978). The structural influence of the massif continued briefly after the late-Cimmerian tectonic episode, with the Lower Cretaceous beds within the district thinning onto the platform. From this time, however, the London–Brabant Platform underwent slow relative regional subsidence, which, coupled with a high global sea level (Vail et al., 1977), resulted in the accumulation of more than 400 m of marine sediments of the Chalk Group within the district.

Regional correlations in East Anglia (Figure 17) have indicated variations in the thicknesess of the Lower and Middle Chalk biozones. Regional studies of the Lower Chalk thickness variations (Dr D J Evans, oral communication, 1990) have shown an area of Lower Chalk attenuation in northern East Anglia which is approximately coincident with the postulated location of the Wash–Saxthorpe Granite (Chroston et al., 1987). While other structurally related causes, such as faulting, may be invoked, it seems possible that the buoyancy effect of the postulated granite may have resulted in the observed differential subsidence of the London–Brabant Massif, in a manner analogous to the sedimentary attenuation of Cretaceous and older rocks caused by the differential subsidence of the postulated Market Weighton Granite in Yorkshire (Kent, 1955; Bott, 1988; Donato and Megson, 1990).

A change in the tectonic setting of the region in late Cretaceous times due to lithospheric compression, crustal uplift and basin inversion (Chadwick, 1985c) can be related to Alpine compression to the south. Northeasterly tilting affected the district and subsequent erosion resulted in removal of progressively older Chalk to the south and west, before the accumulation of the Thanet Formation during the Palaeocene (see Chapters three and four). This unconformity becomes more marked offshore some 35 km to the north of the district where, in the Hewett Gas Field, most of the Chalk Group succession is overstepped by Tertiary strata.

There is evidence that uplift and erosion may have affected this part of Norfolk between the accumulation of the Thanet Formation and that of the London Clay (Knox et al., 1990). The Woolwich and Reading Beds that separate the Thanet and London Clay formations in the London Basin are not present in Norfolk. Furthermore, a northward increase in the depth of erosion is suggested by the absence in the Ormesby Borehole of the youngest element of the Ormesby Clay (Thanet Formation), present under London Clay in the Hales Borehole some 23 km to the south-west.

Eastward tilting, accompanied by broad flexuring about a north-west-trending axis in the Raveningham– Haddiscoe area, recurred in the hiatus between the cessation of London Clay deposition and the marine transgression marked by the base of the Crag Group. The flexuring is demonstrated in the contoured plot of the top surface of the Chalk shown in Figure 15, in the perspective view shown in Figure 19 and in the isopachytes of the Tertiary clay formations (Figure 20). It accounts for a conspicuous eastward offset in the sub-Crag crop of the top of the Chalk, traced from north to south across the southern part of the district. The general structure of the Thanet and London Clay formations dates from that episode.

The late Cretaceous–Tertiary tilting and flexuring events led to shearing and minor faulting within the region. Interpretation of seismic data indicates that the faults, some of which have been identified in the northeast of this district, trend north-west–south-east and have maximum throws of the order of a few tens of metres. There is also some evidence from the seismic data that faulting observed in the Chalk may affect part of the Tertiary sequence. Shear zones of similar trend are a common feature of the Chalk outcrop of East Anglia (C J Wood, oral communication, 1990). The conspicuous north-west–south-east linearity of the Yare–Waveney valley between Brundall and Oulton, near Lowestoft, and of the upper Bure valley to the north of this district may also have an origin in Tertiary shearing. No evidence has been recognised within the district for late Pliocene–early Pleistocene faulting of north-easterly trend such has been postulated in the Stowmarket area of Suffolk as a structural control on Crag deposition (Bristow, 1983).

Regionally in south-eastern England, eastward tilting has recurred through the Quaternary because of the sustained subsidence of the Southern North Sea Basin (e.g. Ziegler and Louwerens, 1979); although no local stratigraphical evidence has been identified, it seems likely that such movement has affected the district, occupying as it does a general hinge-line position between elevated ground to the west and the subsiding southern North Sea Basin to the east. There is some evidence that the coastal strips of countries bordering the southern North Sea are subsiding at rates of up to 3 mm year^{-1} (West, 1968 quoting Fromm, 1953 and Valentin, 1954) and a similar current rate of subsidence may prevail in this district. The extent to which isostatic readjustment from the Devensian glaciation (e.g. Eden et al., 1977; Kooi et al., 1989) remains an appreciable factor in measurements of subsidence in south-eastern England is uncertain.

TEN

Economic geology

ECONOMIC DEPOSITS

Sand and gravel aggregate

Most of the sand- and gravel-dominated parts of the Quaternary succession at outcrop have been worked for aggregate in historical or recent times. Of the recent workings, some of which are no longer active, those at Strumpshaw, Bergh Apton, Norton Subcourse, Haddiscoe and Burgh Castle are the most important (Figure 57). Current onshore production of aggregate from within the district is in the order of 100 to 200 kilotonnes per annum. Offshore, a licensed dredging area for marine aggregate known as Cross Sand extends to within about 7 km of the coastline between Great Yarmouth and Lowestoft (Figure 51). An appraisal of the aggregate resources in this area has been made by the British Geological Survey as part of a more regional study on behalf of the Department of the Environment and the Crown Estate Commissioners (Harrison, 1988).

At Strumpshaw Pit [352 072], now closed, some 1 million cubic metres of sand and gravel within the Lowestoft Till Formation were extracted. About 700 thousand cubic metres were extracted from the old pit at Bergh Apton [300 000] before closure. Recently, up to 40 kilotonnes per annum of hoggin have been dug from new workings at the western end of this pit. The workings at Norton Subcourse [402 995; 413 993] and Haddiscoe [442 972, 444 965; 445 963] (Plate 14) were all in glaciofluvial de-

posits, referred informally to the Haddiscoe Sands and Gravels, and the underlying Corton and Kesgrave formations. The two pits at Norton Subcourse had been partially backfilled at the time of survey, but permission has been granted for 2 million tonnes to be extracted from an adjacent site. The western pit at Haddiscoe is no longer active, but the plant there is used to process material imported from outside the district. The other two pits at Haddiscoe are inactive and partly backfilled.

The sand and gravel pit at Burgh Castle, known as Welcome Pit [482 043], is operational. The workings there are mainly in the Corton Formation (Plate 5, Figure 39), which is unusually gravelly at this locality, and yield some 10 kilotonnes per annum of aggregate. Thin, discontinuous lenses of till occur within the sand of the Corton Formation but do not significantly impede extraction. The increasing thickness of Lowestoft Till cover on the northern side of the pit has made further working from that face uneconomical.

Sand has been extracted from small pits at many localities, particularly from the Corton Formation. It is likely that most of these workings date from or before the early 19th century; many were described by the primary surveyors as being overgrown. Some of the sands dug contained abundant calcareous shell debris (Blake, 1890). Sands of the Corton Formation were commonly encountered in the floors of pits excavated primarily for chalky clay from the Lowestoft Till; in many cases these sands were themselves worked, perhaps for the purpose of im-

Figure 57 Principal sites of sand and gravel extraction and landfill.

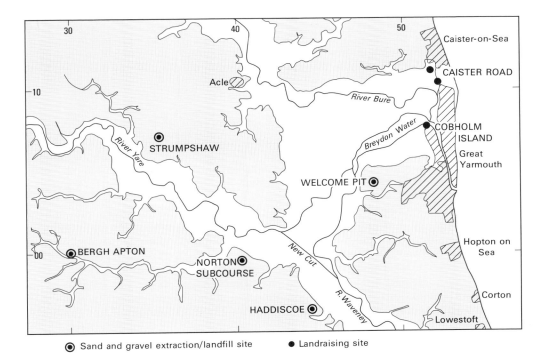

⊙ Sand and gravel extraction/landfill site   ● Landraising site

proving clay soils. Sand was worked also from the Crag in the western and north-western parts of the district around Bramerton and South Walsham [e.g. 3740 1363; 3680 1293], and on a small scale from the Kesgrave Formation, for example at Fishley [4020 1194].

The deposits of the coastal barrier and spit extending between Caister-on-Sea and Gorleston-on-Sea (cover photograph) have served as sources of aggregate and ballast for ships, probably since the formation of the spit during the 13th century. Few obvious traces of these workings are preserved, with the exception of a pit [528 118] in blown sand resting on North Denes Formation at Caister-on-Sea, a pit in blown sand [5283 1036] within the racecourse north of Great Yarmouth and a borrow pit (now a school playing field) [530 101] adjoining the southern end of the Race Course at Newtown. The deposits were formerly worked at a number of sites in Great Yarmouth that have since been backfilled and landscaped; the largest of these reportedly underlies the present recreation grounds [530 085; 530 083] adjoining Sandown Road.

Brick clay

Deposits of till (Norwich Brickearth or Cromer Till) within the Corton Formation were worked for brick clay from many pits within the district, mainly from the mid-19th century, the largest being those adjoining the River Waveney at Burgh Castle [474 043], Somerleyton [4795 9702] and near Freethorpe [414 043]. The sandy clay that typifies these deposits was used for red brick manufacture, while the more clay-rich material was fired as tiles and pipes (Woodward, 1881). At Burgh Castle and Freethorpe, clay from the Lowestoft Till also appears to have been worked to produce white bricks. Many of the pits appear to have been operational at the turn of the present century, but all are now abandoned, that at Burgh Castle in the early 1920s. The silty clays of the Breydon Formation have also served as a source of brickclay, and were fired at the Burgh Castle yard; the precise source of this clay is unclear. Portland cement, also produced at the Burgh Castle Works, was made by firing mud dredged up from Breydon Water with chalk transported by wherry from Whitlingham, on the eastern outskirts of Norwich (Milligan, undated). The resulting clinker was ground into cement at the nearby Berney Arms Mill.

In the Surlingham–Rockland area, workings for brick clay in laminated clays were recorded by Woodward (1881). These pits have been completely backfilled, but at the time of the primary survey the laminated clays were intensively worked for the 'celebrated' Rockland Bricks. Detailed descriptions of the strata exposed in the pits were made by Woodward (1881), who noted two types of 'laminated brickearth'. One, which when fired produced white bricks, was considered to be of glacial origin; the other was thought to be a bed of clay within the Crag and made red bricks. However, the strata were very disturbed and contorted, making it difficult to determine their affinities.

The chalky clay of the Lowestoft Till Formation was also used in the manufacture of sun-dried, unfired bricks, the clay being mixed with chopped straw, then puddled and set in moulds (Woodward, 1881).

Marling and puddling clay

The chalky clay of the Lowestoft Till has been extensively excavated over several centuries, mainly for use as agricultural marl. The practice had all but ceased at the time of the primary survey late in the 19th century (Woodward, 1881), but the pits from which Lowestoft Till was dug remain a characteristic feature of the outcrop of the formation (although many have since been degraded or partially or wholly backfilled). In many of the pits, the Lowestoft Till was completely excavated, typically down to a floor of sand (Corton Formation) that has since provided effective drainage. The sand has itself been excavated in some instances, particularly from pits at the periphery of till outcrops. The pits range in size from shallow workings only a metre or so deep to a working [361 107] 11 m deep and 150 m across, at Burlingham Green.

The Lowestoft Till in its unweathered state has a low permeability and excavations within it (but not penetrating it) hold ponds, some of which may be used as reservoirs for agricultural supply. The excavated clay has also been used as a puddling clay, lining reservoirs dug in more permeable materials, as for example [4498 1418] near Fleggburgh.

Iron ore

A small iron foundry was established during the mid-19th century at Panxworth. It is probable that at least part of the ore used in this enterprise was iron oxide excavated from two pits [3505 1270; 3513 1268] south of the village. The section in another pit nearby [3355 1225] at Pedham, now backfilled, was described by Woodward (1881, p.65) as comprising sand, gravel and clay, with much ironstone and flaggy beds of sandstone. Deposits of iron oxide in the form of irregular pan sheets are a common feature of the weathered Crag and have also been noted in some sections in the Kesgrave Formation. Such iron-pan debris is a typical component of soils derived from the Crag.

Peat

Peat in the Breydon Formation was extracted for fuel in several parts of the marshland between the 12th and 15th centuries AD, and probably mostly in the 13th and 14th centuries (Smith, 1960). The peat diggings, or turbaries, produced the excavations which, on flooding, formed the water bodies now known as broads (Lambert and Jennings, 1960). Typically the sides of the excavations are steep, vertical or stepped, and the floors are generally horizontal except where the excavations abut the valley sides. The excavations are usually 3 to 4 m deep, the steep edges being abandoned working faces; ridges and peninsulas represent balks between adjacent workings (e.g. at Rockland Broad [332 051]) and islands (e.g. in Filby Broad [455 133]), are blocks of the original deposits preserved in situ. Some excavations may be much younger; for example, the existence of Hardley 'Flood', now a shallow broad, is not depicted on the Ordnance Survey maps of the 19th century.

The peat workings are located largely in those marginal parts of the marshland where the discrete Basal, Middle and Upper Peat layers coalesce. Lambert and Jennings (1960, p.24) related the riverward limit of the excavations to an increasing thickness of a flange of Upper Clay, a layer valueless for fuel. Furthermore, they speculated that the combustible quality of the peat improved with depth, thus providing the incentive for deep digging despite the engineering difficulties of controlling the ingress of water.

Such engineering difficulties must have been most acute in the side-valley broads of Fritton and Flixton decoys, and the complex including Filby, Ormesby and (in the adjoining North Walsham district) Rollesby broads, for, according to the data quoted by Lambert and Jennings (1960, pp.40–41), the bases of these supposed excavations lie at some 5 m below OD. However, whether these side valleys were completely filled with peat before the turbaries (peat diggings) were established is conjectural on the present evidence.

WATER SUPPLY AND HYDROGEOLOGY

Historically, the town of Great Yarmouth was largely dependant upon a water supply from wells in the blown sand and North Denes Formation. These deposits are capable of yielding up to 15 ls^{-1} from individual wells, but with the intensive use of such permeable deposits it was impossible to protect the wells from either surface contamination or saline encroachment. As early as 1850, a report to the General Board of Health, quoted by Whitaker (1921), stated that out of the immense number of wells examined only one was found that could be said to be free from organic matter.

The public supply for Great Yarmouth is now obtained from a combination of surface water and groundwater (Figure 58). Surface water is taken from the River Bure at Belaugh (in the North Walsham district to the north) and from Ormesby Broad (near Filby and just within the adjoining North Walsham district). Groundwater is abstracted from two boreholes into the Chalk at Belaugh and transferred to Ormesby for treatment. Lowestoft is served by surface water taken from Fritton Decoy [5024 0072] in conjunction with an intake at Shipmeadow on

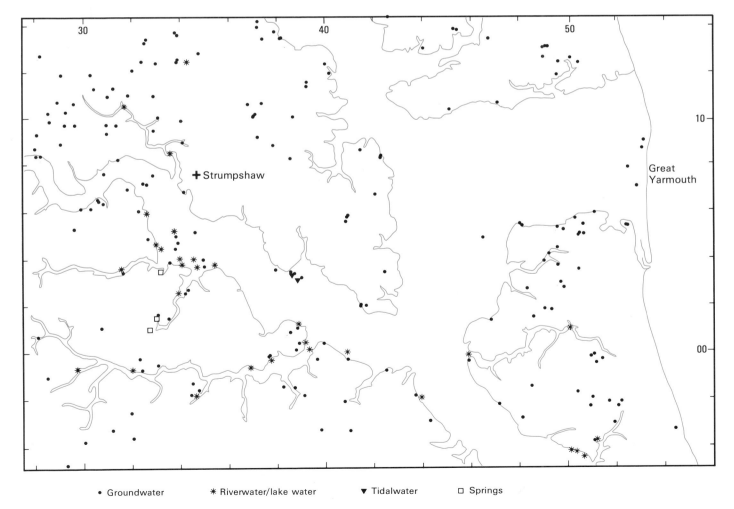

• Groundwater   * Riverwater/lake water   ▼ Tidalwater   □ Springs

Figure 58   Principal sites of water abstraction within the district.

the River Waveney, in the adjoining Lowestoft district. Fritton Decoy and the Filby–Rollesby–Ormesby Broad complex are supported by groundwater discharge issuing from underlying shallow aquifers. A further demand for water in the region is made for agricultural and spray irrigation; this is satisfied primarily by groundwater pumped from boreholes.

In order to maintain public water supplies in the Great Yarmouth region during drought conditions, the River Bure Groundwater Scheme was developed in 1979 by the Anglian Water Authority. This conjunctive use scheme comprises four abstraction boreholes and observation boreholes drilled into the Chalk of the Upper Bure catchment. When additional water is required downstream to meet abstraction requirements at Belaugh and maintain the required minimum flow, groundwater is abstracted and fed into the upper tributaries of the Bure.

The major aquifers in the district are the Upper Chalk and the Crag. The Kesgrave and Corton formations form minor aquifers. In terms of the quantities abstracted, the Chalk is the principal aquifer, but where Palaeogene formations are present (Figure 20) the Crag is of primary importance.

An assessment of the groundwater resource potential of the district, together with information on groundwater quality, is contained in the Section 14 Survey compiled by the East Suffolk and Norfolk River Authority (1971). The hydrogeological properties of the various aquifer units and information relating to groundwater levels in the region are summarised on the Hydrogeological Map of Northern East Anglia (Institute of Geological Sciences, 1976). The abstraction data quoted in this account are drawn from the National Well Record Collection and the National Rivers Authority (Anglian Region) archive. Hydrochemical data are mainly those given by Hiscock (1987), with supplementary data from the Section 14 Survey, the National Rivers Authority and the National Well Record Collection.

In the west of the district, groundwater has been drawn from several boreholes in the Upper Chalk. Eastwards, the top of the Chalk lies progressively deeper, and water boreholes become few and far between, the most easterly being that at Lacon's Brewery (TG 50NW/105; Appendix 2) in Great Yarmouth, where the top of the Chalk lies at 155 m below OD.

The Chalk aquifer

In the west, the Chalk is covered by the semipermeable Crag and younger Pleistocene deposits except for local unconfined conditions where the Chalk crops out in the Yare valley near Postwick and Bramerton. Elsewhere, the Palaeogene Thanet and London Clay formations intervene (Figure 20), forming an aquiclude that confines water in the Chalk. Artesian flow, although not substantial, is recorded at South Walsham and Cantley in the vicinity of the Palaeogene boundary. Apart from minor abstractions in the Great Yarmouth area, there is no discharge from the confined part of the aquifer; thus groundwater flow east of the Palaeogene boundary is vir-

tually absent, with the possible exception of the Chalk structural high at Toft Monks (Figures 15, 19 and 20).

The nature of groundwater flow in the Chalk has been studied in adjoining parts of East Anglia (Woodland, 1946; Ineson, 1962; Downing, 1966; Toynton, 1983; Lloyd and Hiscock, 1990). Despite its high porosity, unfissured chalk is rather impermeable. Boreholes penetrating the Chalk in interfluve areas in this region tend to give unsatisfactory yields, with water levels falling abruptly under test conditions. By contrast, boreholes into the Chalk under, and in the vicinity of the principal valleys, including the Bure and the Yare, generally produce copious supplies. The largest producing boreholes in Norfolk are at Thorpe St Andrew [2532 0840], in the Yare valley just within the adjoining Norwich district; there, a 610 mm diameter public supply borehole penetrating 55.7 m of the Upper Chalk beneath glacial sand and gravel yielded 186 ls[-1] for a drawdown of less than 14 m. The highest yield recorded within the district is 75 ls[-1] from a 457 mm diameter, 91.7 m deep borehole at Cantley [3896 0312]. Two Chalk public supply boreholes are located in the west of the district at Strumpshaw [3414 0680], near to the edge of the River Yare floodplain. Here, the Chalk lies beneath 1 m thick alluvium and about 29 m thick Crag. Whilst a yield of 68 ls[-1] is achievable from each borehole for a drawdown about 22 m, typical yields are in the range 5 to 20 ls[-1] for 200 to 300 mm diameter boreholes.

The difference in yields is attributable to differences in the transmissivity of the Chalk between the valleys and interfluves. At Thorpe St Andrew, a Chalk transmissivity of $2600 \text{ m}^2\text{d}^{-1}$ is recorded (Toynton, 1983), and at Strumpshaw a relatively low value of $300 \text{ m}^2\text{d}^{-1}$ was observed. However, values of Chalk transmissivity of less than $100 \text{ m}^2\text{d}^{-1}$ can be expected in the interfluve areas. This contrast is reflected in the age and chemistry of the groundwaters in the two situations (Wood, 1961; Bath and Edmunds, 1981; Lloyd et al., 1981; Heathcote and Lloyd, 1984; Bath et al., 1985; Lloyd and Hiscock, 1989); groundwater in the interfluves is relatively old, in a reduced state and free from nitrate, and that under or near valleys is modern and high in nitrate and dissolved oxygen.

The high transmissivity in the Chalk associated with valleys may have been influenced by any of the following three factors. First, zones of shear fracturing within the Chalk may have controlled the regional drainage pattern throughout the Quaternary; the evidence in support of the existence of north-west-trending shear zones within the region is presented in Chapter nine. Second, the Chalk near to outcrop in valleys may have been subject to near-surface stress release, resulting in the opening of fissures on bedding surfaces (Ineson, 1962; Price, 1987). Third, a concentration of groundwater flow towards valleys may lead to enhanced solution of chalk along existing fissures (Price, 1987).

The extent to which geological and hydrogeological conditions have influenced the present-day surface drainage network, and thus the distribution of the zones of enhanced transmissivity within the Chalk, is specula-

Location	Great Yarmouth[2]	Kilby Cane No.1[1]	Acle[2]	Thurton[2]	Ludham No.1[1]	No.1[1]	Andrew No.1[1]	Cantley[2]	Lingwood[2]
National Grid Reference	TG 5286 0956	TM 3769 9269	TG 4018 1040	TG 3299 0089	TG 3850 1997	TG 3414 0680	TG 2532 0840	TG 3856 0336	TG 3708 0903
Type of Source	Shaft with adits	Borehole	Shaft	Shaft	Borehole	Borehole	Borehole	Borehole	Borehole
Aquifer	Blown Sand	Glacial Sands	Corton Beds	Corton Beds and ?Crag	Crag	Chalk	Chalk	Chalk	Chalk
Date of Analysis	?	5/10/89	10/5/48	1/7/53	4/10/89	4/10/89	31/10/89	10/7/12	5/11/59
pH		7.5	7.0	7.3	7.6	7.3	7.3		7.0
Electrical conductivity (μmhos/cm)	1296	830			525	740	895	475	700
Total dissolved solids (mg/l)	387	680	300	696	380	590	610		
Total hardness ($CaCO_3$) (mg/l)	158	449.3	104	432	226.8	349.6	336.8	248	345
Bicarbonate (HCO_3^-) (mg/l)	184	359.7		273	243.8	347.5	268.2	297	402
Sulphate (SO_4^{2-}) (mg/l)		113.1			41.8	58.2	80.6	55	19
Chloride (Cl^-) (mg/l)	449	76.5	54	52	44.5	88.0	61.5	77	42
Nitrate (NO^{-3}-N) (mg/l)	3.2	7.4	23.0	19.5	0.7	0.7	13.2	nil	
Calcium (Ca^{2+}) (mg/l)	88.6	156.5			75.1	117.3	112.4	88	118
Magnesium (Mg^{2+}) (mg/l)	40.4	13.9			9.4	13.5	13.4	13	12
Sodium (Na^+) (mg/l)	273	52.0			30.6	53.0	35.4	56	
Potassium (K^+) (mg/l)		3.1			2.6	1.9	4.0	10.5	
Iron (Fe-total) (mg/l)		0.31	absent	nil	1.50	0.95	<0.005	present	
Manganese (Mn-total) (mg/l)			0.10		nil	0.11	0.08	<0.005	

[1] Anglian Water Services Ltd   [2] National Well Record Collection

Table 8   Water quality data from the principal boreholes within or adjacent to the district which feed the public supply (courtesy of the National Rivers Authority).

tive. Beneath valleys, fissuring in the Chalk has been demonstrated by geophysical logging to occur in the upper Bure valley to depths of 10 to 20 m (K M Hiscock, written communication, 1990), the fissures having been formed by the solution of chalk along fractures and bedding planes. The importance of fissure flow in the Chalk is demonstrated at Strumpshaw Pumping Station, where geophysical logging shows a major groundwater inflow horizon associated with fissuring at 41 to 42 m below ground level (about 37 to 38 m below OD) and minor fissuring between 60 and 70 m below ground level (56 to 66 m below OD) (Hiscock and Bishop, 1987).

The quality of water abstracted from the Chalk is normally good (Table 8). Groundwater samples from the semiconfined area in the west of the district have a total hardness of about 250 mgl^{-1} (as $CaCO_3$), of which 200 mgl^{-1} is attributable to carbonates; both increase beneath Lowestoft Till. At Strumpshaw Pumping Station, the groundwater is very hard, with a total hardness of up to 455 mgl^{-1} (as $CaCO_3$) being recorded. Chloride ion concentrations are typically 50 mgl^{-1}, but increase to 100 mgl^{-1} as the Palaeogene boundary is approached. To the east and south of Strumpshaw Pumping Station, the Chalk is overlain by the Tertiary clay formations. In 1985 the chloride concentration in the abstracted groundwater averaged 80 mgl^{-1}, with a recorded maximum of 94 mgl^{-1}. It is likely that mixing between modern, fissure-derived water and old, saline, interstitial water existing at relatively shallow depths at this location, possibly exacerbated by up-coning due to groundwater abstraction, is the explanation for this high chloride content. Where the aquifer is confined, the chloride ion content increases due to old saline water being trapped in the Chalk. There are few analyses, but the existence of a broad saline coastal belt between 10 and 20 km wide may be assumed, where the chloride content exceeds 100 mgl^{-1} and locally reaches several thousand mgl^{-1}. This water shows extremely high values of non-carbonate hardness; for example, a borehole into the Chalk at Lowestoft gave a value of 2800 mgl^{-1} (as $CaCO_3$).

Iron concentrations in the Chalk groundwater are controlled by the chemical conditions within the aquifer. In unconfined Chalk regions the groundwater is oxidising and the iron content is less than 0.01 mgl^{-1}. Where the Chalk is covered by Pleistocene deposits and the groundwater is reducing in nature, iron concentrations as high as 6 mgl^{-1} have been recorded. There are a number of possible sources for this iron, including disseminated iron pyrite in the Lowestoft Till Formation and iron minerals in the older Pleistocene deposits. The nitrate concentration in the semiconfined and confined Chalk aquifers is less than 2 mgl^{-1} (as N) and is commonly undetected; however, concentrations approaching 11.3 mgl^{-1} (as N) are encountered in areas of Chalk outcrop in the Bure and Yare valleys to the west and north-west of the district (Lloyd and Hiscock, 1989).

The Crag aquifer and overlying deposits

The Crag aquifer is an important source of groundwater in the eastern part of the district, serving local, mostly agricultural demand. Yields are generally less dependable than those from the Chalk. The lack of consistency is due in part to the occurrence of low permeability layers of clay and silt within the generally permeable sands that predominate in the formation. The existence of such layers may produce perched aquifers. In the west of the district, the Crag is in hydraulic continuity with the Chalk but, where it is separated from the Chalk by the Palaeogene clay formations, the water levels in the Crag are generally higher than those in the Chalk. Locally, Crag water levels have been lowered below OD by pumped drainage of the marshes.

The type of well or borehole used for abstraction must be taken into account when considering yields from the Crag. Older dug wells and collector systems are shallow and of simple construction; sand entry can be a problem and only low pumping rates (2 to 4 ls^{-1}) are achievable. Properly designed and constructed large-diameter boreholes with a screen and gravel-pack give higher yields. At Ludham Pumping Station [TG 385 199], in the adjoining North Walsham district, a screened 381 mm-diameter borehole 59.7 m deep yielded 40 ls^{-1} on test for a drawdown of 11.9 m, and a 254 mm-diameter, 79 m-deep borehole at Lowestoft [TM 5236 9422], just south of the district, yielded 31 ls^{-1} for 2.3 m drawdown; but these are atypical. Well point systems, used almost exclusively for spray irrigation, consisting of a closely spaced series of shallow, narrow diameter perforated tubes connected by a suction header to a single pump have been successfully constructed in the Crag. The yield of an installation will depend on the number of well points, whose individual yields are likely to be in the range 0.6 to 0.8 ls^{-1}. A system of twelve 70 mm-diameter and 6 m-deep wells at Blofield [330 122] yielded 9 ls^{-1}.

Groundwater from the Crag aquifer is characterised by a high total hardness at outcrop of 300 mgl^{-1} (as $CaCO_3$), of which over half is attributable to carbonates. Where overlying deposits include thick Lowestoft Till the hardness, particularly non-carbonate hardness increases. The chloride concentration ranges between 50 mgl^{-1} (at outcrop) and 120 mgl^{-1} (beneath till) and is derived mainly from surface sources. High chloride values occur in wells on low ground near the coast and in the vicinity of the tidal rivers; they are due to saline intrusion. Over much of the nearshore zone offshore, the Crag occurs at the sea bed or carries a cover of permeable marine sand, and its contained water may be assumed to be saline. Where the onshore Crag in the coastal zone serves as a resource, it should be recognised that its groundwater is in hydraulic continuity with that of the offshore aquifer, and in certain conditions may be vulnerable to saline intrusion.

A feature of water abstracted from the Crag is its high concentration of dissolved and suspended iron, (Forbes, 1952; Wood, 1961; Brereton, 1978). Crag groundwater from the Ludham Pumping Station has an iron concentration of about 1.5 mgl^{-1}. Natural springs and seepages from the Crag are usually conspicuous by the growth of tan-coloured algae and the presence on the surface of standing water of a thin film of hydrous iron oxide (iron concentrations as high as 8 mgl^{-1} have been recorded).

Experience in the use of the Crag as a water resource has been documented by Clarke and Phillips (1984), who also suggested methods for removing the large amounts of iron in pumped water.

The nitrate content of Crag water is high, usually in excess of 11.3 mgl^{-1} (as N). The shallow well supplies are vulnerable to leaching of nitrate resulting from changed agricultural practices in recent decades. Weakly permeable layers of clay and silt within the Crag may restrict vertical movement of contaminants such as nitrate. At Ludham Pumping Station, water is abstracted from the bottom 6 m of the aquifer in order to draw from a layer consisting mainly of sand and shell fragments. The groundwater abstracted at Ludham has a negligible nitrate concentration, and in April 1984 a tritium value of 2.8 TU was measured (Hiscock, 1987). This suggests that the overlying 50 m of Pleistocene deposits, which contain a fairly high proportion of clay, restrict the downward movement of modern water, producing a low nitrate water with a tritium content typical for rainwater which fell before tritium concentration in the environment reached its peak in the early 1960s.

The sands and gravels of the Kesgrave Formation and the sands of the Corton Formation are highly permeable, though recharge may be restricted by local laminae or thin beds of silt and clay and, in the Corton Formation, by units of till. Yields of up to 2 ls^{-1} are generally obtainable from these minor aquifers. However, a borehole at Kirby Cane [TM 3769 9269] (outside the district), into glacial sands, yielded 25 ls^{-1} for less than 4 m drawdown. Arable farming of their outcrops, even where these are draped by a veneer of cover silt, is particularly sensitive to periods of drought. Although abstraction from wells was commonplace, the supplies are no longer dependable. As early as 1881 Woodward noted that, except where the sands carry an impermeable cover of unweathered Lowestoft Till, their water quality has been affected by surface-derived contamination. Nitrate levels are consequently high and the water is also very hard.

Taken together, the sands and gravels of the Crag and the younger Quaternary formations constitute a substantial, if complex, groundwater resource. The presence of impersistent clay layers within the deposits promotes a layering of permeability and the lateral movement of groundwater in the direction of the valley discharge zones (Lloyd and Hiscock, 1990). The deposits have a high groundwater storage and, in the west of the district, where there is hydraulic continuity with the Chalk, this storage is important in controlling recharge to the underlying Chalk aquifer. Farther east, where vertical flow is impeded by the Palaeogene clay formations, the resource discharges at the marshland fringe or into side valleys, including those containing Fritton Decoy and the

Filby, Rollesby and Ormesby broads. The influence of such discharges on the distribution of peat in the Breydon Formation is discussed in Chapter eight.

Interesting aquifer conditions can occur near the coast where the Flandrian deposits are liable to saline intrusuion. Pumped drainage of the marshes has reduced groundwater levels to around or below sea level and allowed the intrusion of high-chloride water. However, present information is insufficient to determine the inland extent of the brackish water. By comparison with a survey by Downing (1966) in the Hickling–Horsey area of Broadland in the adjoining North Walsham district, it is likely that fresh groundwater is present near surface in the vicinity of topographically higher ground with saline water at depth.

The Pleistocene deposits also influence the quality of groundwater abstracted from the Chalk aquifer. Circumstantial evidence for denitrification was presented by Parker and James (1985) for a Chalk borehole site at Mattishall, in the Wensum valley in the Norwich district. Here, tritium and nitrate, at concentrations indicating a modern origin, are detected in the pore water of sands and gravels within the Lowestoft Till Formation, but only tritium is detected in Chalk pore water samples. This suggests removal of nitrate during groundwater recharge to the Chalk aquifer. At Strumpshaw Pumping Station, nitrate is undetected in the abstracted Chalk groundwater. However, a tritium value of 13 TU, indicative of recent recharge, was measured in groundwater from the No. 2 borehole in October 1987 (Hiscock and Bishop, 1987).

The Lowestoft Till Formation, although not an aquifer, is important hydrogeologically. It generally forms drapes of low permeability material over any underlying aquifers, protecting such aquifers from the introduction of modern contaminants. However, the presence of sand bodies within the formation may permit a vertical component of recharge. Supporting evidence for some active recharge is the detection of tritium in Chalk groundwater beneath Lowestoft Till in the Wensum valley (Parker and James, 1985; Parker et al., 1987). Where the formation occurs in buried channels (Chapter six, Figure 35), it may disrupt the regional hydrogeological regime. The buried channels that are completely filled with Lowestoft Till may form barriers to lateral groundwater flow, while those that include sands and gravels increase ground-water flow and enhance groundwater storage (Parker et al., 1987; Lloyd and Hiscock, 1990).

As noted earlier, yields of up to 15 ls^{-1} have been obtained from the blown sand and North Denes Formation in the Great Yarmouth area; however, most sources have high chloride ion concentrations (up to several thousand mgl^{-1}) and are no longer utilised.

ELEVEN
Engineering geology of the Breydon Formation

The Breydon Formation presents particular constraints on the design of engineering structures upon and within it. The soft clays and silts that form the bulk of the formation are inherently weak; included layers of peat tend to have very high moisture contents and are thus highly compressible; and the sand bodies, present within the formation in the vicinity of Great Yarmouth, are likely to be saturated with groundwater, perhaps having a high salinity. In addition, the weathering of iron sulphide contained in the silts and clays may produce acid sulphate soils and groundwater, and the peats provide a potential source of methane gas.

During the course of this survey, a study of archived geological and geotechnical data relating to the Great Yarmouth urban area was carried out jointly by the British Geological Survey and the Geotechnical Consulting Group (civil engineering consultants) on behalf of the Anglian Water Authority. The study covered all of the mapped Quaternary deposits within the area. The results in respect of the Breydon Formation are summarised in this section. The data included some 700 records of boreholes, cone penetration tests and trial pits. Data coverage (Figure 59) was not uniform and the quality of data (particularly for the clayey horizons) varied, depending, for example, upon the sampling method used.

GEOTECHNICAL PROPERTIES

The geotechnical properties of the Breydon Formation are summarised in Table 9; no data are available for the Upper Peat and the Basal Peat, nor for the weathered crust that characterises the top metre or so of the Upper Clay. The values quoted in Table 9 give a broad indication of the geotechnical properties of the Breydon Formation; they should not be used for detailed design calculations for which site specific investigations would be required.

Upper Clay and Lower Clay

The clay contents of the Upper Clay and Lower Clay vary between about 15 and 45 per cent. There is a trend for clay contents to decrease with depth for both these units. Both units show a wide range in plasticity, resulting from variations in the liquid limit rather than the plastic limit. These variations appear to be due to lithological variation rather than changes in mineralogy. Both units can be described (from the Casagrande plasticity chart, Figure 60) as clays of intermediate to very high plasticity. In the Lower Clay there is a consistent trend throughout the area for the liquid limit (and hence the plasticity index) to decrease with depth between 6.5 and 14 m. There are occasional low values where the clay is laminat-

ed and measurements are affected by the presence of sand layers. Generally, the plasticity index for the Lower Clay is slightly lower than that for the Upper Clay, though this is not apparent from the range of values given in Table 9.

Organic contents of 4 to 5 per cent apply generally to the clays, and the presence of organic material will influence other properties such as bulk density, specific gravity, moisture content and compressibility.

Activity is the ratio of the plasticity index to the clay fraction and is indicative of the clay mineralogy for both the Upper Clay and Lower Clay. Activity is generally low (indicating inactive clay minerals such as illite), ranging between 0.3 and 1.7 for the Upper Clay and 0.5 and 1.2 for the Lower Clay. The greater variation in values in the Upper Clay may be due to the influence of sand and silt on measurements of plasticity index.

Liquidity indices[1] range mostly between 0.6 and 0.9 for the Upper Clay and 0.7 and 0.9 for the Lower Clay. These values are typical of recent estuarine or alluvial clays which have suffered no significant postdepositional processes. Variations in bulk density probably reflect variations in organic content.

Sulphate contents for both the Upper Clay and Lower Clay fall mostly into classes 2 and 3 of the Building Research Establishment table on the use of concrete in sulphate-bearing soils and groundwaters (Anon, 1986). Occasionally, values in class 4 are obtained. These values indicate that sulphate resistant cement must be used. Values of pH generally indicate the two clay units to be slightly alkaline. Determinations of chloride content indicate that there may be some seawater infiltration in the vicinity of the rivers Yare and Bure.

From an examination of the data from consolidation and piezocone tests, it has been concluded that the clays exhibit an apparent overconsolidation; that is, they appear to have been loaded in the past more than they are today. As there is no geological evidence to suggest that they have unloaded as a result of erosion, wave compaction or desiccation (except for the weathered crust at the top of the Upper Clay), the apparent overconsolidation is probably an effect of ageing. This is supported by the overconsolidation ratio being approximately constant with depth.

The clays generally are of medium compressibility, with moderate rates of consolidation. Table 9 gives class values for the coefficient of volume compressibility (mv) and coefficient of consolidation (cv) (after Head, 1982 and Lambe and Whitman, 1979, respectively); the pres-

---

1 Liquidity index = $\dfrac{\text{natural moisture content - plastic limit}}{\text{plasticity index}}$

ence of sand and silt layers will give considerably increased values for cv. For laminated clays, cv tends to increase with stress level but, for non-laminated clays, to decrease. The derivation and use of cv depends on a number of assumptions, including that both compressibility and permeability are constant during a stress increment. This will not be true where the stress increment straddles the pre-consolidation pressure; in these circumstances, care is needed in the use of cv. Compressibility tends to reduce with increasing stress level.

Limited permeability data are available (Table 9) and the variation in the results is probably caused by lithological variation relating to the presence or absence of sand or silt laminae or lenses.

Undrained strength values (Cu), quoted in Table 9, are obtained from a variety of tests including field vane, triaxial compression and cone penetration. Average undrained strengths for loading tend to increase with depth from around 5 kPa at 2 m to around 35 kPa at 18 m. Sensitivity, the ratio of intact undrained strength to remoulded undrained strength ranges from 2 to 6, which is consistent with a lack of major postdepositional processes such as leaching. Sensitivity tends to decrease with depth.

Middle Peat

Limited geotechnical data are available for the Middle Peat. Liquid and plastic limits generally have not been measured. Moisture content shows a wide variation ranging from 100 to 700 per cent but mostly falling between 150 and 600 per cent, and tends to decrease with depth; this variation reflects differences in organic content. Bulk densities range between about 1.0 and 1.4 Mg/m^3 and increase with depth; organic contents tend to be greater than 20 per cent. As might be expected, the peat is highly compressible, values of Mv falling into classes 4 or 5 of Head (1982).

ENGINEERING CONSIDERATIONS

The main potential engineering problems associated with the Breydon Formation in the area that were identified in the study are listed below.

Site investigation problems

a. blowing in sands and gravels during standard penetration tests giving low 'N' values
b. difficulties in obtaining good quality 'undisturbed' samples of clay and peat
c. difficulties in identifying thin layers of sand or clay
d. difficulties in locating the groundwater table and/or its fluctuation
e. collapse of trial pits

Construction problems

a. base heave of shafts and trenches in soft clays
b. control of groundwater; piping in shafts, trenches and tunnels

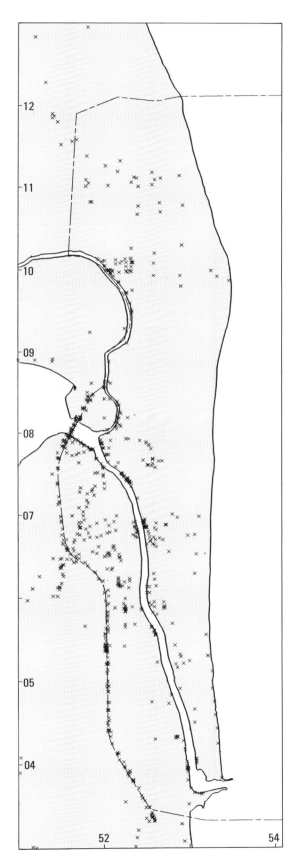

Figure 59   Distribution of borehole, cone penetrometer and trial pits yielding geotechnical data on the Breydon Formation at Great Yarmouth.

Table 9   Summary of the geotechnical properties of the Breydon Formation in the vicinity of Great Yarmouth (based on data courtesy of the Geotechnical Consulting Group).

	+BREYDON FORMATION			Notes
	LOWER CLAY	MIDDLE PEAT	UPPER CLAY	
*Permeability (m s^{-1})	0.3 & 2.2 x10^{-8} 1 to 4.5 x10^{-6}		0.2 & 1.6 x10^{-6} 5 x10^{-8} to 5 x10^{-9}	Falling/rising head test Constant head test
Groundwater level (m OD)		−1.15 to +0.9		Tidal fluctuations likely
Moisture content (%)		150 to 600		
Plastic limit (%)	20 to 40		15 to 30	
Liquid limit (%)	30 to 100		35 to 90	Decreasing with depth
Plasticity index (%)	10 to 60		10 to 55	
Liquidity index (%)	0.7 to 0.9		0.6 to 0.9	
Bulk density (Mg m^{-3})	1.6 to 1.9 Incr. with depth	1.0 to 1.4	1.5 to 1.8	
Specific gravity	2.6 to 2.7		2.6 to 2.7	
Organic content (%)	3 to 8 Decr. with depth	20 to 30	2 to 8 Incr. with depth	
Sulphate class	2 to 3 occasionally 4		2 to 3 occasionally 4	For class definitions refer to Anon (1986)
pH	7 to 8		7 to 8	
Clay (%)	15 to 45		15 to 45	Decreasing with depth
Silt (%)	50 to 60		15 to 55	
Sand (%)	0 to 35		5 to 40	
Cu (KPa)	For loading 5 at 2m increasing to 32 at 15m For excavation 2.5 at 2m increasing to 16 at 15m			Minimum strength profile
ϕ' / c' (KPa)	25 to 35° 0 to 3		25 to 35° 0 to 3	
mv class	3 to 4	4 to 5	3 to 4	For class definition refer to Head (1982)
cv class	∼3		∼3	For non-laminated clay-vertical flow. For class definition refer to Lambe & Whitman (1979)

Notes:

* Limited permeability data are available; variations in the results shown are probably caused by lithological variations relating to the presence or absence of sand or silt laminae or lenses.

+ The values quoted in the table provide a broad indication of the geotechnical properties of the Breydon Formation. They should not be used for detailed design calculations for which site specific investigations would be required.

Figure 60 Plasticity charts for the Upper Clay (top) and Lower Clay of the Breydon Formation.

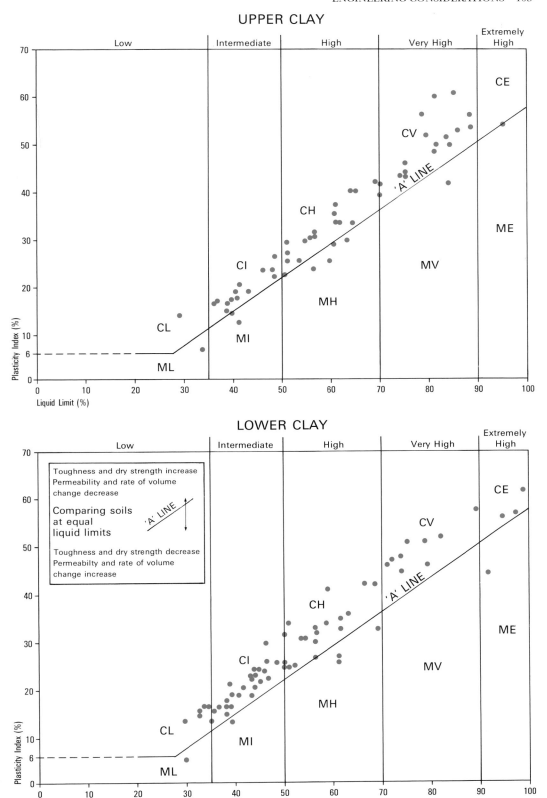

c. settlement due to movement of fines during dewatering

d. settlement or failure of embankments, flood defences and foundations

e. basement and near-surface pipeline flotation

f. problems with cast-in-place bored piles i.e. shaft defects, necking, bulging in very soft clays and peats; base instability

g. problems with driven piles and pile groups in soft clays, i.e. over-driving, excess pore water pressures, heave, lateral displacements, negative skin friction

h. stability of shallow cuts

i. high capacity trench support needed

j. high sulphate and/or chloride contents in groundwater near rivers and the coast

A number of specific points are worth highlighting. The Upper Clay has only a thin weathered crust compared with some soft clay deposits elsewhere. Consequently, care must be taken in applying experience gained at other soft clay sites. Insufficient data are available for carrying out stability and settlement analyses; therefore, strength and other geotechnical parameter values quoted here should be treated with caution. No information is available on the swelling and shrinkage characteristics of the clays.

APPENDIX 1

Upper Cretaceous stratigraphy of the Trunch Borehole (TG 23 SE 8)

[2933 3455] (Mundesley (132) district)   Drilled in 1975; surface level c. + 41 m OD

C J Wood, A A Morter and R W Gallois

The following account is based partly on the unpublished detailed written and graphic logs of the borehole by Mr A A Morter, and partly on a recent reassessment, undertaken for this memoir by Mr C J Wood, of the extensive macrofaunal collections made throughout the succession (also by Mr Morter) and of the total stratigraphy.

The chronostratigraphical range of the Chalk in this borehole is from the Maastrichtian to the base of the Cenomanian (Figures 18 and 61). The Middle Chalk is condensed in comparison with that of the Northern Province, with which it has the greatest affinity; the Lower Chalk is similarly comparable to that in the Northern Province but is very condensed (Figure 17). Core recovery was extremely poor down to about 60 m, but additional information on the upper part of the succession was obtained from a second borehole, Trunch No. 2 [2939 3455], drilled some 60 m east of the main hole.

At the end of this appendix details are given of another shallow cored borehole at Mundesley, which proved some 1.7 m of Chalk belonging unequivocally to the Grey Bed subdivision (Beacon Hill Chalk Member of Johansen and Surlyk, 1990) of the Lower Maastrichtian in the glaciotectonic slices exposed in the cliffs and foreshore between Trimingham and Mundesley (Peake and Hancock, 1961, 1970).

QUATERNARY DEPOSITS

Recorded in Trunch No. 1 from surface to 45.70 m

UPPER CHALK

Lower Maastrichtian

Belemnella lanceolata Zone sensu lato: 44.27 m in Trunch No 2 to about 61 m (inferred preserved Maastrichtian thickness at least 16 m)

Gallois and Morter reported that the borehole commenced in Lower Maastrichtian Sponge Beds (Trimingham Sponge Beds Member of Johansen and Surlyk, 1990) and proved 36 m of Maastrichtian rocks including representatives of the Porosphaera Beds and Sidestrand (pre-Porosphaera) succession (Sidestrand Chalk Member of Johansen and Surlyk, 1990) down to about 82 m. The base of the Maastrichtian is here revised significantly upwards on the basis of new micropalaeontological, nannofloral and stable isotope data.

Core recovery was extremely poor down to about 60 m and there was only limited recovery (mainly flints) below this depth to about 80 m. The poor recovery is probably due to the soft, marly character of the chalk. Trunch No. 2 Borehole recovered some core of weakly indurated chalks with sponges and moulds of bivalves, strikingly reminiscent of the Sponge Beds, immediately below the Pleistocene between 44.27 m and 45.71 m. Beneath these sponge beds, a 14 cm flint at 45.71 to 45.85 m and a 23 cm flint at 47.45 to 47.68 m were tentatively identified with flint bands P and Q of the Porosphaera Beds succession (Peake and Hancock, 1961, fig. 7) respectively (Mr A A Morter, unpublished lithological log).

Dr Bailey (Paleo Services) has kindly carried out an analysis of the foraminiferal faunas of three samples from the uppermost beds in Trunch No. 2 Borehole. He reports (written communication, 1990) that the occurrence of *Angulogavelinella bettenstaedti* Hofker in the samples from 44.91 m and 45.25 m indicates the Early Maastrichtian benthonic foraminifera Zone B6i of Swiecicki (1980). This finding establishes that the sponge beds are the Sidestrand Sponge Beds, since *A. bettenstaedti* first appears at the base of the Sponge Beds and reaches flood proportions within that unit (Swiecicki, 1980, fig. 7:22). The early Maastrichtian dating is supported by the occurrence of *Neoflabellina reticulata* (Reuss) at 45.25 m and possibly *Bolivinoides sidestrandensis* Barr at 44.91 m.

Contrary to the statement by McArthur et al. (1992), it is not possible to infer from the nearby Norfolk coast succession that the base of the Maastrichtian Stage lies at 62.5 m in the Trunch Borehole. Dr Bailey has examined BGS slides of picked foraminifera from the highest part of the recovered succession in Trunch No. 1 Borehole in order to recognise this boundary. He reports (written communication, 1992) that *Reussella szajnochae szajnochae* De Klasz and Knipscheer was poorly represented at 57.3 m, together with rare *Rugoglobigerina rugosa* (Plummer). At 61 m, the former occurred in relative abundance, but virtually no specimens of *R. rugosa* were present. *R. rugosa* was common at 64 m, together with the Upper Campanian marker *Gavelinella monterelensis* Marie. This frequency maximum of *R. s. szajnochae* at 61 m suggests proximity to the flood occurrence of this taxon that is taken to mark the top of the Upper Campanian in wells in the southern part of the North Sea (Bailey et al., 1983). It presumably correlates with the minor acme found in the standard Campanian–Maastrichtian boundary succession at Kronsmoor, northern Germany (Schönfield and Burnett, 1991). A comparable acme was recorded by Swiecicki (1980) from the (Upper Campanian) lowest slice of the Campanian–Maastrichtian glaciotectonic slices comprising the Overstrand Hotel lower mass (Wood, 1967; Peake and Hancock, 1970, p.339G), with *R. rugosa* occurring commonly 3 m below the flood occurrence of *R. s. szajnochae*, exactly as in the borehole. Placing the base of the Maastrichtian at about 61 m is supported by the appearance of *Gavelinella monterelensis* at 64 m; this taxon occurs commonly at and below 71 m. It is also supported by carbon isotope stratigraphy: a significant reduction in $\delta^{13}C$ (bulk rock) values occurs uphole from 61 m (Jenkyns and Gale, in preparation), comparable with the shift in values reported from the base of the Maastrichtian at Kronsmoor by Schönfield et al. (1991).

Some corroboration of the indications from the foraminiferal data and the carbon isotope signature is given by strontium isotope stratigraphy. McArthur et al. (1992) compared data from Trunch with the strontium isotope ($^{87}Sr/^{86}Sr$) curve across the Campanian–Maastrichtian boundary at Kronsmoor and indicated that the boundary in the borehole fell at 66 m, but with a large possible margin of error. A lower limit to the base of the Maastrichtian is provided by nannofloral data. At Kronsmoor, this datum is situated a short distance above the base of boreal nannofloral zone CC/B 23Ab (Burnett, 1991 and unpublished report). In the Trunch Borehole, a second unpublished report by Dr J Burnett (University College Lon-

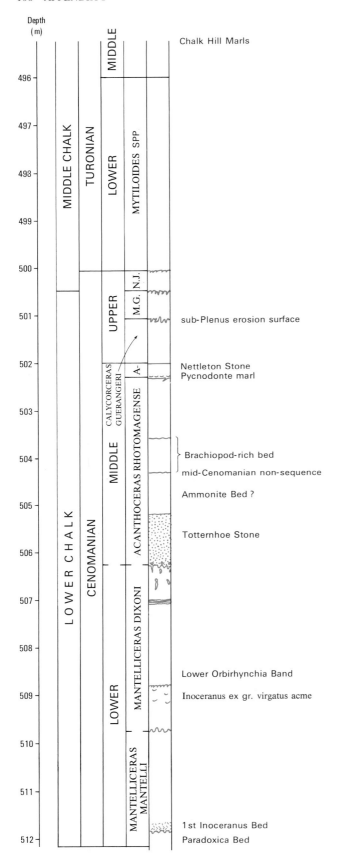

Figure 61 Chalk Group, Trunch Borehole: section of the Lower Chalk and the lower part of the Middle Chalk, showing chronostratigraphical stages and zonal classification.

don places samples from 57.3 m and from 67.51 to 68.53 m in this zone, with a sample from 70.9 m falling into the underlying zone CC/B 23Aa.

Upper Campanian

Belemnitella mucronata Zone sensu lato: about 61 m? to 209.07 m? (about 148.07 m)

In the following discussion, reference is made to the subdivisions of the *mucronata* Zone established by Peake and Hancock (1961, 1970) and in part emended by Wood (1988).

It has not proved possible to recognise the Paramoudra$_1$ and Paramoudra$_2$ faunal belts established by Wood (1988) in the Norwich area. The chalk down to 103 m is rich in fragments of inoceramid shell, large sheet-like fragments being concentrated at 93.50 m. *Belemnitella* cf. *najdini* Kongiel is common over 0.5 m at 85 m and also at 86.50 m. The base of the Paramoudra Chalk as defined on the coast near West Runton (Peake and Hancock, 1970, p.339F; Wood, 1988; Johansen and Surlyk, 1990) is tentatatively drawn, following Gallois and Morter (1976), at a sponge bed at about 121.50 m, but there is no good faunal evidence to support this.

Within the Beeston Chalk, unusually large *Pseudolimea granulata* (Nilsson) with the valves in association are common in the interval between 133 and 134 m. Poor core recovery hinders the placing of the junction between the Beeston Chalk and the underlying Weybourne Chalk, i.e. the upper limit of the main Catton Sponge Bed (see discussion by Wood, 1988). Gallois and Morter (1976) drew this horizon at a weakly developed sponge bed at 152.55 m, but this sponge bed does not mark the upward change to chalk rich in inoceramid fragments that is found at the type locality of the Catton Sponge Bed or in correlative successions elsewhere. It is possible that the main Catton Sponge Bed is situated at a level of core-loss at about 154.7 m, where a marked spike is seen in both the sonic and resistivity logs (Figure 18).

There is no clear evidence of the oyster-rich beds (Weybourne$_2$) in the middle of the Weybourne Chalk in the stratotype section and in the vicinity of Norwich, nor has it proved possible to recognise the boundary between the Weybourne Chalk and the underlying Pre-Weybourne Chalk. The occurrence of *Galerites* at 157 m is noteworthy, this being possibly the first published record from the Weybourne Chalk. *Galeola* sp., perhaps *G. papillosa basiplana* Ernst, occurs at 165.5 m and the record could be taken to indicate a low Weybourne or high Pre-Weybourne Chalk horizon; there is, however, no evidence of the small *Galerites? minor* Rowe MS that characterises the topmost beds of the Pre-Weybourne Chalk in association with *Galeola* (see Wood, 1988, for details).

Unequivocal macrofaunal evidence for the Pre-Weybourne Chalk is provided by several horizons with the barrel-shaped bryozoan *Volviflustrellaria taverensis* (Brydone) between 174.6 and 200 m (i.e. some 25 m); also by occurrences of *Echinocorys* ex gr. *conica* (Agassiz) including a flint-filled specimen at 193.6 m. The highest occurrences can be inferred to correlate with the Pre-Weybourne$_3$ faunal belt of the Norwich district (Wood, 1988) and the lowest with Pre-Weybourne$_2$. The apparent absence of *V. taverensis* from the basal 9 m of the *mucronata* Zone suggests the *Volviflustrellaria*-free Pre-Weybourne₁ faunal belt occurs at this level. The Pre-Weybourne Chalk includes two discrete marl seams: a 7 cm concentration from 182.83 to 182.90 m and a 3 cm seam of flaser marls from 194.99 to 195.02 m, underlain by a fossiliferous horizon with corpulent *Belemnitella* sp. and *Echinocorys* ex gr. *conica*; below this level, some 4 m of core was not recovered. These marl seams may prove to correlate with the marl seams in the basal part of the *mucronata* Zone in southern England (Bailey et al., 1983, fig. 3; Mortimore, 1986, fig. 23).

The base of the *mucronata* zone is tentatively drawn at 209.07 m at the upper limit of a closely spaced pair (within 0.15 m) of relatively hardened beds with pyritised burrow-fills and weakly phosphatised upper surfaces. This composite lithological marker horizon is expressed as a pronounced spike in both the sonic and resistivity logs (Figure 18) and is readily recognisable in the sonic log of the nearby Bacton No. 1 Borehole (Figure 2), and possibly also in that of West Somerton (Figure 2, Appendix 2). It should be noted that there is no convincing macrofaunal evidence for choosing this boundary beyond the fact that *Volviflustrellaria taverensis* extends down to 200 m. Below this depth there was extensive core-loss down to 209.07 m. An alternative interpretation is that the mineralised surfaces are a reflection of the latest early Campanian (high *Gonioteuthis quadrata* Zone) Peine tectonic event, which is expressed by the Downend Hardground in southern England and by the Précy Hardground in northern France (Mortimore and Pomerol, 1991). On this basis, the lower limit of the *mucronata* Zone might be placed at or even above the 3 cm seam of flaser marls. There are some corroborative indications of this from the carbon isotope stratigraphy.

Lower Campanian

Gonioteuthis quadrata Zone: 209.07 to 272.50 m (63.43 m)

The subdivisions (in ascending order) into the *Hagenowia* Horizon, *Applinocrinus cretaceus* Subzone and unnamed post-*cretaceus* Subzone succession used in southern England (Wood and Mortimore, 1988) have not been recognised so far. *Belemnitella* ex gr. *praecursor* Stolley occurs at 209.79 m and 215.37 m. The highest *Gonioteuthis* found was at 239.45 m; *Gonioteuthis quadrata* (Blainville) is common at 244.37 m in association with a flint. None of the distinctive and biostratigraphically restricted forms of *Echinocorys* in southern England, specifically the 'large' and 'small' forms of Gaster, has been positively identified. The occurrence of a flint-filled *Micraster schroederi* Stolley at 232.30 m and a *Micraster* ex gr. s*tolleyi–gibbus* sensu Ernst at 240.14 m is noteworthy. The lower limit of this zone is drawn in relation to the inferred top of the underlying *Offaster pilula* Zone (see below).

Offaster pilula Zone: 272.50 to 306.72 m (34.22 m)

The top of the zone is tentatively drawn at the top of an horizon of medium-sized *Offaster pilula* (Lamarck), which is inferred to represent the local equivalent of the *planoconvexus* horizon with *Offaster pilula planatus* Brydone at the top of the Zone in southern England. This interpretation is supported by the first downhole appearance of the inoceramid bivalve genus *Sphenoceramus* at 275 m and of *Hypoxytoma tenuicostata* (Roemer) at 280 m. The occurrence of *Offaster pilula* at 283.68 m and 284.51 m probably represents the lower of the two belts of *Offaster pilula* recognised in southern England (Wood and Mortimore, 1988, fig. 18). The 6 cm laminated, silty, grey-green marl with its base at 286.55 m probably correlates with

the un-named marl in the middle of the succession at the Wells Quarry [TF 928 429] near Wells-next-the-Sea, Norfolk, with the Old Nore Marl (Mortimore, 1986; Wood and Mortimore, 1988, fig. 18) of southern England and with the M1 marl (Ernst, 1963; Schulz et al., 1984, fig. 1) of the Lägerdorf standard succession in northern Germany. It can be taken as a convenient marker for the boundary between the southern England subzones of *Echinocorys depressula* below and abundant *Offaster pilula* above, the actual boundary in the borehole falling perhaps 1 m lower.

Grobkreide facies, i.e. very coarse-grained chalk largely composed of oyster and inoceramid shell, occurs at intervals from 300 m to the highest record of *Marsupites*. These inoceramid-rich chalks equate with the lower part of the *depressula* Subzone of southern England (Mortimore and Wood, 1988, fig. 18) and with the German *Gonioteuthis granulataquadrata* Zone at Lägerdorf (Ernst, 1963; Schulz et al., 1984).

Santonian

Marsupites testudinarius Zone and *Uintacrinus socialis* Zone undivided: 306.72 to about 335.26 m (possibly to the sponge bed at 341.6 m (following Gallois and Morter, 1976), or even down to the interval of core loss (corresponding to a downhole change from a low resistivity to a high resistivity signature) between 342.34 and 345.21 m).

The top of the *Marsupites* Zone is drawn at a burrowed junction between Grobkreide and non-bioclastic white chalk, which is reflected by an abrupt change from a low resistivity to a high resistivity signature (Figure 18). Although the highest record of *Marsupites* is at 307.35 m, the occurrence of giant *Porosphaera* at 306.80 m and 307.05 m provides a good indication for this zone. It is possible that there is a non-sequence at the boundary between this zone and the overlying *pilula* Zone, since Grobkreide extends down into the *Marsupites* Zone in Germany (Ernst, 1963), and the sculptured nature of the *Marsupites* calyx plate at 307.35 m suggests an horizon significantly below the top of the zone. There is no evidence for the *Uintacrinus anglicus* Zone which is intercalated between the *Marsupites* and *pilula* zones in southern England, and probably extends into the southern part of East Anglia. *Marsupites* occurs over 13.04 m down to 319.54 m, the lowest record being a smooth calyx plate. Unidentified crinoid brachials occur at about 323 m and about 324 m, but the highest definite record of *Uintacrinus* is some 5 m lower at about 325 m. *Uintacrinus* is found over about 10 m down to 335.26 m, with unidentified crinoid brachials 2.2 m lower at 336.8 m.

Santonian–Coniacian

Micraster coranguinum Zone: 335.26 to 411.50 m (76.24 m)

In the absence of other data, the upper limit is provisionally taken at the lowest definite record of *Uintacrinus*. The occurrence of *Conulus* at 354.01 m, *Sphenoceramus* ex gr. *pachti* (Arkhangelsky)–*cardissoides* (Goldfuss) at 352.33 m and 353.54 m and *Cordiceramus cordiformis* (J de C Sowerby) at 355.98 m are indicative of the Santonian. The base of the Santonian Stage is tentatively drawn at a possible *Cladoceramus undulatoplicatus* (Roemer) at 365.80 m, just above a 9 cm flint at 366.50 m; the flint is expressed as a high value spike on the resistivity log (Figure 18) and may be the equivalent of the Bedwell's Columnar Flint of southern England. Occurrences of *Platyceramus mantelli* (Barrois) at 401.65 m, *Volviceramus* aff. *involutus* (J de C Sowerby) at 402.62 m and *V. koeneni* (Muller) at 406.78 m indicate the *Volviceramus*-rich beds at the base of the *coranguinum* Zone, and suggest that the 9 cm flint at 400 m may be the equivalent of the Seven Sisters Flint of Sussex (Mortimore, 1986) and the East Cliff Semitabular Flint of Kent (Gale and Smith, 1982). The base of the zone is taken about 5 m beneath the record of *V. koeneni* at a level of core loss at 411.50 m: this corresponds to a significant low-resistivity spike, which is inferred to represent the marl seams (Shoreham Marls and correlatives) at the base of the zone elsewhere.

Micraster cortestudinarium Zone: 411.50 to 432.03 m (20.53 m)

The higher part of the zone is characterised by *Cremnoceramus* ex gr. *schloenbachi* (Böhm). Large *Cremnoceramus? waltersdorfensis hannovrensis* (Heinz) occur at 426.96 m and are common at 427.88 m, with *Cremnoceramus? rotundatus* (Fiege). Small *C? waltersdorfensis* (Andert) and *C? rotundatus* occur together with *Didymotis* sp. between 431 and 432 m, immediately above the mineralised, convolute hardground at 432.03 m, which marks the top of the underlying *Sternotaxis plana* Zone. This inoceramid– *Didymotis* association is used to recognise the base of the Coniacian Stage (see Wood, Ernst and Rasemann, 1984): it occurs in the equivalent northern England succession 0.15 m beneath the middle of the three Kiplingcotes marls, the highest of which may be represented in the borehole by the marl seam at 430.15 m.

Turonian

Sternotaxis plana Zone: 432.03 to 469.32 m (37.29 m)

The hardground at 432.03 m is inferred to equate with the Navigation Hardground(s) of southern England (Mortimore, 1986), but not with the Top Rock of East Anglia (Bristow, 1990), which represents a condensation of the lower part of the *cortestudinarium* Zone. In the absence of a clear definition of the boundary between the *plana* and *cortestudinarium* zones in the southern England succession, the boundary in the borehole is drawn at this hardground. The *plana* Zone succession in the borehole can be correlated directly with the northern province succession using named marker horizons such as major marl seams and flint bands. The following marker horizons (with their East Anglian equivalents in parentheses) can be recognised:

Ulceby Oyster Bed: 441.50 to 442.00 m

Ulceby Marl (West Tofts Marl): 5 cm marl, crinoidal, with its base at 442.81 m

(In the interval between the Ulceby Marl and the Ludborough Flint, there are significant mineralised, convolute hardgrounds with underlying chalkstones at 449.89 m, 452.19 m and 452.42 m: these presumably correspond in part to the Chalk Rock recognised in the Brandon–Thetford area and elsewhere in East Anglia (see Mortimore and Wood, 1986, fig. 2.3; Bristow, 1990) and to the Kingston nodular chalks (Mortimore, 1986) of the Anglo-Paris Basin succession.)

Ludborough Flint (Floor Stone flint): 30 cm continuous tabular flint with its base at 460.30 m. This flint, which is one of the most important marker horizons in the northern England succession, is well developed in the borehole and is expressed as a high-value sonic and resistivity spike (Figure 18).

North Ormsby Marl (Grimes Graves Marl): 4 cm grey-green, laminated marl with its base at 462.74 m

Triple Tabular Flints (Rough and Smooth Black flints in part): 14 cm tabular flint at 465.47 m; 10 cm tabular flint at 466.37 m. In the interval from the lower flint to the pseudobreccia

marl (see below), thin-tested echinoids including *Infulaster hagenowi* (d'Orbigny) and *Sternotaxis plana* (Mantell) are common, with the former species occurring in abundance at 466.97 to 466.98 m

Ravendale Flint: 9 cm flint at 468.83 m with 2 cm pseudobreccia marl 0.5 m above (normally silicified in northern England and locally fused with the top of the Ravendale Flint).

The base of the *S. plana* Zone is drawn at 469.32 m at an horizon of stylolitic marly partings corresponding to the base of the Burnham Chalk Formation (Wood and Smith, 1978) in northern England. This horizon correlates with the base of the Bridgewick Flints at the base of the *plana* Zone in southern England and can thus be taken as the base of the Upper Chalk (see discussion by Mortimore and Wood, 1986).

MIDDLE CHALK

Terebratulina lata Zone: 469.32 to 493.97 m? (24.65 m?).

The following marker horizons of the northern province *lata* Zone succession (with their East Anglian equivalents in parentheses) can be identified:

(Lower) Deepdale Marl (Twin Marls): 2 cm marl with its base at 471.74 m Deepdale Flints: 9 cm semitabular associated with a *Conulus* horizon at 42.50 m overlain by 8 cm nodular flint at 472.25 m. (It should be noted that, with the exception of a 6 cm flint at 486.46 m, this is the only horizon with flint in the Welton Chalk of the Trunch succession. This contrasts with the relatively flinty correlative succession in the northern province (Wood, 1992, fig. 33).)

Riby Marl: 10 mm marl with its base at 475.44 m

Melton Ross Marl (Mount Ephraim Marl): 8 cm solid marl with its base at 478.03 m

Barton Marls:

   Barton Marl 4 (marly parting only): 481.10 m
   Barton Marl 3 (marly parting only): 481.59 m
   Barton Marl 2 (Pilgrims Walk Marl): thin, 5 mm marl with its base at 482.71 m
   Barton Marl 1 ('Lower Marl'): 1 cm grey-green, laminated marl containing chalk lenses, with its base at 483.66 m

Grasby Marl (Methwold Marl): 2 cm grey-green, laminated marl with its base at 487.59 m

As in the case of the correlative northern province successsion, it has not proved possible so far to recognise the base of the *lata* Zone in the Trunch Borehole. Beneath the Grasby Marl, *Terebratulina lata* (R Etheridge) occurs at 487.94 m and 488.50 m; it is relatively common between 489.05 and 489.32 m, immediately beneath a downhole change to nodular chalk, and just above a *Conulus* horizon. Although there are no records of the zonal index below 489.32 m, with the exception of a single, extremely doubtful example at 492.03 m., the ocurrence of *Inoceramus* ex gr. *cuvieri* (J de C Sowerby) and *I.* ex gr. *lamarcki* Parkinson down to about 493 m is strongly suggestive of a *lata* Zone inoceramid assemblage. The base of the *lata* Zone is provisionally taken at a thin, 2 mm grey-green marl seam on a stylolitised surface at 493.97 m.

Mytiloides labiatus Zone sensu lato*: 493.97 to 500.51 m? (6.54 m)

*(This is an extremely unsatisfactory zonal concept, corresponding to the traditional *Inoceramus labiatus* (formerly *Rhynchonella cuvieri*) Zone, and employed here pending a definitive

zonal scheme for this part of the succession. It comprises the beds between the bottom of the *lata* Zone and the top of the Upper Cenomanian *Metoicoceras geslinianum* Zone and bears no relation whatsoever to the stratigraphical range of the eponymous zone fossil. As so defined, it includes the boundary between the Cenomanian and Turonian stages, with the lower limit marking the base of the Middle Chalk.)

The bed with irregular, ramifying and possibly semisilicified chalkstone nodules between 495.28 and 496 m may correlate with the First Main Flint of the northern province succession (Wood and Smith, 1978; Wood, 1992). The occurrence of a fragmentary *Collignoniceras?* at 495.40 m is suggestive of the basal Middle Turonian *Collignoniceras–Mytiloides subhercynicus* (Seitz) association that has now been recognised in the Shaftesbury (Bristow, in preparation) and Lewes districts in southern England. At the base of this bed, a concentration of stylolites at 495.89 m and thin marly partings at 495.91 m and 496.00 m are taken to represent the Chalk Hill Marls (Wood, 1992), which mark the boundary between the flintless and overlying flinty portions of the Welton Chalk Formation of the northern province (Wood and Smith, 1978; Wood, 1992).

Beneath the presumed Chalk Hill Marls, there is an abrupt lithological change to gritty, shell-detrital chalks rich in *Mytiloides,* which marks the top of the Lower Turonian (Zone of *Mytiloides* spp.). These beds terminate downwards at a planar hardground at 500.07 m, which is provisionally taken as the top of the underlying Upper Cenomanian *Neocardioceras juddii* Zone and, consequently, the boundary between the Cenomanian and Turonian stages.

Upper Cenomanian

Neocardioceras juddii Zone: 500.07 to 500.51 m (0.44 m)

The interval between the planar hardground at 500.07 m and the convolute hardground at 500.51 m is tentatively assigned on general stratigraphical grounds to the *juddii* Zone, there being no biostratigraphical evidence to support this interpretation.

LOWER CHALK

Metoicoceras geslinianum Zone: 500.51 to 501.10 m (0.59 m)

The interval between the non-glauconitised, convolute hardground at 500.51 m and the glauconitised, convolute hardground at 501.10 m is assigned to the *geslinianum* Zone, the marly plexus at 500.96 to 501.02 m representing the thin, north Norfolk equivalent of the Plenus Marls (Jefferies, 1963), and the lower hardground the sub-Plenus erosion surface and the base of the Welton Chalk Formation of the northern province succession.

Calycoceras guerangeri Zone: 501.10 to c.502 m (c.0.9 m)

The marly chalks between the sub-Plenus erosion surface and the top of the Nettleton Stone (see below) are assigned on general stratigraphical grounds to the *Calycoceras guerangeri* Zone. They correspond in part to the Upper Pink Band (Bower and Farmery, 1910) of the northern province and equate with the former *Holaster trecensis* Zone (see Wood, 1980, fig. 20; Wood, 1992, fig. 30).

Middle Cenomanian

Acanthoceras jukesbrownei Zone: about 502 to 502.32 m? (about 0.32 m?)

The chalk below about 502 m is relatively hard and nodular, terminating downwards in a 1 cm marl with abundant *Pycnodonte,* which rests on a hardground at 502.32 m. The hard chalk is a condensed equivalent of the Nettleton Stone of the northern province (Wood, 1992). The underlying marl is the 'Gryphaea Band' recognised in Lincolnshire (Bower and Farmery, 1910) and the Nettleton Pycnodonte Marl (Wood, 1992). It equates with the Pycnodonte Event of northern Germany (Ernst et al., 1983), which is additionally characterised by rare *Acanthoceras jukesbrownei* (Spath). Elsewhere in England, the base of the zone is marked by common *'Inoceramus'* ex gr. *atlanticus* (Heinz), a species which is known to occur in the Pycnodonte Marl; in the absence of this species from the beds beneath the basal hardground, the latter is taken to mark the top of the underlying *Acanthoceras rhotomagense* Zone.

Acanthoceras rhotomagense Zone: 502.32? to 506.30 m (3.98 m)

The interval from 503.58 to 504.33 m equates with the lower part of the Lower Pink Band of the northern province: it is rich in brachiopods, including *Concinnithyris* and *Terebratulina.* The top of the underlying bed at 504.33 m probably corresponds to the mid-Cenomanian non-sequence (Carter and Hart, 1977) and to the top of the *Turrilites costatus* Subzone. The bed itself probably represents the 'ammonite bed' that overlies the Totternhoe Stone. The distinctive gritty lithology with phosphatised clasts characterising the Totternhoe Stone begins at 505.21 m and extends down to the lithified erosion surface at 506.30 m.

In the absence of biostratigraphical evidence to the contrary, the lower limit of the *rhotomagense* Zone and of the Middle Cenomanian is drawn here at at the base of the Totternhoe Stone. By analogy with the succession at Hunstanton, the Totternhoe Stone at Trunch equates with the horizon of the Cast Bed of the southern England succession, i.e. within, but not at the base of the *rhotomagense* Zone (see Gale, 1989, fig. 3). It is possible that the burrowed limestone beneath the Totternhoe Stone and the underlying dark marl between 507.05 and 507.12 m correspond to the higher part of the basal Middle Cenomanian sequence of limestones and marls beneath the Cast Bed in southern England (Gale, 1989, fig. 3); this point requires further investigation.

Lower Cenomanian

Mantelliceras dixoni Zone: 506.30 to 509.80 m (3.50 m)

In the absence of evidence to the contrary, the interval from the hardground beneath the Totternhoe Stone to the high-amplitude erosion surface at 509.80 m is referred to this zone. The latter surface appears to mark the lowest occurrence of *Inoceramus* ex gr. *virgatus* Schlüter and presumably represents the erosion surface (horizon M4 of Gale, 1989, fig. 2) recognised at Folkestone. An acme-occurrence of *I.* ex gr. *virgatus* terminating downwards in a shell-bed at 509.31 to 509.32 m is found over 0.5 m beneath the planar hardground at 508.82 m. This corresponds to the acme-occurrence that occurs over some 3 m beneath the paired limestones with *Mantelliceras dixoni* Spath (horizon M6 of Gale, 1989, fig. 2). The occurrence of *Orbirhynchia mantelliana* (J de C Sowerby) at 508.40 m and 508.43 m represents the lowest of the three *Orbirhynchia* acme-occurrences identified in southern England, and equates with the Lower Orbirhynchia Band (Jeans, 1968) of the northern province succession.

Mantelliceras mantelli Zone: 509.80 to 512.22 m (2.42 m)

The interval from the erosion surface at 509.80 m to the glauconitised hardground at 511.91 m can be assigned to the *Mantelliceras saxbii* Subzone and the higher part (Gale and Friedrich, 1989) of the underlying *Neostlingoceras carcitanense* Subzone. Further work is required before the base of the *saxbii* Subzone can be recognised with confidence. The bioclastic chalks rich in *'Inoceramus' crippsi* Mantell sensu stricto at the base of this interval correspond to the First Inoceramus Bed of the northern province. The underlying chalkstones penetrated by a *Thalassinoides* burrow system represent the Paradoxica Bed of the northern province and equate with the lower part (Gale and Friedrich, 1989) of the *carcitanense* Subzone. They rest with erosive contact on an extremely condensed (0.3 m) Upper Albian Red Chalk succession, which overlies 0.33 m of Lower Albian Carstone. The base of the Lower Chalk is at 512.22 m.

The following is an outline log of the strata proved between the base of the Lower Chalk and the base of the borehole at 651.00 m (Gallois and Morter, 1976, with minor amendment)

	Thickness m	Depth m
CRETACEOUS		
Red Chalk	0.63	
512.85		
JURASSIC		
?Middle Lias	13.80	
526.65		
?Middle/Lower Lias	106.47	
628.32		
?Lower Lias or Penarth Group (Triassic)	4.80	
633.12		
TRIASSIC		
Haisborough Group	17.88	
651.00		

MUNDESLEY BOREHOLE

A cored borehole drilled in 1966 to investigate the stratigraphy of the Pleistocene at Mundesley [317 364] entered Chalk at 13.4 m below the surface (10.5 m below OD) and recovered 1.7 m of richly fossiliferous, grey, calcarenitic chalk with poorly silicified grey flints before terminating (see West, 1980, p.59 and fig. 33). The Chalk core was kindly donated to the British Geological Survey by Professor R G West (University of Cambridge) and the extensive macrofossil and lithological collection made at the time (registered numbers Zt 1484–1628: Book 85, pp. 250–255) has been re-examined for this memoir. The fauna includes *Carneithyris* sp., *Cretirhynchia limbata* (Schlotheim), *Magas chitoniformis* (Schlotheim), large *Terebratulina gracilis* (Schlotheim), *'Pecten' pulchellus* Nilssonand *Cardiaster granulosus* (Goldfuss) and is unequivocally that of the Lower Maastrichtian Grey Beds (Beacon Hill Member of Johansen and Surlyk, 1990), the highest part of the Maastrichtian succession in the glaciotectonic masses in the nearby cliffs and foreshore.

APPENDIX 2

Abstracts of selected borehole logs

Boreholes are identified by their registered numbers in the Survey's 1:10 000 sheet registration system, and are given in alphabetical order.

Acle By-Pass (TG 41 SW/27) TG 4117 1061

Drilled in 1972
Surface level -0.60 m

	Thickness m	Depth m
Soil	0.40	0.40
BREYDON FORMATION		
Clay, silty, mottled, becoming dark grey	2.80	3.20
Peat	3.30	6.50
Clay, silty, grey to blue-grey; pockets of peat at top, shells at base	12.50	9.00
Peat, sandy and silty, with wood fragments	0.45	19.45
YARE VALLEY FORMATION		
Sand, part gravelly, shelly in upper part	2.00	21.45

Carrow Works, Norwich (TG 20 NW/121) TG 2414 0753

Drilled in ?1862 Logged by Rev. J Crompton (in Whitaker, 1921)
Surface level unrecorded

	Thickness m	Depth m
Alluvium	3.66	3.66
CHALK GROUP		
Hard chalk, with flints 6 to 7 ft apart	147.22	150.88
Soft chalk	3.05	153.93
Hard chalk, with flints as above	57.91	211.84
Hard chalk, with flints 4 ft apart	106.89	318.73
Chalk without flints	31.11	349.84
UPPER GREENSAND	1.83	351.67
GAULT	10.98	362.65

Cucumber Corner, Beighton (TG 30 NE/13) TG 3830 0721

	Thickness m	Depth m
Soil	0.65	0.65
LOWESTOFT TILL		
Clay, sandy and silty, with flints	0.05	0.70
Sand, clayey, silty	0.50	1.20
Clay, silty and sandy, with flints	0.50	1.70
CORTON FORMATION		
Sand	2.50	4.20
Sand with grey clay laminae	1.00	5.20
Till		
Clay, sandy, silty, pebbly	0.50	5.70
Clay, sandy and silty, with shell debris	4.50	10.20
Clay, sandy and silty, part pebbly	1.10	11.30
Sand, silty	1.40	12.70

	Thickness m	Depth m
Clay, sandy and silty, pebbly; chalky at 13.70 m	2.00	14.70
Clay, sandy	0.85	15.55
Sand	1.00	16.55
Sand, silty, hard	0.55	17.10
KESGRAVE FORMATION		
Sand	1.40	18.50
Sand and gravel, shelly, with quartz and quartzite	5.30	23.80
Crag		
Sand, shelly	4.20	28.00

The Grange, Langley (TG 30 SW/14) TG 3491 0107

Drilled in 1986
Surface level 25.00 m

	Thickness m	Depth m
LOWESTOFT TILL		
Clay with chalk and flint	4.60	4.60
CORTON FORMATION		
Sand	10.30	14.90
Till		
Clay, sandy with pebbles, laminated	2.20	17.10
KESGRAVE FORMATION		
Sand	1.40	18.50
Sand and gravel, shelly, with quartz and quartzite	5.30	23.80
CRAG		
Sand, shelly	4.20	28.00

Hales Hall (TM 39 NE/6) TM 3673 9597

Drilled in 1986
Surface level + 23.00 m

	Thickness m	Depth m
LOWESTOFT TILL FORMATION		
Clay and gravel, stiff, with flint and chalk clasts	6.80	6.80
CORTON FORMATION		
Sand and silt, partly pebbly	8.50	15.30
Till		
Clay and sand with some flint and chalk clasts	0.60	15.90
KESGRAVE FORMATION		
Sand and gravel, including quartz and quartzite pebbles	2.10	18.00
Clay and silt with shell fragments	0.40	18.00
Clay and sand; ?'Rootlet Bed'	0.70	19.00
Sand and gravel, including quartz and quartzite pebbles	5.50	24.60
CRAG		
Clay, silty, sandy, dark grey-green, shelly	0.90	25.50
Sand, clayey, dark grey-green, shelly, stringers of clay	3.70	29.20

Hales (TM 39 NE/7) TM 3671 9687

Drilled in 1987
Surface level + 9.00 m

	Thickness m	Depth m
Uncored	0.65	0.65
HEAD		
Clay, sandy, gravelly	0.43	1.08
CORTON FORMATION		
Till		
Clay, sandy and sand, part gravelly, poor recovery at 1.44 to 1.65 m	0.63	1.71
KESGRAVE FORMATION		
Sand with some layers of gravel, including quartz pebbles, poor recovery 2.37 to 2.50 m, 3.84 to 4.13 m, 4.76 to 10.0 m, 10.30 to 12.00 m	10.29	12.00
LONDON CLAY FORMATION		
Harwich Member		
Siltstone, sandy, olive-grey; some thin sandstones and many tuffs	4.56	16.56
Hales Clay		
Mudstone, silty, pale greyish brown grading into pale brown sandy siltstone, crudely laminated, and bentonitised tuffs	14.27	30.83
Siltstone, pale brown	1.35	32.18
THANET FORMATION		
Ormesby Clay		
Mudstone, dark greyish brown, waxy	1.93	34.11
Mudstone, greyish brown to brownish grey with pale green banding; glauconitic	3.84	37.95
Mudstone, greyish brown to brownish grey, calcareous, glauconitic, alternating with pale grey marl	2.14	40.09
Mudstone, greyish brown, highly glauconitic, calcareous, with fragments of green clay	2.41	42.50
Mudstone, brown with a slight reddish tinge down to 45.33m, pale reddish brown below; poorly bedded, bioturbated	5.00	47.50
Mudstone, brownish grey to greyish brown, silty, noncalcareous, penetrated at the top by burrows (inc. *Chondrites*) filled with reddish brown clay, down to 47.90m, silty, olive-grey, glauconitic below; phosphatic nodules, calcite concretions, three altered tuffs	10.27	57.77
UPPER CHALK		
Chalkstone with pyritic ghosts of hexactinellid sponges, grading down to white chalk; poor recovery	2.23	60.00

Hellington (Green Lane) (TG 30 SW/12) TG 3197 0231

Drilled in 1986
Surface level + 28.50 m

	Thickness m	Depth m
LOWESTOFT TILL		
Clay with angular flint and, below 2.10 m, chalk clasts	5.70	5.70

	Thickness m	Depth m
CORTON FORMATION		
Sand, partly pebbly, including chalk	9.50	15.20
Clay, sandy	5.20	20.40
KESGRAVE FORMATION		
Sand, pebbly	1.00	21.40
Clay, silty, peat and sand	1.60	23.00
CRAG		
Sand, clayey, with interbedded clay seams	5.00	28.00
Sand and gravel, some shelly	1.80	29.20
Clay, sandy and silty interlaminated, some shelly	0.70	30.50

Lacon's Brewery 1 (1850) (TG 50 NW/105) TG 5229 0793

Drilled in 1841
Surface level + 6.09 m

	Thickness m	Depth m
NORTH DENES FORMATION		
Sand and gravel	15.24	15.24
CRAG		
Sand and shells	2.44	17.68
Clay and shells	15.54	33.22
Sand and shells	14.33	47.55
Sand, shells and gravel	0.61	48.16
LONDON CLAY AND THANET FORMATIONS		
Clay, grey	3.66	51.82
Clay, brown	18.28	70.10
Clay, grey	18.60	88.70
Clay, brown and pyritic	2.74	91.44
Clay, sandy, brown and micaceous	54.86	146.30
Clay, grey becoming brown	6.10	152.40
Clay, grey, with green sand	8.23	160.63
UPPER CHALK	21.34	181.97

Lowestoft (Lake Lothing) (TM 59 SW/53) TM 5380 9260

Drilled in 1912 (log based on Strahan, 1913)
Surface level + 3.7 m

	Thickness m	Depth m
Gravel, sand and clay	21.18	21.18
CRAG		
Clay, sandy, micaceous	1.37	22.55
Sand and shelly sand	50.60	73.15
LONDON CLAY FORMATION		
Clay and sandy clay	48.77	121.92
'READING BEDS'		
Mottled clay	22.86	144.78
CHALK GROUP		
Chalk and flints	321.56	466.34
?UPPER GREENSAND		
Green clay and chalk, black sand	3.35	469.69
GAULT		
Clay and black sand	13.72	483.41
CARSTONE		
Sandstone, soft and glauconitic	12.50	495.91
?SILURIAN ROCKS		
Shale, slate and sandstone	62.48	558.39

Manor Farm, Blofield (TG 30 NW/32) TG 3285 0945

Drilled in 1986
Surface level + 16.00 m

	Thickness m	Depth m
CORTON FORMATION		
Till		
Clay, sandy with ferruginous lenses	3.85	3.85
CRAG		
Clay, silty, sandy with iron pan	0.55	4.40
Sand, silty, pebbly	2.40	6.80
Sand, clayey, ferruginous with iron pan	7.70	14.50
Sand, pebbly	5.50	20.00

Marine Outfall 8 (TG 50 NW/542) TG 5325 0999

Drilled in 1982
Surface level + 4.80 m

	Thickness m	Depth m
NORTH DENES FORMATION		
Sand with subordinate gravel	11.15	11.15
Gravel, with cobbles	1.85	13.00
Sand and gravel, silty	8.20	21.20
Clay, silty, grey, soft	0.30	21.50
Sand and gravel, silty	3.70	25.20
BREYDON FORMATION		
Clay and silt, black to grey-brown, soft	2.80	28.00
Clay and silt, greenish grey, laminated, shelly	1.40	29.40
YARE VALLEY FORMATION		
Sand and gravel, silty and clayey	4.60	34.00
CRAG		
Clay, silty and sandy, firm	1.80	35.80
Sand, silty, clayey and shelly, becoming shelly and gravelly	17.90	53.70
LONDON CLAY FORMATION		
Clay, silty, blue-grey and brown, stiff	4.65	58.35

Mill Lane, Thurlton (TM 49 NW/22) TM 4251 9746

Drilled in 1983
Surface level + 20.94 m

	Thickness m	Depth m
Soil	0.40	0.4
LOWESTOFT TILL		
Clay, sandy and silty, yellow-brown with chalk and flint	1.10	1.50
Silt, pale yellow, layers of chalky sand, laminated	1.20	2.70
Clay, sandy, pale yellowish brown, with flint and chalk pebbles	2.50	4.00
CORTON FORMATION		
Sand, silty, chalky, with flint and quartz; pale yellow	0.90	4.90
Silt, sandy, chalky, pale yellow	0.10	5.00
Sand, silty, with silt laminae, some chalky; pale yellow	7.00	12.00
Sand and gravel, silty, with chalky silt laminae; pale yellow	1.00	13.00

	Thickness m	Depth m
Sand, silty, pebbly, with flint, quartz and chalk	3.70	16.70
KESGRAVE FORMATION		
Sand and gravel, mainly flint but including quartz and quartzite	4.10	20.80
CRAG		
Sand, pebbly, greenish brown; shell debris	1.20	22.00

North Crains 208 (TG 50 NW/417) TG 5156 0782

Drilled in 1980
Surface level + 0.26 m

	Thickness m	Depth m
BREYDON FORMATION		
Sand, silty, clayey and peaty	1.00	1.00
Silt, dark grey, very soft	0.20	1.20
Sand and shelly silt	1.80	3.00
Silt, peaty, sandy and shelly, grey/ grey-green, soft	2.10	5.10
Peat, shelly, firm	0.20	5.30
Silt, peaty and shelly, grey, very soft	1.90	7.20
Silt, clayey and sandy, grey, laminated, soft	3.00	10.20
Sand and silt, shelly, dark grey, laminated	6.70	16.9
Silt, clayey and shelly, dark grey	1.90	18.80
Peat, sandy and shelly, grey-green	0.60	19.40
YARE VALLEY FORMATION		
Sand and gravel	5.60	25.00

Norton Plantation, Norton Subcourse (TM 49 NW/20) TM 4008 9807

Drilled in 1983
Surface level + 22.77 m

	Thickness m	Depth m
Soil	0.50	0.50
LOWESTOFT TILL		
Clay with chalk and flint pebbles	0.70	1.20
CORTON FORMATION		
Sand, silty, chalk grains	7.60	8.80
Sand, clayey and chalky, with flint pebbles	0.10	8.90
Till		
Clay, sand and silt, flint and chalk pebbles, laminated	1.50	10.40
KESGRAVE FORMATION		
Sand, silty, with quartz and flint pebbles	2.00	12.40
Sand and gravel with quartz and quartzite	5.60	18.00
CRAG		
Clay and sand, silty, laminated, yellow-brown becoming grey and dark green	1.20	19.20
Clay, sandy and silt, grey-green	2.20	21.40
Sand and gravel, micaceous and glauconitic	2.00	23.40

Nova Scotia Farm (TG 51 SW/8) TG 5096 1335

Drilled in 1986
Surface level + 18.00 m

	Thickness m	Depth m
Made ground	1.00	1.00

LOWESTOFT TILL FORMATION

Clay, sandy, gravelly, brown	1.50	2.50

CORTON FORMATION

Sand	9.00	11.50
Sand, gravelly	1.00	12.50
Till		
Clay, sandy, scattered pebbles	3.90	16.
Sand, gravelly	1.00	17.
Till		
Clay, sandy, scattered pebbles, shell fragments	4.10	21.50

KESGRAVE FORMATION

Sand, gravelly	7.50	29.00

CRAG

Sand, gravelly and clayey, red-brown, clay laminae	1.00	30.00

Ormesby Borehole (TG 51 SW/7) TG 5145 1425

Drilled in 1982
Surface level + 5.33 m

	Thickness m	Depth m
MADE GROUND	1.03	1.03
CORTON FORMATION		
Sand	5.96	6.99
Till		
Sand and silt	0.22	7.21
Clay and sand, pebbly, some shell	1.00	8.21
Sand with abundant shell debris	2.75	10.96
Till		
Clay, sandy, grey-brown, some pebbles and shell fragments	1.00	11.96
KESGRAVE FORMATION		
Sand, some pebbles, clay clasts	1.00	12.96
Sand and gravel including quartz pebbles yellow-brown	1.00	13.96
Sand, gravelly, clayey, grey-brown	0.40	14.36
CRAG		
Sand, olive-grey to yellow-brown	11.63	25.99
Clay, sand and silt, olive-grey	3.18	29.17
Sand, some micaceous, glauconitic, shelly	5.43	34.60
Clay, sand and silt, olive-grey	1.40	36.00
Sand, some micaceous, glauconitic, shelly	1.15	37.15
Sand, with shells and glauconite-coated flint pebbles	1.75	38.90
Sand, olive-grey, micaceous, glauconitic, with shells	6.83	45.73
Clay and silt, sandy, olive-grey, laminated, glauconitic and micaceous	13.86	59.59
Clay and silt, sandy, olive-grey, with sand and shell laminae	7.11	66.70
Sand, shelly, olive-grey, abundant glauconite	3.73	70.43
LONDON CLAY FORMATION		
Harwich Member		
Siltstone, brown-grey, many layers of tuff	26.27	96.70
Hales Clay		
Siltstone, glauconitic and pyritic, some tuffs	14.40	112.40
THANET FORMATION		
Ormesby Clay		
Clay, silty, sandy, glauconitic, some tuffs; reddish brown between 119.5 and 123.3 m	27.45	139.85

Upper Chalk	8.15	148.00

Oxpit Lane, Freethorpe (TG 40 SW/3) TG 4102 0381

Drilled in 1986
Surface level + 15.00 m

	Thickness m	Depth m
CORTON FORMATION		
Till		
Clay, sandy	3.26	3.26
KESGRAVE FORMATION		
Sand, silty with flint pebbles	0.98	4.24
Sand, clayey with clay beds up to 0.2 m	1.11	5.35
Sand and gravel, including quartzite pebbles	4.15	9.50
Sand, pebbly	2.00	11.50
CRAG		
Sand with clay laminae	0.50	12.00
Sand and gravel, ferruginous	3.50	15.50
Sand, silty	2.50	18.00
Sand and gravel with disturbed clay laminae	2.50	20.50
Clay and sand, interlaminated	0.79	21.29
Sand, shelly	0.26	21.55
Sand, shelly and pebbly	8.95	30.50

Pockthorpe (TM 49 NW/21) TM 4097 9663

Drilled in 1983
Surface level + 23.06 m

	Thickness m	Depth m
Soil	0.40	0.40
LOWESTOFT TILL		
Clay, sandy and silty, dark yellow-brown with flint and chalk pebbles	2.70	3.10
CORTON FORMATION		
Sand, silty, chalky in parts	5.00	8.10
Sand, silty and clayey, with chalk and flint, and clay pellets	9.00	17.10
Sand and gravel, mainly flint but including quartz and quartzite	0.80	17.90
Till		
Clay, yellowish brown, sandy and silty with flint, quartz and chalk	1.50	19.40
KESGRAVE FORMATION		
Sand, pebbly, with flint and quartz	4.00	23.40
Sandy gravel, mainly flint with quartz and quartzite	4.90	28.30
CRAG		
Clay, silty, sandy and shelly, green, laminated	0.70	29.00
Sand, silty, shelly, greenish brown	1.00	30.00

Royal Society Borehole, Ludham (TG 31 NE 16) TG 3855 1992

Drilled in 1959
Surface level + 6.1 m
(Abridged and metricated from West, 1961)

	Thickness m	Depth m
?NORWICH BRICKEARTH (CORTON FORMATION)		
Sand, brown; stones	3.20	3.20

CRAG

	Thickness m	Depth m
Sand, brown; clay seams, iron pan, sporadically pebbly	9.60	12.80
Sand, grey; clay partings, micaceous	3.35	16.15
Clay and silt, grey; sand partings, shell fragments	4.73	20.88
Core lost, except between 22.86 and 23.47 m; probably shelly sand	3.81	24.69
Clay, silty with sand partings, grey; locally shelly	9.14	33.83
Sand, shelly, grey; thin clay seams	18.90	52.73
Sand, shelly, grey; gravelly in places	2.74	55.47
Sand, shelly, grey; black flints up to 75 mm in diameter	0.31	55.78

LONDON CLAY

Clay, brown	0.30	56.08

Runham (TG 41 SE/4) TG 4588 1129

Drilled in 1984
Surface level + 12.00 m

	Thickness m	Depth m
Soil and cover silt	0.50	0.50

LOWESTOFT TILL

Clay, sandy and silty with pebbles	1.35	1.85

CORTON FORMATION

Sand, silty and clayey	2.75	4.60
Clay, sandy and silty with shell debris	10.30	14.90

KESGRAVE FORMATION

Sand and gravel, including quartz pebbles	7.00	21.90

CRAG

Sand, silty, part shelly, iron pan at top	3.60	25.50

Runham/Yare 8 (TG 50 NW/480) TG 5165 0810

Drilled in 1981
Surface level 0.00 m

	Thickness m	Depth m
Deck	0.70	0.70

BREYDON FORMATION

Silt, clayey and gravelly, mottled grey-brown, soft	0.90	1.60

NORTH DENES FORMATION

Sand and gravel, silty	1.70	3.30

BREYDON FORMATION

Silt, clayey and shelly, grey, soft	0.50	3.80
Silt, dark brown and grey, soft and organic	1.10	4.90
Clay, silty, sandy, grey, soft	13.50	18.40
Peat, sandy, dark brown	0.30	18.70

YARE VALLEY FORMATION

Sand and gravel, silty	5.20	23.90

CRAG

Clay, silty and sandy, grey, becoming shelly and gravelly	1.65	25.55
Sand, shelly, grey	8.65	34.20

Somerton No. 1 (TG 42 SE/1) TG 4607 2120

Drilled in 1968
Surface level + 4.19 m

	Thickness m	Depth m
No recovery	4.19	4.19

ALLUVIUM

Sand, silt and peat	22.03	26.22

CRAG

Sandstone, loose, with chert fragments	28.64	54.86

LONDON CLAY FORMATION

Claystone, with occasional siltstones	50.64	105.50

CHALK GROUP

Upper Chalk

Chalk and flint	381.5	487.0

Middle Chalk

Chalk and flint	36.0	523.0

Lower Chalk

Chalk	16.5	539.5

GAULT

Mudstone, partly calcareous	5.6	545.1

CARSTONE

Sandstone, soft and glauconitic	17.9	563.0

LOWER CRETACEOUS (BARREMIAN) CLAYS

	8.2	571.2

HAISBOROUGH GROUP

Mudstones with anhydrite/gypsum and siltstones	145.0	716.2

BACTON GROUP

Bunter Sandstone Formation

Sandstone, minor mudstones	36.8	753.0

Bunter Shale Formation

Mudstones, anhydritic with siltstones and fine sandstones	85.9	838.9

?Bröckelschiefer Member

Mudstones, silty, anhydritic and dolomitic	12.1	851.0

Hewett Sandstone Member

Sandstone	17.8	868.8

ZECHSTEIN GROUP
Upper Zechstein (Z3–Z5) Clastics

Sandstones, siltstones and mudstones	32.2	901.0

Plattendolomit (Brotherton [Magnesian Limestone] Formation)

Dolomitic limestone	7.3	908.3

?Grauer Salzton

Red mudstone	5.2	913.5

Lower Zechstein (Z1–Z2) Clastics

Sandstones and mudstones, dolomitic	35.5	949.0

?Zechsteinkalk

Muddy limestone	1.8	950.8

ROTLIEGEND GROUP

Leman Sandstone Formation

Sandstone, conglomeratic at base	28.1	978.9

COAL MEASURES
Mudstones and sandstones 60.9 1039.8

DINANTIAN LIMESTONES
Limestones, dolomitic, with occasional
 mudstones 141.0 1180.8

?SILURIAN ROCKS
Shales, siltstones and slates 220.1 1400.9

Strumpshaw Hill (TG 30 NE/12) TG 3545 0703

Drilled in 1984
Surface level + 40.00 m

	Thickness m	Depth m
Soil	0.30	0.30
LOWESTOFT TILL FORMATION		
Sand and gravel, with cobbles	9.60	9.90
Till		
Clay, silty, with chalk granules	1.10	11.00
Sand, silty	0.20	11.20
Clay, stiff, with chalk pebbles and flints	6.30	17.50
CORTON FORMATION		
Sand	3.30	20.80
Sand, clayey, with clay layers and chalk pebbles	0.90	21.70
Till		
Clay, silty	1.50	23.20
Sand with chalk and quartz pebbles	0.60	23.80
Clay, sandy, silty with chalk and flint pebbles	4.80	28.60
Sand and gravel	0.80	29.40
Clay, stiff, with chalk and flint pebbles	3.00	32.40
KESGRAVE FORMATION		
Sand and gravel	0.70	33.10

Toft Monks House (TM 49 NW/23) TM 4301 9570

Drilled in 1983
Surface level + 26.90 m

	Thickness m	Depth m
Soil and cover silt	1.10	1.10
LOWESTOFT TILL		
Clay, silty and sandy, with flints	0.20	1.30
Clay, silty, with flints and chalk	1.90	3.20
Silt, clayey, sandy, laminated; granular chalk sand at base	2.10	5.30
Clay, silty, with flints and chalk	2.05	7.35
CORTON FORMATION		
Sand, silty, chalky, pale yellow	9.15	16.50
Till		
Clay, sandy and silty with shell fragments, pebbles of flint, quartz and chalk; greyish brown and orange-brown	1.30	17.80
KESGRAVE FORMATION		
Sand and silt, interlaminated, including quartz and flint pebbles	4.50	22.30
CRAG		
Sand, micaceous, much iron pan	7.00	29.30
Sand, shelly, very shelly below 30.30 m	2.00	31.30

Upton Hall, Upton (TG 31 SE/30) TG 3940 1224

Drilled in 1986
Surface level + 15.00 m

	Thickness m	Depth m
CORTON FORMATION		
Till		
Clay, sandy, pebbly	4.37	4.37
Clay, pebbly and sand, interbedded	1.13	5.50
Sand	0.50	6.00
Sand and gravel with flint, quartz and quartzite	0.05	6.05
Till		
Clay, sandy, pebbly with iron pan	5.11	11.16
Clay, sandy, pebbly, including quartz and chalk pebbles; ferruginous	2.44	13.60
KESGRAVE FORMATION		
Sand, silty	0.60	14.20
Sand, clayey and pebbly, including quartz and quartzite pebbles	10.30	24.50
CRAG		
Silt, grey-green, micaceous	0.50	25.00
Sand, grey-green, micaceous	1.00	26.00

Waste Disposal Site, West Caister (TG 51 SW/31) TG 5184 1082

Drilled in 1974
Surface level + 2.00 m

	Thickness m	Depth m
Made ground	3.00	3.00
BREYDON FORMATION		
Clay, peat and shells	4.10	7
Peat, brown, fibrous, woody	1.80	8.90
Clay, grey, very soft	4.60	13.50
Clay	7.50	21.00
Clay, shell and gravel	1.70	22.70
Silt, sandy and shelly	0.90	23.60
Peat, brown, tough, woody	0.10	23.70
?CRAG		
Sand, coarse-grained, grey	0.50	24.20

West Somerton No. 1 (TG 41 NE/3) TG 4736 1935

Drilled in 1987
Surface level +24.56 m
Published with permission from AmBrit Resources Ltd

	Thickness m	Depth m
No recovery	3.5	3.5
Sand, silt, clay and peat	50.5	54.0
CRAG		
Sandstone, loose, with chert fragments	33.5	87.5
LONDON CLAY FORMATION		
Claystone with some siltstone	44.5	132.0
CHALK GROUP		
Upper Chalk		
Chalk and flint	372.0	504.0
Middle Chalk		
Chalk and flint	36.0	540.0

Lower Chalk
Chalk | 15.7 | 555.7

GAULT
Mudstone, partly calcareous | 8.3 | 564.0

CARSTONE
Sandstone, soft and glauconitic | 16.7 | 580.7

LOWER CRETACEOUS (BARREMIAN) CLAYS | 9.8 | 590.5

HAISBOROUGH GROUP
Mudstones with anhydrite/gypsum
  and siltstones | 116.7 | 707.2

BACTON GROUP

Bunter Sandstone Formation
Sandstone | 37.6 | 744.8

Bunter Shale Formation
Mudstones, anhydritic with siltstones and
  fine sandstones | 81.4 | 826.2

?Bröckelschiefer Member
Mudstones, silty, anhydritic and dolomitic | 12.4 | 838.6

Hewett Sandstone Member
Sandstone | 15.5 | 854.1

ZECHSTEIN GROUP

Upper Zechstein (Z3–Z5) Clastics
Sandstones, siltstones and mudstones | 33.4 | 887.5

*Plattendolomit (Brotherton [Magnesian
  Limestone] Formation)*
Dolomitic limestone | 8.0 | 895.5

?Grauer Salzton
Red mudstone | 5.5 | 901.0

Lower Zechstein (Z1–Z2) Clastics
Sandstones, and mudstones, dolomitic | 22.0 | 923.0

?Zechsteinkalk
Muddy limestone | 2.0 | 925.0

ROTLIEGEND GROUP

Leman Sandstone Formation
Sandstone, | 18.2 | 943.2

COAL MEASURES
Mudstones and sandstones | 36.3 | 979.5

DINANTIAN LIMESTONES
Limestones, dolomitic with occasional
  mudstones | 8.0 | 987.5

White Lodge Farm, Mundham (TM 39 NW/12) TM 3346 9804

Drilled in 1986
Surface level + 8.84 m

	Thickness m	*Depth* m
LOWESTOFT TILL		
Clay with chalk clasts and flints	4.60	4.60
CORTON FORMATION		
Sand, pebbly at base	6.10	10.70
Sand, clay and gravel, interbedded	6.60	17.30
CRAG		
Sand and clay, interlaminated, micaceous, pebbly	5.00	22.30
Sand, grey-green, micaceous	4.70	27.00

Witton House, Brundall (TG 30 NW/31) TG 3130 0912

Drilled in 1986
Surface level + 24.50 m

	Thickness m	*Depth* m
GLACIOFLUVIAL DEPOSITS		
Sand, pebbly	1.40	1.40
Sand, clayey, pebbly	0.15	1.55
Sand, pebbly	1.45	3.00
CORTON FORMATION		
Till		
Clay, sand and gravel, chalky	4.00	7.00
CRAG		
Sand, part clayey, ferruginous, with layers and laminae of clay; some iron pan	1.20	8.20
	12.05	20.25

APPENDIX 3

Geological Survey photographs

Copies of these photographs are deposited for reference in the library of the British Geological Survey, Keyworth, Nottingham NG12 5GG. Black and white prints can be supplied and, in addition, colour prints are available for all the photographs with 5-figure numbers. All numbers belong to Series A. Numbers 5654–5673 were taken in 1931 by J Rhodes, 14179–14199 and 14209–14213 in 1983 by R Collins, and 15048–15064 in 1990 by H J Evans.

5654   View across the Waveney joining Breydon Water, from Burgh Castle
5655   Marshland drainage mills along the River Yare
5656   A marsh farm with drainage mills on River Bure
5657   River Waveney and marshes from St Olaves Bridge
5658   The confluence of River Waveney and New Cut
5659   Fritton Lake (Decoy)
5660   Fritton Lake (Decoy)
5661   Rollesby Broad from Rollesby-Ormesby road (Sheet 148)
5662   Ormesby Broad from Rollesby–Ormesby road (Sheet 148)
5663   Filby Broad from Filby Church
5664   Filby Broad from Filby Bridge
5665   Cliffs of glacial deposits at Corton
5666   Broken Sea wall due to wave action, Corton
5667   Houses on cliff edge, partly demolished due to land slips, Corton
5668   Cliffs of glacial deposits, Corton
5669   Landslips affecting glacial deposits, Corton Cliffs
5670   Peat overlying the 'Rootlet Bed', Corton Cliffs
5671   Peat underlying glacial deposits, Corton Cliffs
5672   General view of cliffs of glacial deposits, Corton Cliffs
5673   Glacial deposits at Corton Cliffs
14179   Cliff section in glacial and glaciofluvial deposits (Corton Formation), Corton [5474 9653]
14180   Cliff section and coastal defences, Corton [5468 9652]
14181   'Plateau Gravels' (Corton Woods Sands and Gravels), and Pleasure Gardens Till and Oulton Beds (Lowestoft Till Formation), Corton [5468 9652]
14182   Pleasure Gardens Till and Oulton Beds (Lowestoft Till Formation, Corton [5468 9652]
14183   Dewatering structure at top of Corton Sands (Corton Formation), Corton [5468 9652]
14184   'Ball and pillow' structures in Corton Sands, Corton [5458 9689]
14185   'Ball and pillow' structures in Corton Sands, Corton [5458 9689]
14186   Junction of Lowestoft Till with Corton Sands, Corton [5446 9740]
14187   Cliff section in Corton Sands, Corton [5411 9835]
14188   Periglacial involutions in the Corton Sands, Corton [5395 9873]
14189   Microfaulting in the Corton Sands, Corton [5451 9722]
14190   Fining-upwards sequence of sands, silts and clays (Corton Formation), Corton [5441 9755]

14191   Channel scour in Corton Sands (Corton Formation), [5412 9830]
14192   Dewatering structure in Corton Sands, Corton [5411 9835]
14193   Typical bedforms developed in Corton Sands, Corton [5412 9829]
14194   Lithological variations within Corton Sands, Corton [5391 9886]
14195   Margin of till sheet (Corton Formation), Corton [5404 9852]
14196   Margin of till sheet (Corton Formation), Corton [5404 9852]
14197   Ice-wedge casts [5401 9864]
14198   Section in 'Norwich Brickearth' (till in Corton Formation), Corton [520 145]
14199   Interbedded sands and slightly pebbly silty clays (Corton Formation) Corton [520 145]
14209   Sands and gravels at Haddiscoe [447 962]
14210   Sands and gravels at Haddiscoe [447 962]
14211   Raft of sand incorporated in overlying gravels at Haddiscoe [446 963]
14212   Close-up of 14211 [446 963]
14213   Channel of well-rounded flint gravel at Haddiscoe [445 962]
15048   Anglian glacial deposits in cliffs at Corton [547 965]
15049   Sands of the Corton Formation in cliffs at Corton [5468 9652]
15050   Gravels of the Corton Formation at Welcome Pit, Burgh Castle [485 041]
15051   Sands and pebbly sands of the Corton Formation at Welcome Pit, Burgh Castle [485 042]
15052   Corton Formation — sands and pebbly sands resting on till, Welcome Pit, Burgh Castle [485 042]
15053   Cliffs of Corton Formation composed largely of till, California (Sheet 148) [520 145]
15054   Cliffs of Corton Formation comprising till with a layer of sand, California (Sheet 148) [5196 1453]
15055   Lowestoft Till resting on Corton Formation in cliffs at California, (Sheet 148) [5184 1476]
15056   Lowestoft Till resting on Corton Formation, Welcome Pit, Burgh Castle [484 043]
15057 oft   Laminated silts and clays of the Oulton Beds (Lowestoft Till Formation) in cliffs at Corton [5468 9652]
15058   Corton Woods Sands and Gravels in the cliffs at Corton [5468 9648]
15059   Close-up of 15058 [5468 9648]
15060   Foredunes on North Beach, Great Yarmouth [532 090]
15061   Foredunes on beach deposits at North Beach, Great Yarmouth [533 090]
15062   Tidal flats and salt marsh flanking Breydon Water [517 082]
15063   Salt marsh at Breydon Water [517 082]
15064   Fritton Decoy [476 000]

REFERENCES

Most of the references listed below are held in the Library of the British Geological Survey at Keyworth, Nottingham. Copies of the references can be purchased subject to the current copyright legislation.

ALDERTON, A M. 1983. Flandrian vegetational history and sea-level change of the Waveney valley. Unpublished PhD thesis, University of Cambridge.

ALLEN, P. 1984. Kesgrave Sand and Gravel Formation. 15–24 in *Field guide to the Gipping and Waveney valleys, Suffolk, May, 1982*. ALLEN, P (editor). (Norwich: Quaternary Research Association.)

ALLSOP, J M. 1984. Geophysical appraisal of a Carboniferous basin in northeast Norfolk, England. *Proceedings of the Geologists' Association*, Vol. 95, 175–180.

— 1985. Geophysical investigations into the extent of the Devonian rocks beneath East Anglia. *Proceedings of the Geologists' Association*, Vol. 96, 371–379.

— 1987. Patterns of late Caledonian intrusive activity in eastern and northern England from geophysics, radiometric dating and basement geology. *Proceedings of the Yorkshire Geological Society*, Vol. 46, 335–353.

— and JONES, C M. 1981. A pre-Permian palaeogeological map of the East Midlands and East Anglia. *Transactions of the Leicester Literary and Philosophical Society*, No. 75, 28–33.

ANDERTON, R, BRIDGES, P H, LEEDER, M R, and SELLWOOD, B W. 1979. *A dynamic stratigraphy of the British Isles*. (London: George Allen and Unwin.)

ANON. 1986. Concrete in sulphate-bearing soils and groundwater. *Digest*, No. 250. (Watford: Building Research Establishment.)

ASGAARD, U. 1975. A revision of Sahni's types of the brachiopod subfamily Carneithyridinae. *Bulletin of the British Museum (Natural History)*, Geology Series, Vol. 25, No. 5.

BADEN-POWELL, D F W. 1948. The chalky boulder clays of Norfolk and Suffolk. *Geological Magazine*, Vol. 85, 279–296.

— 1950. Field meeting in the Lowestoft district. *Proceedings of the Geologists' Association*, Vol. 61, 191–197.

— and REID MOIR, J. 1942. On a Palaeolithic industry from the Norfolk coast. *Geological Magazine*, Vol. 79, 209–296.

BAILEY, H W, GALE, A S, MORTIMORE, R N, SWIECICKI, A, and WOOD, C J. 1983. The Coniacian–Maastrichtian stages of the United Kingdom, with particular reference to southern England. *Newsletters on Stratigraphy*, Vol. 12, 19–42.

BALCHIN, D A, and RIDD, M F. 1970. Correlation of the younger Triassic rocks across eastern England. *Quarterly Journal of the Geological Society of London*, Vol. 126, 91–101.

BALSON, P S, and CAMERON, T D J. 1985. Quaternary mapping offshore East Anglia. *Modern Geology*, Vol. 9, 221–239.

BANHAM, P H. 1970. 2–4 in *Quaternary Research Association field guide, Norwich area*. BOULTON, G S (editor). (Norwich: Quaternary Research Association.)

— 1971. Pleistocene beds at Corton, Suffolk. *Geological Magazine*, Vol. 108, 281–285.

— 1975. Glacitectonic structures: a general discussion with particular reference to the contorted drift of Norfolk. 69–94 *in* Ice ages: ancient and modern. WRIGHT, A E, and MOSELEY, F (editors). *Geological Journal Special Issue*, No. 6. (Liverpool: Seel House Press.)

— 1988. Polyphase glaciotectonic deformation in the Contorted Drift of Norfolk. 27–32 in *Glaciotectonics: forms and processes*. CROOT, D G (editor). (Rotterdam: Balkema.)

— and ROSE, J. 1977. 15–16 in *Guidebook for excursions A1 and C1: X INQUA Congress Excursion Guides*. BOWEN, D Q (editor). International Union for Quaternary Research. Congress X, Birmingham 1977.

BATH, A H, and EDMUNDS, W M. 1981. Identification of connate water in interstitial solution of Chalk sediment. *Geochimica et Cosmochimica Acta*, Vol. 45, 1449–1461.

— DOWNING, R A, and BARKER, J A. 1985. The age of groundwaters in the Chalk and Pleistocene sands of north-east Suffolk. *British Geological Survey Research Report*, WD/ST/85/1.

BECK, R B, FUNNELL, B M, and LORD, A R. 1972. Correlation of the Lower Pleistocene Crag at depth in Suffolk. *Geological Magazine*, Vol. 109, 137–139.

BELL, A, and BELL, R. 1871. The English Crags, and their stratigraphical divisions as indicated by their invertebrate fauna. *Geological Magazine*, Vol. 108, 256–263.

BERGGREN, W A, KENT, D V, and FLYNN, J J. 1985. Jurassic to Palaeogene: Part 2. Palaeogene geochronology and chronostratigraphy. 141–195 *in* The chronology of the geological record. SNELLING, N J (editor). *Memoir of the Geological Society of London*, No. 10.

BLAKE, J H. 1884. Explanation of horizontal sections, Sheet 128. Sections of the Suffolk cliffs at Kessingland and Pakefield, and at Corton. *Geological Survey of England and Wales*.

— 1890. Geology of the country near Yarmouth and Lowestoft (explanation of Sheet 67). *Memoir of the Geological Survey* (England and Wales).

BLOOMFIELD, C. 1972. The oxidation of iron sulphides in soils in relation to the formation of acid sulphate soils, and of ochre deposits in field drains. *Journal of Soil Science*, Vol. 23, No. 1, 1–16.

BOSWELL, P G H. 1914. On the occurrence of the North Sea Drift (Lower Glacial), and certain other brickearths in Suffolk. *Proceedings of the Geologists' Association*, Vol. 25, 121–153.

— 1916. The stratigraphy and petrology of the Lower Eocene deposits of the north-eastern part of the London Basin. *Quarterly Journal of the Geological Society of London*, Vol. 71, 536–591.

— 1920. On the surface and dip of the Chalk in Norfolk. *Transactions of the Norwich and Norfolk Naturalists' Society*, Vol. 11, Pt. 1, 22–58.

BOULTON, G S, and HINDMARSH, R C A. 1987. Sediment deformation beneath glaciers: rheology and geological consequences. *Journal of Geophysical Research,* Vol. 92, (B9), 9059–9082.

BOTT, M H P. 1988. The Market Weighton gravity anomaly — granite or graben? *Proceedings of the Yorkshire Geological Society,* Vol. 47, 47–53.

BOWEN, D Q, ROSE, J, MCCABE, A M, and SUTHERLAND, D G. 1986. Correlation of Quaternary glaciations in England, Ireland, Scotland and Wales. 299–340 *in* Quaternary glaciations in the Northern Hemisphere. ŠIBRAVA, V, BOWEN, D Q, and RICHMOND, G M (editors). *Quaternary Science Reviews,* Vol. 5.

BOWER, C R, and FARMERY, J R. 1910. The zones of the Lower Chalk of Lincolnshire. *Proceedings of the Geologists' Association,* Vol. 21, 333–359.

BRENNAND, T P. 1975. The Triassic of the North Sea. 295–312 in *Petroleum and the continental shelf of North-west Europe,* Vol. 1. WOODLAND A W (editor). (Barking: Applied Science, for the Institute of Petroleum.)

BRERETON, N R. 1978. The effects of iron bacteria on the yield and efficiency of groundwater supply boreholes. *Water Research Centre Report,* ILR 895.

BRIDGE, D McC. 1985. Geological notes and local details for 1:10 000 Sheets TM 49 NE, TM 59 and part of TM 59 NE (Somerleyton and Corton). (Keyworth: British Geological Survey.)

— and HOPSON, P M. 1985. Fine gravel, heavy mineral and grain-size analyses of mid-Pleistocene glacial deposits in the lower Waveney valley, East Anglia. *Modern Geology,* Vol. 9, 129–144.

BRIDGLAND, D R. 1988. The Pleistocene fluvial stratigraphy and palaeogeography of Essex. *Proceedings of the Geologists' Association,* Vol. 99, 291–314.

BRISTOW, C R. 1983. The stratigraphy and structure of the Crag of mid-Suffolk, England. *Proceedings of the Geologists' Association,* Vol. 94, 1–12.

— 1990. Geology of the country around Bury St Edmunds. *Memoir of the British Geological Survey,* Sheet 189 (England and Wales).

— In preparation. Geology of the country around Shaftesbury. *Memoir of the British Geological Survey,* Sheet 313 (England and Wales).

— and COX, F C. 1973. The Gipping Till: a reappraisal of East Anglian glacial stratigraphy. *Journal of the Geological Society of London,* Vol. 129, 1–37.

BRITISH GEOLOGICAL SURVEY. 1988. East Anglia Sheet 52°N–00°. Sea Bed Sediments. 1:250 000 Series. (Southampton: Ordnance Survey, for the British Geological Survey.)

BRITISH GEOLOGICAL SURVEY and RIJKS GEOLGISCHE DIENST. 1984. Flemish Bight Sheet 52°N– 02°. Quaternary Geology. 1:250 000 Series. (Southampton: Ordnance Survey, for the British Geological Survey.)

BROADS AUTHORITY. 1981. Acid sulphate soils in Broadland. *Broads Authority Research Series,* No. 3.

BROMLEY, R G, SCHULZ, M-G, and PEAKE, N B. 1975. Paramoudras: giant flints, long burrows and the early diagenesis of chalks. *Kongelige Danske Videnskabernes Selskab. Geologi Skrifter,* No. 20.

BRUNSTROM, R G W, and WALMSLEY, P J. 1969. Permian evaporites in the North Sea Basin. *Bulletin of the American Association of Petroleum Geologists,* Vol. 53, 870–883.

BULLARD, E C, GASKELL, T F, HARLAND, W B, and KERR-GRANT, C. 1940. Seismic investigations of the Palaeozoic floor of east England. *Philosophical Transactions of the Royal Society of London,* A, Vol. 239, 29–94.

BURNETT J. 1991. New nannofossil zonation scheme for the Boreal Campanian. *International Nannoplankton Association Newsletter,* Vol. 12, 67–70

BURTON, R G O, and HODGSON, J M (editors). 1987. Lowland peat in England and Wales. *Soil Survey Special Survey,* No. 15.

BUTLER, J B. 1975. The West Sole Gas-field. 213–222 in *Petroleum and the continental shelf of North-west Europe,* Vol. 1, WOODLAND, A W (editor). (Barking: Applied Science, for the Institute of Petroleum.)

CAMBRIDGE, P G. 1975. Field meeting to Bramerton, near Norwich, 14–15th September, 1974. *Bulletin of the Geological Society of Norfolk,* No. 27, 31–46.

CAMERON, T D J, CROSBY, A, BALSON, P S, JEFFERY, D H, LOTT, G K, BULAT, J, and HARRISON, D J. 1992. *UK offshore regional report: The geology of the southern North Sea.* (Keyworth: British Geological Survey.)

— BONNY, A P, GREGORY, D M, and HARLAND, R. 1984. Lower Pleistocene dinoflagellate cyst, foraminiferal and pollen assemblages in four boreholes in the southern North Sea. *Geological Magazine,* Vol. 121, 85–97.

— STOKER, M S, and LONG, D. 1987. The history of Quaternary sedimentation in the UK sector of the North Sea Basin. *Journal of the Geological Society of London,* Vol. 144, 43–58.

CARTER, D J, and HART, M B. 1977. Aspects of mid-Cretaceous stratigraphical micropalaeontology. *Bulletin of the British Museum (Natural History),* Geology Series, Vol. 29, No. 1.

CASEY, R. 1961. Geological age of the Sandringham Sands. *Nature, London.* Vol. 190, 1100.

— and GALLOIS, R W. 1973. The Sandringham Sands of Norfolk. *Proceedings of the Yorkshire Geological Society,* Vol. 40, 1–22.

CASTON, V N D. 1972. Linear sand banks in the southern North Sea. *Sedimentology,* Vol. 18, 63–78.

— 1977. A new isopachyte map of the Quaternary of the North Sea. 1–8 *in* Quaternary sediments of the central North Sea, 1 and 2. *Report of the Institute of Geological Sciences,* No. 77/11.

CATT, J A, CORBETT, W M, HODGE, C A H, MADGETT, P A, TATLER, W, and WEIR, A H. 1971. Loess in the soils of North Norfolk. *Journal of Soil Science,* Vol. 22, 444–452.

CAVELIER, C, and POMEROL, C. 1986. Stratigraphy of the Palaeogene. *Bulletin de la Société Géologique de France,* 8ᵉ Série 2, 255–265.

CHADWICK, R A. 1985a. End Jurassic–early Cretaceous sedimentation and subsidence (late Portlandian to Barremian), and the late-Cimmerian unconformity. 52–56 in *Atlas of onshore sedimentary basins in England and Wales.* WHITTAKER, A (editor). (Keyworth: British Geological Survey, and Glasgow and London: Blackie.)

— 1985b. Cretaceous sedimentation and subsidence (Aptian–Albian). 57–58 in *Atlas of onshore sedimentary basins in England and Wales.* WHITTAKER, A (editor). (Keyworth: British Geological Survey, and Glasgow and London: Blackie.)

— 1985c. Cenozoic sedimentation and subsidence and tectonic inversion. 61–63 in *Atlas of onshore basins in England and Wales.* WHITTAKER, A (editor). (Keyworth: British Geological Survey, and Glasgow and London: Blackie.)

CHARLESWORTH, E. 1835. Observations on the Crag Formation and its organic remains: with a view to establishing a division of the Tertiary strata overlying the London Clay in Suffolk. *London, Edinburgh and Dublin Philosophical Magazine*, Series 3, Vol. 7, 81–94.

— 1837. A notice of the remains of vertebrate animals found in the Tertiary beds of Norfolk and Suffolk. *Report of the British Association for the Advancement of Science*, (for 1836), Sections 84–86.

CHATWIN, C P. 1961. *British regional geology: East Anglia and adjoining areas* (4th edition). (London: HMSO for Geological Survey and Museum.)

CHROSTON, P N, and SOLA, M A. 1982. Deep boreholes, seismic refraction lines and the interpretation of gravity anomalies in Norfolk. *Journal of the Geological Society of London*, Vol. 139, 255–264.

— ALLSOP, J M, and CORNWELL, J D. 1987. New seismic refraction evidence of the origin of the Bouguer anomaly low near Hunstanton, Norfolk. *Proceedings of the Yorkshire Geological Society*, Vol. 46, 311–319.

CLARKE, K B, and PHILLIPS, J H. 1984. Experiences in the use of East Anglian sands and gravels ('Crags') as a source of water supply. *Journal of the Institution of Water Engineers and Scientists*, Vol. 38, 543–549.

CLARKE, M R, and AUTON, C. 1982. The Pleistocene depositional history of the Norfolk–Suffolk borderland. *Report of the Institute of Geological Sciences*, No. 82/1, 23–29.

— and CORNWELL, J D. 1983. The buried glacial channels of the Woolpit (Suffolk) area—a preliminary report. *Report of the Institute of Geological Sciences*, No. 83/10, 31–36.

CLAYTON, C J. 1986. The chemical environment of flint formation in Upper Cretaceous chalks. 43–54 in *The scientific study of flint and chert: proceedings of the Fourth International Flint Symposium*. SIEVEKING, G DE G, and HART, M B (editors). (Cambridge University Press.)

CLAYTON, K M. 1977. Beach profile and volume changes. *Report of the East Anglian Coastal Research Programme, University of East Anglia, Norwich*, No. 5.

— 1980. Coastal protection along the East Anglian coast, UK. *Zeitschrift für Geomorphologie*, N F Supplementband, 34, 165–172.

— 1989. Sediment input from the Norfolk Cliffs, Eastern England — a century of coast protection and its effect. *Journal of Coastal Research*, Vol. 5, 433–442.

— McCAVE, I N, and VINCENT, C E. 1983. The establishment of a sand budget for the East Anglian coast and its implications for coastal stability. 91–96 in *Shoreline Protection* (Proceedings of a conference organised by the Institute of Civil Engineers, University of Southampton, 14th September 1982). (London: Thomas Telford.)

COLES, B P L. 1977. The Holocene foraminifera and palaeogeography of Central Broadland. Unpublished PhD thesis, University of East Anglia.

— and FUNNELL, B M. 1981. Holocene palaeoenvironments of Broadland, England. *International Association of Sedimentologists Special Publication*, No. 5, 123–131.

CONYBEARE, W D, and PHILLIPS, W. 1822. *Outlines of the geology of England and Wales*. London.

COOPER, J. 1976. British Tertiary stratigraphical and rock terms, formal and informal, additional to Curry 1959, Lexique Stratigraphique International. *Tertiary Research Special Paper*, No. 1.

CORBETT, W M. 1977. Distribution of loess in north east Norfolk. *Bulletin of the Geological Society of Norfolk*, Vol. 29, 3–22.

— and TATLER, W. 1970. Soils in Norfolk: Sheet TM 49 (Beccles North). *Soil Survey Records*, No. 1.

— — 1974. Soils in Norfolk II. *Soil Survey Records*, No. 21.

COSTA, L I and DOWNIE, C. The distribution of the dinoflagellate *Wetzeliella* in the Palaeogene of north-western Europe. *Palaeontology*, Vol. 19, 591–694.

COX, F C. 1985a. The East Anglia Regional Geological Survey: an overview. *Modern Geology*, Vol. 9, 103–115.

— — 1985b. The tunnel valleys of East Anglia. *Proceedings of the Geologists' Association*, Vol. 96, 357–369.

— and NICKLESS, E F P. 1972. Some aspects of the glacial history of central Norfolk. *Bulletin of the Geological Survey of Great Britain*, No. 42, 79–98.

— GALLOIS, R W, and WOOD, C J. 1989. Geology of the country around Norwich. *Memoir of the British Geological Survey*, Sheet 161 (England and Wales).

— HAILWOOD, E A, HARLAND, R, HUGHES, M J, JOHNSTON, N, and KNOX, R W O'B. 1985. Palaeocene sedimentation and stratigraphy in Norfolk, England. *Newsletters on Stratigraphy*, Vol. 14, 169–185.

COXON, P. 1979. Pleistocene environmental history in central East Anglia. Unpublished PhD thesis, Unversity of Cambridge.

CRAIG-SMITH, S J. 1972. The changing system. *Report of the East Anglian Coastal Study, University of East Anglia, Norwich*, No. 3.

— SIMMONDS, A C, and CAMBERS, G. 1975. East Anglian sea defence policy. *Report of the East Anglian Coastal Research Programme, University of East Anglia, Norwich*, No. 2.

CRONIN, T M. 1983. Rapid sea-level and climatic changes: evidence from continental and island margins. *Quaternary Science Reviews*, Vol. 1, 177–214.

CUMMING, A D, and WYNDHAM, C L. 1975. The geology and development of the Hewett Gas-field. 313–326 in *Petroleum and the continental shelf of North-west Europe*, Vol. 1, WOODLAND, A W (editor). (Barking: Applied Science, for the Institute of Petroleum.

CURRY, D, ADAMS, C G, BOULTER, M C, DILLEY, F C, EAMES, F E, FUNNELL, B M, and WELLS, M K. 1978. A correlation of Tertiary rocks in the British Isles. *Special Report of the Geological Society of London*, No. 12.

DALE, S. 1704. Letter concerning Harwich Cliff, and the fossil shells there. *Philosophical Transactions*, Vol, 24, No. 291, 1568–1578. Reprinted in *The History and Antiquities of Harwich and Dovercourt*, 18–19, London, 1730.

DENT, D L, DOWNING, E J B, and ROGAAR, H. 1976. Changes in the structure of marsh soils following drainage and arable cultivation. *Journal of Soil Science*, Vol. 27, 250–265.

DEWEY, J F. 1982. Plate tectonics and the evolution of the British Isles. *Journal of the Geological Society of London*, Vol. 139, 371–412.

DONATO, J A, and MEGSON, J B. 1990. A buried granite batholith beneath the East Midland Shelf of the Southern North Sea Basin. *Journal of the Geological Society of London*, Vol. 147, 133–140.

DOWNING, R A. 1966. Hydrogeology of northern East Anglia with special reference to the Chalk. *Water Supply Papers of the Geological Survey of Great Britain*. Unpublished report.

EAST SUFFOLK AND NORFOLK RIVER AUTHORITY. 1971. *First survey of resources and demands.* Section 14 Survey.

EDEN, R A, HOLMES, R, and FANNIN, N G T. 1977. Depositional environment of offshore Quaternary deposits of the Continental Shelf around Scotland. *Report of the Institute of Geological Sciences,* No. 77/15.

ELLIOTT, R E. 1961. The stratigraphy of the Keuper Series in southern Nottinghamshire. *Proceedings of the Yorkshire Geological Society,* Vol. 33, 197–234.

EISMA, D, MOOK, W G, and LABAN, C. 1981. An early holocene tidal flat in the Southern Bight. 229–237 *in* Holocene marine sedimentation in the North Sea Basin.
NIO, S-D, SHÜTTENHELM (sic), R T E, and WEERING, TJ C E VAN (editors). *Special Publication of the International Association of Sedimentologists,* No. 5.

ERNST, G. 1963. Stratigraphische und Gesteinschemische Untersuchungen im Santon und Campan von Lägerdorf (SW-Holstein). [Stratigraphical and rock chemistry researches in the Santonian and Campanian at Lägerdorf (SW Holstein)]. *Mitteilungen aus dem Geologischen Staatsinstitut in Hamburg,* Vol. 32, 72–127. [In German]

— 1972. Grundfragen der Stammesgeschichte bei irregulären Echiniden der Nordwesteuropäischen Oberkreide. [Fundamental questions on the phylogeny of irregular echinoids of the Upper Cretaceous of north-west Europe.] *Geologisches Jahrbuch,* A4, 63–175. [In German]

EVANS, C J, and ALLSOP, J M. 1987. Some geophysical aspects of the deep geology of eastern England. *Proceedings of the Yorkshire Geological Society,* Vol. 46, 321–333.

EYLES, N, EYLES, C H, and McCABE, A M. 1989. Sedimentation in an ice-contact subaqueous setting: the mid-Pleistocene 'North Sea Drifts' of Norfolk, UK. *Quaternary Science Reviews,* Vol. 8, 57–74.

FISHER, M J. 1986. Triassic. 113–132 in *Introduction to the petroleum geology of the North Sea* (2nd edition). GLENNIE, K W (editor). (Oxford: Blackwell.)

FITCH, R. 1836. Letter on the discovery of the tooth of a mastodon in the Crag at Thorpe, near Norwich. *Proceedings of the Geological Society of London,* Vol. 2, 417.

FORBES, C L. 1952. Ludham Borehole: a gravel pack well in the Norwich Crag. *Journal of the Institution of Water Engineers,* Vol. 6, 362–369.

FRANCE, D S. 1975. The geology of the Indefatigable Gas-field. 233–240 in *Petroleum and the continental shelf of North-west Europe,* Vol. 1, WOODLAND, A W (editor). (Barking: Applied Science, for the Institute of Petroleum.)

FUNNELL, B M. 1958. Yare Valley buried glacial channel. *Transactions of the Norfolk Naturalists' Society,* Vol. 18, 10–14.

— 1961. The Palaeogene and Early Pleistocene of Norfolk. *Transactions of the Norfolk Naturalists' Society,* Vol. 19, 340–364.

— 1979. History and prognosis of subsidence and sea level change in the lower Yare valley. *Bulletin of the Geological Society of Norfolk,* Vol. 31, 35–44.

— 1987. Late Pliocene and Early Pleistocene stages of East Anglia and the adjacent North Sea. *Quaternary Newsletters,* Vol. 52, 1–11.

— and WEST, R G. 1977. Preglacial Pleistocene deposits of East Anglia. 246–265 in *British Quaternary studies: recent advances.* SHOTTON, F W (editor). (Oxford: Clarendon Press.)

— NORTON, P E P, and WEST, R G. 1979. The Crag at Bramerton, near Norwich, Norfolk. *Philosophical Transactions of the Royal Society of London,* B, Vol. 287, 489–534.

FYFE, J A, ABBOTTS, I, and CROSBY, A. 1981. The subcrop of the mid-Mesozoic unconformity in the UK area. 236–244 in *Petroleum geology of the continental shelf of North-west Europe.* ILLING, L V, and HOBSON, G D (editors). (London: Heyden and Sons.)

GALE, A S. 1989. Field meeting at Folkestone Warren, 29th November, 1987. *Proceedings of the Geologists' Association,* Vol. 100, 73–82.

— and SMITH, A B. 1982. The palaeobiology of the Cretaceous irregular echinoids *Infulaster* and *Hagenowia.* *Palaeontology,* Vol. 25, 1–42.

— and FRIEDRICH, S. 1989. Occurrence of the ammonite genus *Sharpeiceras* in the Lower Cenomanian Chalk Marl of Folkestone. 80–82 *in* appendix to Field meeting at Folkestone Warren , 29th November, 1987. GALE, A S. 1989. *Proceedings of the Geologists' Association,* Vol. 100.

GALLOIS, R W. 1984. The late Jurassic to mid Cretaceous rocks of Norfolk. *Bulletin of the Geological Society of Norfolk,* Vol. 34, 3–64.

— and MORTER, A A. 1976. Trunch Borehole, Mundesley (132) Sheet. *In* IGS Boreholes 1975. *Report of the Institute of Geological Sciences,* No. 76/10.

— — 1982. The stratigraphy of the Gault of East Anglia. *Proceedings of the Geologists' Association,* Vol. 93, 351–368.

GARDNER, K, and WEST, R G. 1975. Fossil ice-wedge polygons at Corton, Suffolk. *Bulletin of the Geological Society of Norfolk,* Vol. 27, 47–53.

GEIGER, M E, and HOPPING, C A. 1968. Triassic stratigraphy of the southern North Sea Basin. *Philosophical Transactions of the Royal Society of London,* B, Vol. 254, 1–36.

GIBBARD, P L, WEST, R G, ZAGWIJN, W H, BALSON, P S, BURGER, A W, FUNNELL, B M, JEFFERY, D H, JONG J DE, KOLFSCHOTEN, T VAN, LISTER, A M, MEIJER, T, NORTON, P E P, PREECE, R C, ROSE, J, STUART, A J, WHITEMAN, C A, and ZALASEIWICZ, J A. 1991. Early and early Middle Pleistocene correlations in the Southern North Sea Basin. *Quaternary Science Reviews,* Vol. 10, 23–52.

GLENNIE, K W. 1972. Permian Rotliegendes of North-west Europe interpreted in the light of modern desert sedimentation studies. *Bulletin of the American Association of Petroleum Geologists,* Vol. 56, 1048–1071.

— 1986. Early Permian–Rotliegend. 63–86 in *Introduction to the petroleum geology of the North Sea* (2nd edition). GLENNIE, K W (editor). (Oxford: Blackwell.)

GODWIN, H, and WILLIS, E H. 1964. Cambridge University natural radiocarbon measurements VI. *Radiocarbon,* Vol. 6, 116–137.

GOODCHILD, M W, and BRYANT, P. 1986. The geology of the Rough Gas Field. 223–235 *in* Habitat of Palaeozoic gas in NW Europe. BROOKS, J, GOFF, J C, and HOORN, B VAN (editors). *Special Publication of the Geological Society of London,* No. 23.

GRAY, I. 1975. Viking Gas-field. 241–248 in *Petroleum and the continental shelf of North-west Europe.* Vol. 1. WOODLAND, A W (editor). (Barking: Applied Science, for the Institute of Petroleum.)

GREEN, C, and HUTCHINSON, J N. 1960. Archaeological evidence. 113–146 *in* The making of the Broads. LAMBERT, J M, JENNING, J N, SMITH, C T, GREEN, C, and HUTCHINSON, J N. *Memoir of the Royal Geographical Society,* No. 3.

GREEN, C P, and McGREGOR, D F M. 1978. Pleistocene gravel trains of the River Thames. *Proceedings of the Geologists' Association,* Vol. 89, 143–156.

—— 1990. Pleistocene gravels of the north Norfolk coast. *Proceedings of the Geologists' Association,* Vol. 101, 197–202.

—— and EVANS, A H. 1982. Development of the Thames drainage system in Early and Middle Pleistocene times. *Geological Magazine,* Vol. 119, 281–290.

GUNN, J. 1867. The order of succession of the preglacial, glacial and postglacial strata in the coast sections of Norfolk and Suffolk. *Geological Magazine,* Vol. 4, 371–372 and 561.

HANCOCK, J M. 1986. Cretaceous. 161–176 in *Introduction to the petroleum geology of the North Sea.* GLENNIE, K W (editor). (London: Blackwell Scientific.)

HARLAND, R, BONNY, A P, HUGHES, M J, and MORIGI, A N. In press. The Lower Pleistocene stratigraphy of the Ormesby Borehole, Norfolk, England. *Geological Magazine.*

HARMER, F W. 1898. The Pliocene deposits of the east of England—Part I. Lenham Beds and Coralline Crag. *Quarterly Journal of the Geological Society of London,* Vol. 54, 308–356.

— 1900a. On a proposed new classification for the Pliocene deposits of the east of England. *Report of the British Association for the Advancement of Science, (Dover), Transactions of Section C,* (for 1899), 751–753.

— 1900b. The Pliocene deposits of the east of England— Part II. The crag of Essex (Waltonian) and its relation to that of Suffolk and Norfolk. With a report on the inorganic constitutents of the Crag by Joseph Lomas. *Quarterly Journal of the Geological Society of London,* Vol. 56, 705–738.

— 1902. A sketch of the later Tertiary history of East Anglia. *Proceedings of the Geologists' Association,* Vol. 17, 416–479.

— 1904. The Great Eastern Glacier. *Geological Magazine,* Vol. 51, 509–510.

— 1909a. The Pliocene deposits of the eastern counties of England. 86–102 in *Geology in the field.* MONKTON, H W, and HERRIES, R S (editors). *Geologists' Association Jubilee Volume.*

— 1909b. The Pleistocene period in the eastern counties of England. 103–123 in *Geology in the field.* MONKTON, H W, AND HERRIES, R S (editors). *Geologists' Association Jubilee Volume.*

— 1928. The distribution of erratics and drift. *Proceedings of the Yorkshire Geological Society,* Vol 21, 79–150.

HARRISON, D J. 1988. The marine sand and gravel resources off Great Yarmouth and Southwold, East Anglia. *British Geological Survey Technical Report,* WB/88/9.

HART, J K. 1987. The genesis of the North East Norfolk Drift. Unpublished PhD thesis, University of East Anglia.

— HINDMARSH, R C A, and BOULTON, G S. 1990. Styles of subglacial glaciotectonic deformation within the context of the Anglian ice-sheet. *Earth Surface Processes and Landforms,* Vol. 15, 227–241.

HART, M B, BAILEY, H W, CRITTENDEN, S, FLETCHER, B N, PRICE, R J, AND SWIECICKI, A. 1989. Cretaceous. 273–371 in *Stratigraphical atlas of fossil foraminifera* (second edition). JENKINS, D G, and MURRAY, J W (editors). (London: Ellis Horwood.)

HAZELDEN, J. 1989. Soils in Norfolk VIII: Sheet TG 40 (Halvergate). *Soil Survey Records,* No. 115.

HEAD, K H. 1982. *Manual of soil laboratory testing. Volume 2: permeability, shear strength and compressibility test.* (London: Pentech Press.)

HEATHCOTE, J A, and LLOYD, J W. 1984/1985. Groundwater chemistry in south-east Suffolk (UK) and its relation to Quaternary geology. *Journal of Hydrology,* Vol. 75, 143–165.

HEY, R W. 1967. The Westleton Beds reconsidered. *Proceedings of the Geologists' Association,* Vol. 78, 427–445.

— 1976. Provenance of far-travelled pebbles in the Pre-Anglian Pleistocene of East Anglia. *Proceedings of the Geologists' Association,* Vol. 87, 69–82.

— 1980. Equivalents of the Westland Green Gravels in Essex and East Anglia. *Proceedings of the Geologists' Association,* Vol. 91, 279–290.

— and BRENCHLEY, P J. 1977. Volcanic pebbles from Pleistocene gravels in Norfolk and Essex. *Geological Magazine,* Vol. 114, 219–225.

HILL, E. 1902. On the matrix of the Suffolk Chalky Boulder Clay. *Quarterly Journal of the Geological Society of London,* Vol. 58, 179–184.

HISCOCK, K M. 1987. Groundwater chemistry study in the vicinity of Norwich. Unpublished PhD thesis, University of Birmingham.

— and BISHOP, P K. 1987. Borehole logging and groundwater dating at Strumpshaw Pumping Station, Norfolk. Unpublished report to Anglian Water, ALTA Geophysics, University of Birmingham.

HOLLINGWORTH, S E, and TAYLOR, J H. 1946. An outline of the geology of the Kettering district. *Proceedings of the Geologists' Association,* Vol. 57, 204–233.

HOPSON, P M, and BRIDGE, D McC. 1987. Middle Pleistocene stratigraphy in the lower Waveney valley, East Anglia. *Proceedings of the Geologists' Association,* Vol. 98, 171–186.

HORTON, A. 1970. The drift sequence and subglacial topography in parts of the Ouse and Nene basin. *Report of the Institute of Geological Sciences,* No. 70/9.

HOUBOLT, J J H C. 1968. Recent sediments in the Southern Bight of the North Sea. *Geologie en Mijnbouw,* Vol. 47, 245–273.

INESON, J. 1962. A hydrogeological study of the permeability of the Chalk. *Journal of the Institution of Water Engineers,* Vol. 16, 449–463.

INSTITUTE OF GEOLOGICAL SCIENCES. 1976. IGS boreholes 1975. *Report of the Institute of Geological Sciences,* No. 76/10.

— 1976. Hydrogeological map of northern East Anglia. 1:125 000. (London: HMSO for Institute of Geological Sciences.)

JEANS, C V. 1968. The origin of the montmorillonite of the European Chalk with special reference to the Lower Chalk of England. *Clay Mineralogy,* Vol. 7, 311–329.

JEFFERIES, R P S. 1963. The stratigraphy of the *Actinocamax plenus* Subzone (Turonian) in the Anglo-Paris Basin. *Proceedings of the Geologists' Association,* Vol. 74, 1–33.

JELGERSMA, S. 1979. Sea-level changes in the North Sea basin. 233–248 in *The Quaternary history of the North Sea.* OELE, E, SCHÜTTENHELM, R T E, and WIGGERS, A J (editors). *Acta Universitatis Upsaliensis Symposia Universitatis Upsaliensis annum Quingentesimum Celebrantis; 2.* (Uppsala.)

JENNINGS, J N. 1952. The origin of the Broads. *Memoir of the Royal Geographical Society,* No. 2, 1–66.

— 1955. Further pollen data from the Norfolk Broads. Data for the study of post-glacial history, XIV. *New Phytologist,* Vol. 54, 199–207.

JOHANSEN, M B, and SURLYK, F. 1990. Brachiopods and the stratigraphy of the Upper Campanian and Lower Maastrichtian Chalk of Norfolk, England. *Palaeontology,* Vol. 33, 823–872.

KEMP, R A. 1980. The Valley Farm Soil in southern East Anglia. 179–196 in *Soils and Quaternary landscape evolution.* BOARDMAN, J (editor). (Chichester: Wiley and Sons.)

KENT, P E. 1955. The Market Weighton structure. *Proceedings of the Yorkshire Geological Society,* Vol. 30, 197–227.

— 1967. Outline geology of the southern North Sea basin. *Proceedings of the Yorkshire Geological Society,* Vol. 36, 1–22.

KENYON, N H, BELDERSON, R H, STRIDE, A H, and JOHNSON, M A. 1981. Offshore tidal sand-banks as indicators of net sand transport and as potential deposits. *International Association of Sedimentologists Special Publication,* No. 5, 257–268.

KING, C. 1981. The stratigraphy of the London Clay and associated deposits. *Tertiary Research Special Paper,* No. 6.

— 1983. Cenozoic micropalaeontological biostratigraphy of the North Sea. *Report of the Institute of Geological Sciences,* No. 82/7.

KNOX, R W O'B. 1984. Nannoplankton zonation and the Palaeocene/Eocene boundary beds of NW Europe: an indirect correlation by means of volcanic ash layers. *Journal of the Geological Society of London,* Vol. 141, 993–999.

— 1990. Thanetian and early Ypresian chronostratigraphy in south-east England. *Tertiary Research,* Vol. 11, 57–64.

— and MORTON, A C. 1983. Stratigraphical distribution of early Palaeogene pyroclastic deposits in the North Sea Basin. *Proceedings of the Yorkshire Geological Society,* Vol. 44, 355–363.

— — 1988. The record of early Tertiary N Atlantic volcanism in sediments of the North Sea Basin. 407–419 *in* Early Tertiary volcanism and the opening of the Atlantic. MORTON, A C, and PARSONS, L M (editors). *Special Publication of the Geological Society of London,* No. 39.

— — and HARLAND, R. 1981. Stratigraphical relationships of Palaeocene sands in the UK sector of the central North sea. 261–287 in *Petroleum geology of the continental shelf of North-west Europe.* ILLING, L V, and HOBSON, G D (editors). (London: Heydon and Sons.)

— MORIGI, A N, ALI, J R, HAILWOOD, E A, and HALLAM, J R. 1990. Early Palaeogene stratigraphy of a cored borehole at Hales, Norfolk. *Proceedings of the Geologists' Association,* Vol. 101, 145–151.

KOOI, H, CLOETINGH, and REMMELS, G. 1989. Intraplate stresses and the stratigraphic evolution of the North Sea Central Graben. *Geologie en Mijnbouw,* Vol. 68, 49–72.

LAMBE, T W, and WHITMAN, R V. 1979. *Soil mechanics (SI version).* (Chichester: Wiley-Interscience.)

LAMBERT, J M, and JENNINGS, J N. 1969. Stratigraphical and associated evidence. 1–66 *in* The making of the Broads. LAMBERT, J M, JENNINGS, J N, SMITH, C T, GREEN, C, and HUTCHINSON, J N. *Memoir of the Royal Geographical Society,* No. 3.

LARWOOD, G P. 1961. The Lower Cretaceous deposits of Norfolk. 280–292 *in* The geology of Norfolk. LARWOOD, G P, and FUNNELL, B M. *Transactions of the Norfolk and Norwich Naturalists Society,* Vol. 19.

LEE, M K, PHARAOH, T C, and SOPER, N J. 1990. Structural trends in central Britain from images of gravity and aeromagnetic fields. *Journal of the Geological Society of London,* Vol. 147, 241–258.

LLOYD, J W, and HISCOCK, K M. 1990. Importance of drift deposits in influencing Chalk hydrogeology. 271–278 in *International Chalk Symposium, 1989.* (London: Thomas Telford.)

— HARKER, D, and BAXENDALE, R A. 1981. Recharge mechanisms and groundwater flow in the chalk and drift deposits of southern East Anglia. *Quarterly Journal of Engineering Geology,* Vol. 14, 87–96.

LOTT, G K, KNOX, R W O'B, HARLAND, R, and HUGHES, M J. 1983. The stratigraphy of Palaeogene sediments in a cored borehole off the coast of north-east Yorkshire. *Report of the Institute of Geological Sciences,* No. 83/9.

LUDWIG, G, MULLER, H, and STREIF, H. 1981. New dates on Holocene sea-level changes in the German Bight. *International Association of Sedimentologists Special Publication,* No. 5, 211–219.

LYELL, C. 1833. *Principles of geology* (1st edition). Vol. 3, 171–182. (London: Murray.)

— 1839. On the relative ages of the Tertiary deposits commonly called 'Crag' in the counties of Norfolk and Suffolk. *Magazine of Natural History,* Series 2, Vol. 3, 313–322.

MARIE, J P P. 1975. Rotliegendes stratigraphy and diagenesis. 205–212 in *Petroleum and the continental shelf of North-west Europe,* Vol. 1, WOODLAND, A W (editor). (Barking: Applied Science, for the Institute of Petroleum.)

MARRIOTT, W, and GRIBBLE, T G. 1904. The Breydon viaduct at Great Yarmouth. *Proceedings of the Institution of Civil Engineers,* Vol. 157, 268.

MATHERS, S J, and ZALASIEWICZ, J A. 1986. A sedimentation pattern in Anglian marginal channels from Suffolk, England. *Sedimentology,* Vol. 33, 559–573.

— — BLOODWORTH, A J, and MORTON, A C. 1987. The Banham Beds: a petrologically distinct suite of Anglian glacigenic deposits from central East Anglia. *Proceedings of the Geologists' Association,* Vol. 98, 229–240.

MAYHEW, D F, and STUART, A J. 1986. Stratigraphic and taxonomic revision of the fossil vole remains (Rodentia microtinae) from the Lower Pleistocene deposits of eastern England. *Philosophical Transactions of the Royal Society of London,* B, Vol. 312, 431–485.

McARTHUR, J M, KENNEDY, W J, GALE, A S, THIRLWALL, M F, CHEN, M, BURNETT, J, and HANCOCK, J M, 1992. Strontium isotope stratigraphy in the Late Cretaceous: intercontinental correlation of the Campanian/Maastrichtian boundary. *Terra Nova,* Vol. 4, 385–393.

McCAVE, I N. 1978. Grain-size trends and transport along beaches: an example from eastern England. *Marine Geology,* Vol. 28, M43–M51.

— 1981. Location of coastal accumulations of fine sediments around the southern North Sea. *Rapport et procès-verbaux des réunions. Conseil permanent international pour l'exploration de la mer,* Vol. 181, 15–27.

— 1987. Fine sediment sources and sinks around the East Anglian coast (UK). *Journal of the Geological Society of London,* Vol. 144, 149–152.

McGREGOR, D F M, and GREEN, C P. 1978. Gravels of the River Thames as a guide to Pleistocene catchment changes. *Boreas,* Vol. 7, 197–203.

— — 1983. Post-depositional modification of Pleistocene terraces of the River Thames. *Boreas,* Vol. 12, 23–34.

MILLWARD, D, ELLISON, R A, LAKE, R D, and MOORLOCK, B S P. 1987. Geology of the country around Epping. *Memoir of the British Geological Survey,* Sheet 240 (England and Wales).

MITCHELL, G F, PENNY, L F, SHOTTON, F W, and WEST, R G. 1973. A correlation of Quaternary deposits in the British Isles. *Special Report of the Geological Society of London,* No. 4.

MITCHELL, M. 1982. Dinantian macrofossils from the Somerton Borehole, Norfolk. *Report of the Palaeontology Research Group, British Geological Survey,* No. PDL/82/220.

MORTIMORE, R N. 1986. Stratigraphy of the Upper Cretaceous White Chalk of Sussex. *Proceedings of the Geologists' Association,* Vol. 97, 97–139.

— and POMEROL, B. 1991. Upper Cretaceous tectonic disruptions in a placid Chalk sequence in the Anglo-Paris Basin. *Journal of the Geological Society of London,* Vol. 148, 391–404.

— and WOOD, C J. 1986. The distribution of flint in the English Chalk, with particular reference to the 'Brandon Flint Series' and the high Turonian flint maximum. 7–20 in *The scientific study of flint and chert; proceedings of the Fourth International Flint Symposium,* Vol. 1. SIEVEKING, G DE G, and HART, M B (editors). (Cambridge University Press.)

NORTON, P E P. 1967. Marine molluscan assemblages in the Early Pleistocene of Sidestrand, Bramerton and the Royal Society Borehole at Ludham, Norfolk. *Philosophical Transactions of the Royal Society of London,* B, Vol. 253, 161–200.

O'RIORDAN, T. 1980. A case study in the politics of land drainage. *Disasters,* Vol. 4, 393–410.

ONYETT, D, and SIMMONDS, A. 1983. Final report: Beach changes and longshore transport 1974–1980. *Report of the East Anglian Coastal Research Programme, University of East Anglia, Norwich,* No. 8.

OWEN, H G. 1971. The stratigraphy of the Gault in the Thames Estuary and its bearing on the Mesozoic tectonic history of the area. *Proceedings of the Geologists' Association,* Vol. 82, 187–207.

OWENS, B. 1982. Palynological report on the cutting samples from Somerton No. 1 borehole. *Report of the Palaeontology Research Group, British Geological Survey,* No. PDL/82/243.

PALLIS, M. 1911. The cause of salinity of the Broads of the River Thurne. *Geographical Journal,* Vol. 37, 284–291.

PARKER, J M, and JAMES, R C. 1985. Autochthonous bacteria in the Chalk and their influence on groundwater quality in East Anglia. *Journal of Applied Bacteriology,* Symposium Supplement, 15S–25S.

— BOOTH, S K, and FOSTER, S D D. 1987. Penetration of nitrate from agricultural soils into the groundwater of the Norfolk Chalk. *Proceedings of the Institution of Civil Engineers,* Part 2, Vol. 83, March, 15–32.

PARKINSON, J. 1811. Observations on some of the strata in the neighbourhood of London, and on the fossil remains contained in them. *Transactions of the Geological Society,* Vol. 1, 325–354.

PEAKE, N B, and HANCOCK, J M. 1961. The Upper Cretaceous of Norfolk. *Transactions of the Norfolk and Norwich Naturalists' Society,* Vol, 19, 293–339. Reprinted with addenda in 1970:

293–339J in *The geology of Norfolk.* LARWOOD, G P, and FUNNELL, B M (editors). (London and Ashford: Geological Society of Norfolk.)

PERRIN, R M S, DAVIES, H, and FYSH, M D. 1973. Lithology of the Chalky Boulder Clay. *Nature, London,* Vol. 245, 101–104.

— — — 1974. Distribution of late Pleistocene aeolian deposits in eastern and southern England. *Nature, London,* Vol. 248, 320–324.

— ROSE, J, and DAVIES, H. 1979. The distribution, variation and origins of pre-Devensian tills in eastern England.

Philosophical Transactions of the Royal Society of London, B, Vol. 287, 535–570.

PHARAOH, T C, MERRIMAN, R J, WEBB, B C, and BECKINSALE, R D. 1987. The concealed Caledonides of eastern England: preliminary results of a multidisciplinary study. *Proceedings of the Yorkshire Geological Society,* Vol. 46, 355–369.

— — EVANS, J A, BREWER, T S, WEBB, B C, and SMITH, N J P. 1991. Early Palaeozoic arc-related volcanism in the concealed Caledonides of southern Britain. In *Brussels Caledonide Symposium Volume. Annales de la Société Geologique de Belgique.*

POINTON, W K. 1978. The Pleistocene succession at Corton, Suffolk. *Bulletin of the Geological Society of Norfolk,* Vol. 30, 55–76.

PRESS, M H. 1956. The seven havens of Great Yarmouth and their bridges. *Edgar Allen News,* Vol. 35, No. 414, 272–274.

PRESTWICH, J. 1847. On the main points of structure and probable age of the Bagshot Sands, etc. *Quarterly Journal of the Geological Society of London,* Vol. 3, 378–409.

— 1849. On some fossiliferous beds overlying the Red Crag at Chillesford near Orford, Suffolk. *Quarterly Journal of the Geological Society of London,* Vol. 5, 343–353.

— 1850. On the structure of the strata between the London Clay and the Chalk, etc. Part i. Basement-Beds of the London Clay. *Quarterly Journal of the Geological Society of London,* Vol. 6, 252–281.

— 1852. On the structure of the strata between the London Clay and the Chalk, etc. Part iii. The Thanet Sands. *Quarterly Journal of the Geological Society of London,* Vol. 8, 235–264.

— 1854. On the structure of the strata between the London Clay and the Chalk, etc. Part ii. The Woolwich and Reading Series. *Quarterly Journal of the Geological Society of London,* Vol. 10, 75–157.

— 1860. On the presence of London Clay in Norfolk, as proved by a well-boring at Yarmouth. *Quarterly Journal of the Geological Society of London,* Vol. 16, 449–452.

— 1871a. On the structure of the Crag-beds of Suffolk and Norfolk with some observations on their organic remains. Part I. The Coralline Crag of Suffolk. *Quarterly Journal of the Geological Society of London,* Vol. 27, 115–146.

— 1871b. On the structure of the Crag-beds of Suffolk and Norfolk with some observations on their organic remains. Part II. The Red Crag of Essex and Suffolk. *Quarterly Journal of the Geological Society of London,* Vol. 27, 325–356.

— 1871c. On the structure of the Crag-beds of Suffolk and Norfolk with some observations on their organic remains. Part III. The Norwich Crag and Westleton Beds. *Quarterly Journal of the Geological Society of London,* Vol. 27, 425–496.

PRICE, J R. 1980. Acid sulphate and potential acid sulphate soils in the peatlands of the Norfolk Broads. Unpublished report, Soil Survey of England and Wales.

PRICE, M. 1987. Fluid flow in the Chalk of England. 141–156 *in* Fluid flow in sedimentary basins and aquifers. GOFF, J C, and WILLIAMS, B P J (editors). *Special Publication of the Geological Society of London,* No. 34.

— BIRD, M J, and FOSTER, S S D. 1976. Chalk pore-size measurements and their significance. *Water Services,* Vol. 80, 596–600.

RAWSON, P F, CURRY, D, DILLEY, F C, HANCOCK, J M, KENNEDY, W J, NEALE, J W, WOOD, C J, and WORSSAM, B C. 1978. A correlation of the Cretaceous rocks in the British Isles. *Special Report of the Geological Society of London,* No. 9.

REID, C. 1882. The geology of the country around Cromer. *Memoir of the Geological Survey.*

— 1890. The Pliocene deposits of Britain. *Memoir of the Geological Survey.*

REINECK, H-E, and SINGH, I B. 1973. Depositional sedimentary environments. (Berlin: Springer-Verlag.)

RESTON, T J, and BLUNDELL, D J. 1987. Possible mid-crustal shears on the edge of the London Platform. *Geophysical Journal of the Royal Astronomical Society,* Vol. 89, 251–258.

RHYS, G H. 1974. A proposed standard lithostratigraphic nomenclature for the southern North Sea and an outline structural nomenclature for the whole of the (UK) North Sea. *Report of the Institute of Geological Sciences,* No. 74/8.

RICE, R J. 1968. The Quaternary deposits of central Leicestershire. *Philosophical Transactions of the Royal Society of London, A,* Vol. 262, 459–509.

ROBINSON, A H W. 1966. Residual currents in relation to shoreline evolution of the East Anglian coast. *Marine Geology,* Vol. 4, 57–84.

ROSE, J. 1987. Status of the Wolstonian Glaciation in the British Quaternary. *Quaternary Newsletter.* No. 53.

— 1989. Stadial type sections in the British Quaternary. 15–20 in *Quaternary type sections.* ROSE, J, and SCHLUCTER, CH (editors). (Rotterdam: Balkema.)

— and ALLEN, P. 1977. Middle Pleistocene stratigraphy in south-east Suffolk. *Journal of the Geological Society of London,* Vol. 133, 85–102.

— — and HEY, R W. 1976. Middle Pleistocene stratigraphy in southern East Anglia. *Nature, London,* Vol. 263, 492–494.

— — KEMP, R A, WHITEMAN, C A, and OWEN, N. 1985. The early Anglian Barham Soil of eastern England. 197–229 in *Soils and Quaternary landscape evolution.* BOARDMAN, J (editor). (Chichester: John Wiley and Sons.)

RUSSELL, M J. 1976. A possible Lower Permian age for the onset of ocean floor spreading in northern North Atlantic. *Scottish Journal of Geology,* Vol. 12, No. 4, 315–323.

SAUNDERS, R L. 1979. Engineering characteristics of soft normally consolidated clays with reference to the Breydon clays of Norfolk. Unpublished MSc thesis, University of London.

SCHÖNFELD, J, SIROCKO, F, and JORGENSEN, N O. 1991. Oxygen isotope composition of upper Cretaceous chalk at Lägerdorf (NW Germany): its original environmental signal and palaeoclimatic interpretation. *Cretaceous Research, Vol. 12, 27–46.*

— and BURNETT, J. 1991. Biostratigraphical correlation of the Campanian–Maastrichtian boundary: Lägerdorf– Hemmoor (northwestern Germany), DSDP Sites 548A, 549 and 551 (eastern North Atlantic) with palaeobiogeographical and palaeoceanographical implications. *Geological Magazine,* Vol. 128, 479–503.

— SIROCKO, F and JØRGENSEN, N O. 1991. Oxygen isotope composition of Upper Cretaceous chalk at Lägerdorf (northwest Germany): its original environmental sidnal and palaeotemperature interpretation. *Cretaceous Research,* Vol. 12, 27–46.

SCHULZ, M-G. 1978. Zur Litho-und Biostratigraphie des Obercampan–Untermaastricht von Lägerdorf und Kronsmoor (SW-Holstein). [On the litho- and biostratigraphy of the Upper Campanian–Lower Maastrichtian at Lägerdorf and Kronsmoor (SW Hostein).] *Newsletters on Stratigraphy,* Vol. 7, 73–89. [In German]

— 1979. Morphometrisch-variationsstatistische Untersuchungen zur Phylogenie der Belemniten-Gattung *Belemnella* im Untermaastricht NW-europas. [Statistical studies of morphometric variation in the phylogeny of the Belemnite genus *Belemnella* in the Lower Maastrichtian of north-west Europe.] *Geologisches Jahrbuch,* A47, 3–157. [In German]

— ERNST, G, ERNST, H, and SCHMID, F. 1984. Coniacian to Maastrichtian stage boundaries in the standard section for the Upper Cretaceous white chalk of NW Germany (Lägerdorf-Kronsmoor-Hemmoor): definitions and proposals. *Bulletin of the Geological Society of Denmark,* Vol. 33, 203–215.

SMITH, C T. 1960. Historical evidence. 63–111 in The making of the Broads. LAMBERT, J M, JENNINGS, J N, SMITH, C T, GREEN, C, and HUTCHINSON, J N. *Memoir of the Royal Geographical Society,* No. 3.

SMITH, D B, BRUNSTROM, R G W, MANNING, P I, SIMPSON, S, and SHOTTON, F W. 1974. Correlation of the Permian rocks of the British Isles. *Special Report of the Geological Society of London,* No. 5.

— HARWOOD, G M, PATTISON, J, and PETTIGREW, T. 1986. A revised nomenclature for Upper Permian strata in eastern England. 9–17 in The English Zechstein and related topics. SMITH, D B, and HARWOOD, G M (editors). *Special Report of the Geological Society of London,* No. 22.

SMITH, I F. 1985. Mesozoic basins. 42–83 in *Geothermal energy: the potential in the United Kingdom.* DOWNING, R A, and GRAY, D A (editors). (Keyworth: British Geological Survey.)

SMITH, M V. 1985. The compressibility of sediments and its importance on Flandrian Fenland deposits. *Boreas,* Vol. 14, 1–18.

SMITH, N J P (compiler). 1985. Map 1, Pre-Permian geology of the United Kingdom (South). (Keyworth: British Geological Survey.)

— 1987. The deep geology of central England: the prospectivity of the Palaeozoic rocks. 217–224 in *Petroleum geology of North-west Europe; proceedings of the 3rd conference ... London 26–29 October 1986.* BROOKS, J, and GLENNIE, K (editors). (London: Graham and Trotman.)

SOIL SURVEY OF ENGLAND AND WALES. 1986. *Annual report.* (Harpenden: Soil Survey of England and Wales.)

SOLOMON, J D. 1932a. The glacial succession on the north Norfolk coast. *Proceedings of the Geologists' Association,* Vol. 43, 241–270.

— 1932b. On the heavy mineral assemblages of the Great Chalky Boulder-clay and Cannon-shot Gravels of East Anglia, and their significance. *Geological Magazine,* Vol. 69, 314–320,

SOPER, N J, WEBB, B C, AND WOODCOCK, N H. 1987. Late Caledonian (Acadian) transgression in north-west England: timing, geometry and geotectonic significance. *Proceedings of the Yorkshire Geological Society,* Vol. 46, 175–192.

STOKER, M S, LONG, D, and FYFE, J A. 1985. The Quaternary succession in the central North Sea. *Newsletters on Stratigraphy,* Vol. 14, 119–128.

— SKINNER, A C, FYFE, J A, and LONG, D. 1983. Palaeomagnetic evidence for early Pleistocene in the central and northern North Sea. *Nature, London,* Vol. 304, 332–334.

STRAHAN, A, 1913. Boring at the East Anglian Ice Co.'s works, Lowestoft. 87–88 in *Summary of Progress for 1912. Geological Survey of Great Britain.* (London: His Majesty's Stationery Office.)

STRANK, A R E. 1982. Foraminifera from the Somerton Borehole, Norfolk. *Report of the Palaeontology Research Group, British Geological Survey*, No. PDL/82/191.

STRAW, A. 1960. The limit of the 'Last' Glaciation in north Norfolk. *Proceedings of the Geologists' Association*, Vol. 71, 379–390.

— 1965. A reassessment of the Chalky Boulder Clay or Marly Drift of north Norfolk. *Zeitschrift für Geomorphologie*, Vol. 9, 209–221.

STRIDE, A H. 1988. Indications of long term episodic suspension transport of sand across the Norfolk Banks, North Sea. *Marine Geology*, Vol. 79, 55–64.

STUBBLEFIELD, C J. 1967. Some results of a recent Geological Survey boring in Huntingdonshire. *Proceedings of the Geological Society of London*, No. 1637, 35–44.

SWIECICKI, A. 1980. A foraminiferal biostratigraphy of the Campanian and Maastrichtian chalks of the United Kingdom. Unpublished CNAA PhD thesis, Plymouth Polytechnic.

SWIFT, D J P. 1975. Tidal sand ridges and shoal-retreat massifs. *Marine Geology*, Vol. 18, 105–134.

TAYLOR, J C M. 1986. Late Permian–Zechstein. 87–111 in *Introduction to the petroleum geology of the North Sea* (second edition). GLENNIE, K W (editor). (Oxford: Blackwell.)

— and COLTER, V S. 1975. Zechstein of the southern North Sea Basin. 249–263 in *Petroleum and the continental shelf of North-west Europe*, Vol. 1, WOODLAND, A W (editor). (Barking: Applied Science, for the Institute of Petroleum.)

TAYLOR, R C. 1824. On the Crag Strata at Bramerton, near Norwich. *Transactions of the Geological Society*, 2nd series, Vol. 1, 371–373.

— 1827. On the geology of East Norfolk; with remarks upon the hypothesis of Mr Robberds, respecting the former level of the German Ocean. *Philosophical Magazine*, Ser. 2, Vol. 1.

TERWINDT, J H R. 1971. Litho-facies of inshore estuarine and tidal inlet deposits. *Geologie en Mijnbouw*, Vol. 50, 515–526.

TOYNTON, R. 1983. The relation between fracture patterns and hydraulic anisotropy in the Norfolk Chalk, England. *Quarterly Journal of Engineering Geology*, Vol. 16, 169–185.

TRIMMER, J. 1851. Generalizations respecting the erratic Tertiaries or Northern Drift, etc. *Quarterly Journal of the Geological Society of London*, Vol. 7, 19–31.

— 1858. On the upper and lower boulder clays of the Gorlston Cliffs in Norfolk. *Quarterly Journal of the Geological Society of London*, Vol. 14, 171–172.

TUBB, S R, SOULSBY, A, and LAWRENCE, S R. 1986. Palaeozoic prospects on the northern flanks of the London Brabant Massif. 55–72 in Habitat of Palaeozoic gas in NW Europe. BROOKS, J, GOFF, J C, and HOORN, B van (editors). *Special Publication of the Geological Society of London*, No. 23.

VAIL, P R, MITCHUM, R M, TODD, R G, WIDMIER, J M, THOMPSON III, S, SANGREE, J B, BUBB, J N, and HATFIELD, W G. 1977. Seismic stratigraphy and global changes of sea-level. 42–212 in Seismic stratigraphy, application to hydrocarbon exploration. PAYTON, C E (editor). *Memoir of the American Association of Petroleum Geologists*, No. 26.

VAN ADRICHEM BOOGAERT, H A, and BURGERS, W K J. 1983. The development of the Zechstein in the Netherlands. 83–92 in Petroleum geology of the southeastern North Sea and the adjacent areas. KAASSCHIETER, J P H, and REIJERS, T J A (editors). *Geologie en Mijnbouw*, Vol. 62.

VAN VEEN, F R. 1975. Geology of the Leman Gas-field. 223–232 in *Petroleum and the continental shelf of North-west Europe*. Vol. 1. WOODLAND, A W (editor). (Barking: Applied Science, for the Institute of Petroleum.)

VINCENT, C E. 1979. Longshore sand transport rates—a simple model for the East Anglian coastline. *Coastal Engineering*, Vol. 3, 113–136.

WARRINGTON, G, AUDLEY-CHARLES, M G, ELLIOT, R E, EVANS, W B, IVIMEY-COOK, H C, KENT, P E, ROBINSON, P L, SHOTTON, F W, and TAYLOR, F M. 1980. A correlation of Triassic rocks in the British Isles. *Special Publication of the Geological Society of London*, No. 13.

WEST, R G. 1961. Vegetational history of the Early Pleistocene of the Royal Society borehole at Ludham, Norfolk. *Philosophical Transactions of the Royal Society of London*, B, Vol. 155, 437–453.

— 1963. Problems of the British Quaternary. *Proceedings of the Geologists' Association*, Vol. 74, 147–186.

— 1968. *Pleistocene geology and biology with special reference to the British Isles*. (London: Longman.)

— 1980. *The Pre-glacial Pleistocene of the Norfolk and Suffolk coasts*. (Cambridge University Press.)

— and DONNER, J J. 1956. The glaciations of East Anglia and the East Midlands: a differentiation based on stone orientation measurements of the tills. *Quarterly Journal of the Geological Society of London*, Vol. 112, 69–91.

WHITAKER, W. 1866. On the Lower London Tertiaries of Kent. *Quarterly Journal of the Geological Society of London*, Vol. 22, 404–435.

— 1921. The water supply of Norfolk from underground sources. *Hydrogeological Memoir of the Geological Survey of Great Britain*.

— and DALTON, W G. 1887. The geology of the country around Halesworth and Harleston. *Memoir of the Geological Survey of Great Britain*.

WHITEMAN, C A. 1992. The palaeogeography and correlation of pre-Anglian-Glaciation terraces of the River Thames in Essex and the London Basin. *Proceedings of the Geologists' Association*, Vol. 103, 37–56.

— and ROSE, J. 1992. Thames river sediments of the British Early and Middle Pleistocene. *Quaternary Science Reviews*, Vol. 11, 363–375.

WHITTAKER, A (editor). 1985. *Atlas of onshore sedimentary basins in England and Wales*. (Keyworth: British Geological Survey, and Glasgow and London: Blackie.)

— HOLLIDAY, D W, and PENN, I. 1985. Geophysical logs in British stratigraphy. *Special Report of the Geological Society of London*, No. 18.

WHITTLESEA, P S. 1985. Notes on Chalk fossils. 1. Note on a temporary section at Bramerton, near Norwich. *Bulletin of the Geological Society of Norfolk*, Vol. 35, 39–41.

— 1991. The Maastrichtian in Norfolk. *Bulletin of the Geological Society of Norfolk*, Vol. 40, 33–51.

WILLS, L J. 1978. A palaeogeological map of the Lower Palaeozoic floor beneath the cover of Upper Devonian, Carboniferous and later formations. *Memoir of the Geological Society of London*, No. 8.

WOOD, C J. 1967. Some new observations on the Maastrichtian Stage in the British Isles. *Bulletin of the Geological Survey of Great Britain*, No. 27, 271–288.

— 1980.   Upper Cretaceous.   92–105 in *British regional geology: Eastern England from the Tees to the Wash* (2nd edition). KENT, P E. (London: HMSO for British Geological Survey.)

— — 1988.   The stratigraphy of the Chalk of Norwich. *Bulletin of the Geological Society of Norfolk*, Vol. 38, 3–120.

— 1992.   Chapter 5: The Chalk.   71–101 in Geology of the country around Kingston upon Hull and Brigg.   GAUNT, G D, FLETCHER, T P, and WOOD, C J. *Memoir of the British Geological Survey*, Sheets 80 and 89 (England and Wales).

— and MORTIMORE, R N.   1988.   Biostratigraphy of the Newhaven and Culver Members.   58–65 in Geology of the country around Brighton and Worthing. YOUNG, B, and LAKE, R D. *Memoir of the British Geological Survey*, Sheets 318 and 333 (England and Wales).

— and SMITH, E G.   1978.   Lithostratigraphical classification of the Chalk in North Yorkshire, Humberside and Lincolnshire. *Proceedings of the Yorkshire Geological Society*, Vol. 42, 263–287.

— ERNST, G, and RASEMANN, G.   1984.   The Turonian–Coniacian stage boundary in Lower Saxony (Germany) and adjacent areas: The Salzgitter-Salder Quarry as a proposed international standard section. *Bulletin of the Geological Society of Denmark*, Vol. 33, 225–238.

WOOD, E C.   1961.   Some chemical and bacteriological aspects of East Anglian waters. *Proceedings of the Society of Water Treatment Examiners*, Vol. 10, 76–86.

WOOD, S V (junr.).   1864.   On the Red Crag, and its relation to the Fluvio-marine Crag, and on the Drift of the Eastern Counties. *Annals and Magazine of Natural History*, Series 3, Vol. 13, 203.

WOOD, S V.   1866.   On the Structure of the Red Crag. Explanation of the diagram-section by WOOD, S V junr. *Quarterly Journal of the Geological Society of London*, Vol. 22, 538–552.

— 1880.   The newer Pliocene period in England. *Quarterly Journal of the Geological Society of London*, Vol. 36, 457–528.

— and HARMER, F W.   1868.   The glacial and post-glacial structure of Norfolk and Suffolk. (Abstract). *Geological Magazine*, Vol. 5, 452–456.

— — 1872.   An outline geology of the Upper Tertiaries of East Anglia.   ii–xxxi in Supplement to the Crag Mollusca. Part 1 (univalves) with an introduction on the Crag district by S V Wood. (junr.) and F W Harmer. WOOD, S V. *Palaeontographical Society Monograph*, No. 113, 25.

WOODLAND, A W.   1946.   Water supply from underground sources of the Cambridge Ipswich district. *Geological Survey of Great Britain, Wartime Pamphlet*, No. 20, Pt. 10.

— 1970.   The buried tunnel-valleys of East Anglia. *Proceedings of the Yorkshire Geological Society*, Vol. 37, No. 22, 521–578.

WOODWARD, H B.   1881.   Geology of the country around Norwich.   *Memoir of the Geological Survey* (England and Wales).

— 1882.   Notes on the Bure Valley Beds and the Westleton Beds.   *Geological Magazine*, Vol. 9, 452–457.

WOODWARD, J.   1728–29.   *An attempt towards a natural history of the fossils of England; in a catalogue of the English fossils in the collection of J Woodward, Tome, I. A catalogue of the additional English native fossils, in the collection of J Woodward, M D. Tome II.* (London: Printed for F Fayram, J Senex, J Osborn, and T Longman.)

ZALASIEWICZ, J A, and GIBBARD, P L.   1988.   The Pliocene to early Middle Pleistocene: an overview.   1–31 in *The Pliocene–Middle Pleistocene of East Anglia*. GIBBARD, P L, and ZALASIEWICZ, J A (editors). (Cambridge: Quaternary Research Association.)

— and MATHERS, S J.   1985.   Lithostratigraphy of Red and Norwich Crags of the Aldeburgh–Orford area, south-east Suffolk. *Geological Magazine*, Vol. 122, 287–296.

— — GIBBARD, P L, PEGLAR, S M, FUNNELL, B M, CATT, J A, HARLAND, R, LONG, P E, and AUSTIN, T J F.   1991.   Age and relationships of the Chillesford Clay (Early Pleistocene: Suffolk, England). *Philosophical Transactions of the Royal Society of London*, B. Vol. 333, 81–100.

— — HUGHES, M J, GIBBARD, P L, PEGLAR, S M, HARLAND, R, BOULTON, G S, NICHOLSON, R A, CAMBRIDGE, P, and WEALTHALL, G P.   1988.   Stratigraphy and palaeoenvironments of the Red Crag and Norwich Crag formations between Aldeburgh and Sizewell, Suffolk, England. *Philosophical Transactions of the Royal Society of London*, B, Vol. 322, 221–272.

ZAGWIJN, W H, and DOPPERT, J W Chr.   1978.   Upper Cenozoic of the Southern North Sea Basin: palaeoclimatic and palaeogeographic evolution. *Geologie en Mijnbouw*, Vol. 57, 577–588.

ZIEGLER, P A.   1975.   North Sea Basin history in the tectonic framework of North-west Europe.   131–150 in *Petroleum and the continental shelf of North-west Europe*, Vol. 1. WOODLAND, A W (editor). (Barking: Applied Science, for the Institute of Petroleum.)

— 1981.   Evolution of sedimentary basins in north-west Europe.   3–39 in *Petroleum geology of the continental shelf of North-west Europe*. ILLING, L V, and HOBSON, G D (editors). (London: Heyden and Sons.)

— 1982.   *Geological atlas of Western and Central Europe.* (Shell Internationale Petroleum Maatschappi BV.)

— and LOUWERENS, C J.   1979.   Tectonics of the North Sea. 7–22 in *The Quaternary history of the North Sea*. OELE, E SCHÜTTENHELM, R T E, and WIGGERS, A J (editors). *Acta Universitatis Upsaliensis Symposia Universitatis Upsaliensis annum Quingentesimum Celebrantis; 2.* (Uppsala.)

FOSSIL INDEX

Page numbers in italic indicate figures and tables, P after a page number indicates a plate.

GENERAL INDEX

BRITISH GEOLOGICAL SURVEY

Keyworth, Nottingham NG12 5GG
(0602) 363100

Murchison House, West Mains Road, Edinburgh
EH9 3LA   031-667 1000

London Information Office, Natural History Museum
Earth Galleries, Exhibition Road, London SW7 2DE
071-589 4090

The full range of Survey publications is available through the
Sales Desks at Keyworth and at Murchison House, Edinburgh,
and in the BGS London Information Office in the Natural
History Museum Earth Galleries. The adjacent bookshop
stocks the more popular books for sale over the counter. Most
BGS books and reports are listed in HMSO's Sectional List 45,
and can be bought from HMSO and through HMSO agents
and retailers. Maps are listed in the BGS Map Catalogue, and
can be bought BGS approved stockists and agents as well as
direct from BGS.

*The British Geological Survey carries out the geological survey of Great
Britain and Northern Ireland (the latter as an agency service for the
government of Northern Ireland), and of the surrounding continental
shelf, as well as its basic research projects. It also undertakes
programmes of British technical aid in geology in developing countries
as arranged by the Overseas Development Administration.*

*The British Geological Survey is a component body of the Natural
Environment Research Council.*

HMSO publications are available from:

HMSO Publications Centre
(Mail, fax and telephone orders only)
PO Box 276, London SW8 5DT
Telephone orders 071-873 9090
General enquiries 071-873 0011
Queueing system in operation for both numbers
Fax orders 071-873 8200

HMSO Bookshops
49 High Holborn, London WC1V 6HB
(counter service only)
071-873 0011   Fax 071-873 8200
258 Broad Street, Birmingham B1 2HE
021-643 3740   Fax 021-643 6510
33 Wine Street, Bristol BS1 2BQ
0272-264306   Fax 0272-294515
9 Princess Street, Manchester M60 8AS
061-834 7201   Fax 061-833 0634
16 Arthur Street, Belfast BT1 4GD
0232-238451   Fax 0232-235401
71 Lothian Road, Edinburgh EH3 9AZ
031-228 4181   Fax 031-229 2734

HMSO's Accredited Agents
(see Yellow Pages)

And through good booksellers